P9-BBT-374

THE CANTERBURY TALES OF GEOFFREY CHAUCER

DANIEL COOK was born in Bismarck, North Dakota, in 1914. He received his M.A. degree from the University of Wisconsin and a Ph.D. degree from the University of California (Berkeley) in linguistics and medieval languages and literature. He was associate editor of Webster's New International Dictionary, Third Edition, and has taught at Duke University and Southern Illinois University. He is now Professor of English at the American University of Beirut, where he is currently doing research on Middle Eastern dialects of the Gypsy language.

He has recently published in Anchor Books a companion volume to THE CANTERBURY TALES, Chaucer's *Troilus and Criseyde*.

the CANTERBURY TALES of GEOFFREY CHAUCER

A SELECTION EDITED WITH
INTRODUCTION AND NOTES
BY DANIEL COOK

Anchor Books
Doubleday & Company, Inc.
Garden City, New York

TYPOGRAPHY BY SUSAN SIEN
COVER DESIGN BY ROBIN JACQUES

The Anchor Books edition is the first publication of *The Canterbury Tales of Geoffrey Chaucer* edited by Daniel Cook.

Anchor Books edition: 1961

Library of Congress Catalog Card Number 61-9496

Printed in the United States of America

CONTENTS

PREFACE

This edition has grown out of a conviction that it is a needless deprivation of pleasure to be obliged to read Chaucer in a translation. It has been remarked that no poet rewards so generously as does Chaucer the relatively small effort required to learn his language. But while this is unquestionably true, it is true also that there are today large numbers of otherwise quite well-read persons who, for one reason or another, know the poems only in translation.

It is to the task of relieving this condition that the present edition addresses itself. The innovation is, of course, the location of notes and glosses on facing pages. Though this procedure is admittedly extravagant of space, it is hoped that the gain for the reader will more than compensate for the necessary reduction in the amount of text which can be provided. The first advantage lies in the paralleling of text and notes, a device which considerably increases the ease and speed with which the latter may be consulted. The second and principal advantage results from the generous amount of space which such a system provides. Where space is severely limited, as in editions with footnote glosses, the editor must choose between two unsatisfactory alternatives. He may confine himself to glosses and brief explanatory notes, a solution which places the burden of translation on the reader where it belongs, but which, as a result of the limitation of space, is often inadequate to clear explanation of the text. Or he may, for difficult passages, substitute a translation of one or more lines of text for the glossing of vocabulary and the explanation of syntactical structures. While this usually provides satisfactory explication of the text, it does nothing to promote in the reader an understanding of constructions which may occur again and again in his subsequent reading. The facing-page notes avoid both of these difficulties by permitting full glossing and explanation of all passages without ever relying on paraphrase alone to clarify an obscure line.

It has been my intention in this edition to take full advantage of the opportunities which this system affords. In the notes and glosses, as well as in the introductions to the various prologues and tales, a consistent effort has been made to supply all information that might reasonably be required for an understanding of the poet's work. In order to promote learning of the more useful items of vocabulary, glosses of common words and constructions are not, in the earlier pages of the edition, duplicated at the second and subsequent occurrences. Instead, the reader is referred by a line reference to the first occurrence, thus increasing, it is hoped, his awareness of the importance of these terms.

The reader should assume that an unfamiliar word which is not glossed is to be found in any good dictionary of modern English. He is urged to use the dictionary not only for these words but also as an encyclopedic reference for technical terms, many of which may be especially unfamiliar to those not already acquainted with the terminology of the Catholic Church. Such terms as *confession, absolution, shrive, penance, indulgence, Fathers* are important to one's understanding of many of the religious references in the *Tales.* Scientific and legal terms such as *zodiac, sign, assize, advocate* may also require checking in a good reference source. Useful reference works are *Webster's New International Dictionary* (unabridged), The Encyclopaedia Britannica, and The Catholic Encyclopedia.

The general introduction and the prefatory notes affixed to each prologue and tale have been limited to such informational and evaluative material as would seem useful in increasing the reader's enjoyment of the *Tales.* The general outline of the author's career seems particularly relevant to a work as broadly reflective of English life as is this. The brief sections on Chaucer's language and versification should be noticed by those who wish to reach a fuller perception of the graceful fluidity and ease of this poetry. A particular effort has been made throughout the edition to place the tales here selected within a framework of summaries and descriptions of the omitted portions, so that the reader may obtain a fair idea of the character of the whole work. This idea should of course be supplemented by the introductory discussion of the text of the *Tales.*

The selections in this edition include some of the best known of Chaucer's *Tales* and all are generally recognized as among his best. The text of the edition is derived from the Chaucer Society's *A Six-Text Print of Chaucer's Canterbury Tales.* Chief reliance for readings is of course on the Ellesmere and Hengwrt manuscripts, and with a few exceptions the spelling is that of Ellesmere. The text thus derived has been compared throughout with the text and textual notes in F. N. Robinson's *Complete Works of Geoffrey Chaucer,* second edition, Boston, 1957, and J. M. Manly and Edith Rickert's *The Text of the Canterbury Tales,* Chicago, 1940. For the notes and introductions I am obligated of course to many more Chaucer scholars than I could name here. Particularly useful have been the Robinson edition, Manly's earlier edition of the *Canterbury Tales* (New York, 1928), and the great edition of W. W. Skeat, *The Complete Works of Geoffrey Chaucer,* Oxford, 1894. In addition to these, I have levied also, consciously and unconsciously, upon many of the great number of excellent articles and books that have contributed so much to our knowledge of this subject in the last sixty years.

I am happy to declare also my indebtedness and my gratitude to Professor Kemp Malone for his numerous kindnesses to me, particularly for reading parts of this book in manuscript and for his helpful suggestions and corrections, and to my colleague Professor Edith Krappe for her generous assistance in clearing the text and notes of numerous errors and inconsistencies. Much warm thanks are due also to my friends Alan Cohn, Humanities Librarian of Southern Illinois University Library, for his invariably ready, painstaking, and learned assistance in a multitude of problems, and Pyke Johnson of Doubleday and Company for encouraging me in a thoroughly enjoyable and rewarding undertaking.

DANIEL COOK

INTRODUCTION

Geoffrey Chaucer is one of the most learned of English writers. While not much is known of the specific nature of his education, nothing is clearer than that he was throughout his life a voracious reader of everything that he could lay hands on and an enthusiastic and acute observer of all that surrounded him. To both of these generalizations his whole work bears witness, but for his reading habits we have the additional testimony of his own words. The humorously rueful observation that he put in the mouth of the eagle in *The House of Fame* describes the poet's practice at a time when he was a busy and responsible officer of the king's customs.

For when thy labour doon al is,
And hast maad alle thy rekenynges,
In stede of reste and newe thynges,
Thou goost hom to thy hous anoon,
And, also domb as any stoon,
Thou sittest at another book
Til fully daswed is thy look.

If his temperament was bookish, the events of his life make it clear that he was a man of considerable experience and practical ability. Perhaps the most striking feature of his career is its extraordinary suitability to the author of the *Canterbury Tales.* There is in it opportunity for study, for travel, for contact with the world's great writers and great doers, for observation of the worlds of the court and of the market place and of the high and the low.

Chaucer was born about 1340, the son of a wealthy London merchant and a member of a family which for several generations had been active in government service. He was educated at a grammar school in London and at sometime before 1357 was appointed a page in the household of the wife of Prince Lionel, second son of Edward III. In 1359-60 he was in the army which the king and his sons led into France. He was captured in an engagement near Rheims and was ransomed in March 1360, the king contributing a substantial sum for that purpose.

From 1361 to 1367 he almost certainly continued his education, quite possibly at the study of the law, probably remaining at the same time a member of one of the royal households. In 1367-68 his name appears on the list of yeomen, and then of esquires, in the king's household. In 1369 he served again in France with the king's third son, the powerful John of Gaunt, Duke of Lancaster, and probably near the end of that year wrote his first long poem, *The Book of the Duchess,* on the occasion of the death of Gaunt's wife. He was married at sometime during this period to Philippa de Roet, whose sister, Katherine, became Gaunt's mistress and later his third wife.

On a number of occasions in the next few years Chaucer was a member of diplomatic missions to Italy, France, Flanders, and perhaps elsewhere. Some of these were of considerable importance, and in them Chaucer was associated with men of influence and distinction. In 1374 he was appointed controller of the customs on wool and hides in the port of London, and for a number of years served in this and various business and governmental capacities in London. In the middle eighties he moved from the city into Kent, not far from London, and was made justice of the peace for Kent in 1385 and elected member of Parliament in 1386.

From 1389 he held important appointments from the king in connection with the administration of various royal works and properties. For these and other services he received annuities and gifts both from Richard II and, after 1399, from Henry IV in amounts sufficient to maintain him in reasonably prosperous estate. He died in 1400—according to the inscription on his tomb, on October 25—and was buried in Westminster Abbey.

This long, successful, and varied career is clearly reflected in the variety of styles and subjects to be found in Chaucer's work. The poetry of his early period is in the fashionable French manner of the English and French courtly tradition of his day. His later work shows clearly the influence of the Italians, Dante, Petrarch, and Boccaccio, with whose writings he probably became familiar as a result of his trips to Italy. And finally, in his last work, the *Canterbury Tales,* there is found in its most mature form his characteristic fusion of wide learning and close and accurate observation of the men and women of the England in which he lived and worked.

THE CANTERBURY TALES

The *Canterbury Tales* as a whole is what is known as a "frame story." This is to say that it is a single narrative within whose framework are placed other separate and distinct narratives. This is not, of course, a new device with Chaucer. But his use of the frame is unlike that of any writer known to him. For his frame is not, as is often the case, merely a perfunctory setting for a variety of tales; it is a remarkable story in itself, rich in events and in characters whose lifelike reality surpasses anything previously known in English.

Chaucer's frame is, of course, the story of a pilgrimage to the shrine of St. Thomas Becket at Canterbury. And it would be hard to think of a setting better suited to his purposes. For the pilgrimage was one of the most popular of medieval institutions, on which at one time or another all ranks and classes of society might have been seen. It was primarily, of course, an act of piety, the fulfillment, perhaps, of a vow to the saint to visit his shrine as a thank offering for some favor asked and received, such as good fortune in war, the success of a voyage, or a bountiful harvest. But it was very pleasant also to ride slowly through the spring countryside with pleasant companions, and pleasant to stop at an occasional ale stake; and, besides, one might hope for agreeable adventures, especially if one were an agreeable Wife of Bath. There must have been in many a Canterbury pilgrimage just such a mingling of piety and worldliness, of seriousness and levity as are to be found in the group assembled by Chaucer at the Tabard Inn in Southwark.

It is from this variety of *personae* that what has been called the "drama" of the *Canterbury Tales* derives. The contrast of opposites, for example, provides the first incident of the story. At the conclusion of the courtly tale of the gentle, courteous knight, the seemly order of rank in the narratives is rudely shattered by the intrusion of the drunken, bawdy Miller. His somewhat heated exchange with the Host then becomes the first of the many amusing "links" which comprise much of the drama and which we are likely to think of as most characteristically Chaucerian.

A second type of dramatic incident is seen in the disputes among various members of the group, in the prosecution of which each party is likely to employ his tale as a means of enforcing his argument or ridiculing his opponent. Two of the most acrimonious of these disputes arise between the Miller and the Reeve and between the Summoner and the Friar. The Wife of Bath appears also to have evoked a reaction from certain of her fellow pilgrims. Though her discussion of the ascendancy of women in the marital relationship can probably not be said exactly to have provoked a dispute, it does seem to have set off a series of tales in which dramatically diverse views of marriage play a central role and in which allusion appears to be made to her statement of the theme.

Most important, perhaps, in the drama of the frame story is the role of the Host. In the present edition the links attached to the selected tales have been included specifically for the purpose of giving the reader some idea of this remarkable character. He is the director of the proceedings, firm, commanding, and gracious, respectful almost to comic excess when addressing the lady Prioress, jovial and condescending to the Clerk. But faced with impertinence from the Pardoner, he is a lion. And always he is the literary critic: his aesthetic is outraged by the doggerel of *Sir Thopas;* he is immensely moved by the rather obvious pathos of the *Physician's Tale* and boisterously delighted with the Nun's Priest. He is always forthright in reaction, transparently obvious, and, above all, naïve.

THE TEXT

The text of the *Canterbury Tales* survives in a large number of manuscripts in which the order of the tales varies considerably. The variation, however, is not absolute, for in all of the good, complete manuscripts the frame story with its tales is presented in a number of connected narratives of stages of the journey. Most of these comprise two or more tales and the so-called "links" preceding or following them which give an account of the conversation among the pilgrims or the events of the journey. There are, in all, ten of these segments of narrative, or "fragments," as they are usually called. While the order of tales within the fragments is thus usually fixed by the allusions in the links to them or to their tellers and by the fact that in most manuscripts the contents of the fragments do not vary significantly, the order of the fragments themselves is largely undetermined. Not only is there considerable variation among the manuscripts as to the order in which the fragments are presented but the fragments themselves give little unambiguous evidence as to the order in which the author intended them to be presented.

This absence of an internally verifiable coherent order for all the tales is only one item of the considerable evidence that the *Canterbury Tales* was never completely finished by its author. It is indeed highly probable that Chaucer himself had not settled upon a final order for the tales. The present edition, therefore, follows most modern practice in adopting the order supported by the best manuscripts and reflected in the now standard numbering of the fragments. In line numbering also, this edition follows conventional practice in using numbers derived from numerating each fragment independently. Thus the reader will find that the *Nun's Priest's Tale,* for example, because it is preceded in fragment VII by four other tales, begins with line VII: 2821.

CHAUCER'S LANGUAGE

The enjoyment of Chaucer's poetry depends greatly, of course, upon the ease and accuracy with which one is able to read and understand it. The following brief discussions of his language and versification are provided in the hope that the general reader will profit by them, but, more especially, in the belief that teachers may find them useful. Some understanding and command of the pronunciation and metrics is particularly recommended to all. The colloquial ease and fluidity of much of Chaucer's verse is one of its most striking characteristics and one which is impossible to experience without some command of his sounds and metrics.

PRONUNCIATION

This discussion of the pronunciation of Middle English—or of Chaucer's dialect of Middle English—is written for the reader with no experience in the scientific description of the sounds of speech. Accordingly, it necessarily relies on terminology that is regrettably inexact, not to say sometimes perhaps misleading. The rules themselves, while generally sound, are of course subject under certain circumstances to exceptions which it is not practical to describe in so brief a treatment. The reader who learns to apply these elementary principles, however, should acquire an acceptable pronunciation.

The sounds represented by Chaucer's spelling are conventionally classified into long and short vowels, diphthongs, and consonants.

vowels

The distinction between long and short vowels was a significant one in ME (=Middle English) and is still used, though somewhat misleadingly, by many school grammars of MnE (=Modern English). This modern distinction can in most cases be safely used to determine the length of ME vowels. To review the usual modern classification, the "long" vowels are said to be the sounds of *a* in *late*, *e* in *meet*, *i* in *bite*, *o* in *note*, *u* in *flute;* the "short" vowels the *a* in *hat*, *e* in *set*, *i* in *hit*, *o* in *hot*, *u* in *pull*. In general, a word having one of these "long" vowels in MnE had a long vowel in its ME form, and words with "short" vowels in MnE had short vowels in ME. Thus, in the following table of ME long vowels it will be seen that the illustrative words all have "long" vowels in MnE.

long vowels

The long vowels of ME have all undergone qualitative change in MnE. For speakers of English it is a convenient generalization to say that they can be read with "European" qualities, i.e., those of French or German. There were seven long vowels in ME, which can be classified according to the usual ME spelling as follows. The illustrative words are given in their MnE spellings, but they are all common ME words and should be pronounced as shown in the table.

ME *a* was similar to the vowel heard in MnE f*a*ther (ME words having this vowel are *April, take, lady)*.

ME *e* (open): like the vowel of MnE th*e*re *(sea, heath, great, meat)*.

ME *e* (close): like the vowel of MnE f*a*te *(meet, see, he, deep)*.

ME *i* and *y:* like the vowel of MnE mach*i*ne *(smiling, wide, ride)*.

ME *o* (open): like the vowel of MnE l*aw* *(coat, holy, home, go)*.

ME *o* (close): like the vowel of MnE f*oe* *(root, foot, boot, good)*.

ME *ou* or *ow:* like the vowel of MnE t*oo*l *(fowl, house, mouse)*.

Notes:

1. *a, i* or *y*, and *ou* or *ow* were generally pronounced in one way only.
2. *e* (often doubled in Chaucer's spelling) may represent either of two sounds. It will be noticed in the table that these two ME sounds have for the most part become identical in MnE (*see,* ME close *e; meat,* ME open *e*), but modern spelling usually offers a clue as to which of the two sounds the word had in ME. Most words which are now spelled *ea* had open *e* in their ME form; most that are now spelled *e* or *ee* had close *e* in ME.
3. *o* (often doubled in Chaucer's spelling) may represent either of two sounds. Here not only the modern spelling but also modern pronunciation provides a clue: most words now spelled with *o* or *oa* and pronounced as in *go* or *coat* had open *o* in their ME form; most now spelled *oo* and pronounced as in *boot* or as in *good* had close *o* in ME.

short vowels

The short vowels of ME have undergone little qualitative change in MnE. Thus most words pronounced with a "short" vowel in MnE may be pronounced with the same vowel in ME. ME *a* is the most obvious exception.

ME *a* was pronounced like the vowel of American English *hot* as in ME *that, had, shall, was)*.

ME *e* like the vowel of MnE *get (set, ever, leg, met)*.

ME *i* and *y* like the vowel of MnE *hit (it, visit, his, pilgrimage)*.

ME *o* like the vowel of British English *hot* (a rounded vowel—*hollow, lot, ox)*.

ME *u* (often spelled with an *o)* like the vowel of MnE *pull*—never with the vowel of *cut (but, full, young, some)*.

Notes:

1. *a* has changed in MnE in most words. ME has no sound like the vowel of MnE *cat.*

2. *e* and *i (y* is an alternative spelling for *i)* are the same in ME as in MnE.

3. the sound of ME *u* was always that of MnE *pull,* though it was sometimes spelled with an *o* in certain words *(love, yong, corteisye).* Words with ME *u* can be recognized by their MnE pronunciation which is in all instances with the vowel of *cut* or *pull.* Note that there was no sound in ME like the vowel of MnE *cut.*

unstressed vowels

Vowels completely without stress in ME usually tended as in MnE toward the quality of the final sound represented by the *a* in MnE *sofa.* This is particularly true of the final unstressed *e* in *mille, nighte, dwelle,* etc.

diphthongs

ME *ai, ay* and *ei, ey* may be pronounced like the *ai* in American English *rain (faith, seyd).* More precisely, this sound may be distinguished from ME long close *e* (the sound of the vowel in MnE *lady*) by having as the first element of the diphthong a vowel similar to that of MnE *cat.*

ME *au, aw* like the *ou* of MnE *house (chaunce, lawe).*

ME *oi, oy* like the *oy* of MnE *boy (joye).*

consonants

ME *gh* This sound has been entirely lost in MnE. It was a spirant similar to the consonant in German *ich* or *ach.* It is usually preceded by a short vowel *(right, night).*

ME *wr, gn, kn* When these consonant combinations appear initially in words, both consonants are pronounced *(write, gnaw, knee).*

ME *l* Pronounced in combination where it has been lost in MnE *(half, palm).*

ME *g* or *gg* Pronounced either like the *j* in MnE *judge* or the *g* in MnE *get.* Modern usage is a good guide.

ME *h* Not pronounced initially in French loan words (honor) or in common short English words *(he, him)* in unstressed position.

ME *r* Pronounced with a tongue-tip trill.

GRAMMAR

The principal grammatical differences between Chaucer's language and Modern English are relatively few and simple. The following is a brief summary of the most important. A little time spent with this summary will considerably increase the accuracy with which one is able to read the poetry.

nouns

Most plurals and possessives are formed by the addition of *-es* (or *-s* when a word already ends in *-e);* some monosyllables also double the final consonant.

sing. *thank*	plu. *thankes*	possessive *thankes*
cat	*cattes*	*cattes*
tale	*tales*	*tales*

This final *-es* is usually pronounced as a separate syllable.

Some nouns preserve a plural in *-n* that is now rare in Modern English: sing. *sho* (shoe), *to* (toe); plu. *shoon, toon.*

pronouns

	singular			plural		
	subject	possessive	object	subject	possessive	object
1st pers.	*I*	*my, *myn*	*me*	*we*	*oure*	*us*
2nd pers.	**thou*	**thy, *thyn*	**thee*	**ye*	*youre*	*you*
3rd pers.	*he*	*his*	*him*			
	she	*hir*	*hire*	*they*	**hire*	**hem*
	(h)*it*	**his*	(h)*it*			

The forms marked with an asterisk differ from the forms in Modern English. Most are specially commented on below.

1. Note that the second-person forms *thou, thy, thyn, thee* are used in the singular only. These forms are usually confined to familiar use between intimates or to inferiors.
2. The possessives *thy* and *my* are used before words beginning

with a consonant, *thyn* and *myn* before vowels: *my bretheren, myn opinioun.*

3. Note that the possessive of *it* is not the modern *its,* but *his: April with* his *shoures.*

4. Note that the possessive of *they* is not *their,* but *hir* and that the objective is not *them,* but *hem: so priketh* hem *Nature in* hir *corages* (so Nature pricks *them* in *their* spirits).

5. Note that *that* and *which* are the relative pronouns used for Modern English *who* or *whom: a gentil Manciple of* which.

adjectives

In the comparative and superlative degrees some adjectives change the vowel of the stem, sometimes also doubling the final consonant: *sweete/ swettere; greet/ gretteste; strong/ strenger.* Certain adjectives, usually of one syllable, (e.g., *good*) have two declensions, a "strong" and a "weak." In the strong declension they appear without final *-e* in the singular and with final *-e* in the plural *(goode).* In the weak declension they appear with final *-e* in both singular and plural. The weak declension is used when the adjective is preceded by *the* (the yonge sonne), a demonstrative (this yonge wyf), a possessive (his halfe cours, Epicurus owene sone), a noun in direct address (faire Pertelote).

adverbs

1. Adverbs are formed from adjectives by the addition of *-e* and *-liche* as well as of *-ly: wel koude he sitte on hors and* faire *ryde; And have a mantel* roialliche *ybore.*

2. The negative particle *ne,* which is usually translated *not* or *nor,* often combines with certain following verbs:

I ne woot (know) becomes *I noot* (I don't know)

I ne hadde becomes *I nadde* (I had not)

verbs

The verb endings of Middle English differ somewhat from those of Modern English, and there is some difference between the endings of strong and weak verbs (often called in school grammars "regular" and "irregular").

	Present	Past
	singular	
1st pers.	*I love, take*	*I loved, took*
2nd pers.	*thou *lovest, *takest*	*thou *lovedest, took*
3rd pers.	*he *loveth, *taketh*	*he loved, took*
	plural	
1st pers.	*we* }	*we* }
2nd pers.	*ye* } **love(n),*take(n)*	*ye* } **lovede(n), * tooke(n)*
3rd pers.	*they* }	*they* }

1. Note that 2nd sing. (with *thou*) has the characteristic ending *-est* in the present and past of weak verbs but only in the present of strong verbs.

2. Note that 3rd sing. (with *he, she, it*) has the characteristic ending *-eth* in the present only.

3. Note that the plural forms of all verbs may and often do have a final *-n: forth they* goon *towardes that village.*

subjunctive

sing.	*I, thou, he*	*love*
plu.	*we, ye, they*	*love(n)*

The subjunctive is very much more common in Middle English than in Modern English. Its usual sense is conditional where Modern English would use *would* or *should: it is no curteisye to speken to an old man vileynye, but* (unless) *he* trespasse *in word or deed* (it is not courteous to speak rudely to an old man, unless he *should offend* in word or deed).

infinitive

The Middle English infinitive is often formed with final *-n: it is no curteisye to* speken *to an old man vileynye; whan shal my bones* been *at reste.*

past participle

The past participle in Middle English is variously formed:
1. with no distinctive affix: *of which the taverner hadde* spoke *biforn; that in my chambre longe tyme hath* be.
2. with final *-n: he shal be* slayn; *when he hath* goon.
3. with final *-ed: hadde* filled *with wyn.*

4. with a prefix *y-: this tresor moste* ycaried *be by nyghte* (must be carried at night); *if ther were no seed* ysowe (sown).

syntax

1. *word order*

Unfamiliar word order is perhaps the most obvious of the problems of translation that Middle English presents. Some of the characteristics of Middle English order follow.

verb-first constructions: *to hire biwreyed I my conseil al* (I revealed to her all my secrets); *thanne maistou (may-est thou) chese* (then you may choose); *by him shal other men corrected be* (other men shall be corrected by him).

verb-last constructions: *that eech of hem ful blissful was* (that each of them was very blissful).

2. *indirect object* (without *to*): *now wol I tellen forth what happed* me (now I will tell what happened *to me); as* me *was taught* (as was taught *to me).*

3. *impersonal constructions*

A number of common verbs, most of which have changed slightly in meaning in Modern English, appear regularly in this construction. Though the position of the pronoun often suggests that it is subject, it is an indirect object or object: *me thoughte he hadde a paire of legges (thought* = seemed; it seemed to me that he had a pair of legs); *him thoughte his dreem nas* (was not) *but a vanitee* (it seemed to him that his dream was but a vain folly); *right as you lest (lest* = pleases; just as it pleases you).

4. *reflexive constructions*

In Middle English there is much more frequent use of the simple pronoun reflexives than is found in Modern English: *her husband hidde him* (hid himself); *er that the cok him croweth* (before the cock crows); *of one thyng I avaunte me* (of one thing I boast).

VERSIFICATION

All of the selections in this book except the *Prioress's Tale* are in rhymed iambic-pentameter couplets. In a regular line of this kind there are five metric feet, each consisting of one unstressed followed by one stressed syllable. In the following examples, such a foot is marked, or scanned, by setting it off with vertical lines and by marking the stressed syllable with an acute accent: | al thóugh |. Unstressed syllables will ordinarily not be marked.

He wás | as fréssh | as ís | the mónth | of Máy |

final e

Final *e* is, of course, common in Chaucer's language and may generally be assumed to be pronounced. The resulting extra syllable is very important to a correct reading of the verse, forming as it commonly does the necessary unstressed syllable between two otherwise adjacent stressed syllables. Pronounced final *e* is here marked with a diaeresis *(ë)*.

As lée|në wás | his hórs | as ís | a rá|kë

The final *ë* of *leene* provides the necessary unstressed syllable of the second foot. It may be noticed here also that the final *ë* of the last word forms an extra unstressed syllable outside the fifth foot of the pentameter line. This extra unstressed syllable at the end of the line produces what is called a "feminine" line, or, in the case of rhyming words, a "feminine" rhyme. This is very common in Chaucer's verse.

exceptions to the pronunciation of final e

Instances in which final *e* is not pronounced in this verse may be grouped under three heads.

1. Before a word beginning with a vowel or *h* (especially in English pronouns, as *he* or *him*, or words borrowed from French, as *honour)*.

And he | was clad | in cote | and hood | of gre|në
(no ë in *cote* before *and)*

Up on | the cop | right of | his nose | he had|dë
(no ë in *nose* before *he)*

2. At the end of common short words, as some auxiliary verbs, adverbs, pronouns *(hadde, wile; thanne; youre, hire, thise)*.

This il|kë wor|thy knyght | hadde been | al so |
(no ë in *hadde)*

Thanne lon|gen folk | to goon | on pil|grim a|ges
(no ë in *thanne)*

Hire gir|dles and | hir pou|ches e|very deel |
(no ë in *hire)*

3. Irregularly at the demand of the meter.

But sore | wepte she | if oon | of hem | were deed |
(no ë in *sore,* in *wepte)*

syncope

Also before a vowel or *h,* an unstressed syllable containing an *r, l, n, w,* or consonantal *i* or *y* is commonly elided so as to fuse the consonant with the following sound.

For he | hadde ge|ten him yet | no be|ne fi|cë

Here the unstressed vowel in *geten* is elided so as to fuse the *n* and the following *him* into a single unstressed syllable: get | nim yet |. Other examples of this elision, or syncope, of an unstressed vowel are

Wel koude | she ca|rie a mor|sel and | wel ke|pë
That of | hir smy|lyng was | ful sym|ple and coy |
And won|der ly | de ly|vere and of | greet streng|thë
Un to | his or|dre he was | a no|ble post |

Similar instances of syncope are seen in the disappearance of the medial syllables of words like *evere, nevere, owene,* resulting in the pronunciation *ne'er, e'er, ownë.*

> For be | we never | so vi|ci ous | with in|në
>
> Of yon|gë wom|men at | his owe|në cost |

shifting stress

Many French borrowings in which the accent has shifted in Modern English to the first or second syllable had still in Middle English a strong stress on a final or next-to-final syllable.

> Up on | his arm | he bar | a gay | bra cer |
>
> And on | that o|ther syde | a gay | dag ge|rë
>
> But for | to spe|ken of | hir con|sci en|cë
>
> By pa|tente and | by pleyn | com mis|si oun

irregular feet

An effective device for introducing variety and emphasis into the verse is the occasional employment of irregular feet. One of the commonest of these is the inverted iamb.

> Ful se|me ly | af ter | her mete | she raugh|të

Here the foot | af ter | is an inverted iamb, or trochee, a foot with one stressed syllable followed by one unstressed.

Another common feature of Chaucer's verse is the truncated line, which he often uses as a means of emphasizing the first syllable. Here the first unstressed syllable in the line is omitted, leaving the first foot with only a single stressed syllable.

> Gyn|glen in | a whis|tlynge wynd | as clee|rë

rhyme royal

The *Prioress's Tale,* instead of being written in the usual pentameter couplets of the *Canterbury Tales,* is a stanzaic poem in a form known as rhyme royal. This is a seven-line stanza in iambic pentameter, rhyming *ababbcc.*

THE CANTERBURY TALES
OF GEOFFREY CHAUCER

FRAGMENT I.

GENERAL PROLOGUE

Here Bygynneth the Book of the Tales of Caunterbury

Whan that Aprill with his shoures soote *1*
The droghte of March hath perced to the roote,
And bathed every veyne in swich licour,
Of which vertu engendred is the flour;
Whan Zephyrus eek with his sweete breeth *5*
Inspired hath in every holt and heeth
The tendre croppes, and the yonge sonne
Hath in the Ram his halfe cours yronne,
And smale foweles maken melodye
That slepen al the nyght with open yë— *10*
So priketh hem Nature in hir corages—
Thanne longen folk to goon on pilgrimages,
And palmeres for to seken straunge strondes
To ferne halwes, kouthe in sondry londes;

1 *whan that:* when; *his:* its; *shoures soote:* sweet showers.
2 *droghte:* drought; *perced:* pierced.
3 *veyne:* vessel of sap; *swich licour:* that liquid.
4 *of which vertu:* by the power of which; *engendred:* produced.
5 *Zephyrus:* the west wind; *eek:* also.
6 *inspired:* breathed upon; *holt:* woodland; *heeth:* field.
7 *croppes:* sprouts; *yonge sonne:* the sun is young because it has run *(yronne)* only halfway through the first division or "sign" of the zodiac (the Ram), a position in its annual course across the sky which it enters in March and leaves in April.
9 *foweles:* birds.
10 *open yë:* open eye. They are so spurred (pricked) by springtime amorousness that they sing all night.
11 *hir:* their; *corages:* hearts.
12 *thanne:* then; *longen:* long, desire; *goon:* go; *pilgrimages:* journeys to worship at a holy shrine.
13 *palmeres:* pilgrims; *strondes:* strands, shores.
14 *ferne halwes:* far-off shrines; *kouthe:* well-known; *sondry londes:* various lands.

And specially from every shires ende 15
Of Engelond to Caunterbury they wende,
The holy blisful martir for to seke
That hem hath holpen whan that they were seeke.

Bifel that in that seson on a day,
In Southwerk at the Tabard as I lay, 20
Redy to wenden on my pilgrymage
To Caunterbury with ful devout corage,
At nyght was come into that hostelrye
Wel nyne and twenty in a compaignye
Of sondry folk, by aventure yfalle 25
In felaweshipe, and pilgrimes were they alle
That toward Caunterbury wolden ryde.
The chambres and the stables weren wyde,
And wel we weren esed atte beste.
And shortly, whan the sonne was to reste, 30
So hadde I spoken with hem everichon
That I was of hir felaweshipe anon,
And made forward erly for to ryse
To take oure way ther-as I yow devyse.
But nathelees, whil I have tyme and space, 35
Er that I ferther in this tale pace,
Me thynketh it acordaunt to resoun
To telle yow al the condicioun
Of ech of hem, so as it semed me,
And whiche they weren, and of what degree, 40
And eek in what array that they were inne;
And at a knyght than wol I first bigynne.
A Knyght ther was, and that a worthy man,
That fro the tyme that he first bigan

15 *shire:* one of the political divisions into which England is divided.
16 *Caunterbury:* the city containing the shrine of the martyr, St. Thomas Becket; *wende:* go.
17 *seke:* seek.
18 *that:* who; *hem:* them; "who hath helped them when they were sick *(seeke).*"
19 *bifel:* it happened.
20 *Southwerk:* a borough of London on the south side of the Thames; *Tabard:* the name of an inn.
21 *wenden:* go.
22 *ful:* fully; *corage:* see l. 11.
23 *was come:* had come; *hostelrye:* inn.
24 *wel:* fully.
25 *sondry:* l. 14; *aventure:* chance; *yfalle:* fallen.
26 *felaweshipe:* companionship.
27 *wolden:* would, wished (to).
28 *wyde:* roomy.
29 *esed:* accommodated; *atte:* at the.

30 *shortly:* in short; *to reste:* set.
31 *so:* in such a manner; *hem:* them; *everichon:* everyone.
32 *anon:* at once.
33 *made forward:* (we) made agreement; *erly:* early.
34 *ther-as:* as; *you devyse:* describe to you.

35 *nathelees:* nevertheless; *space:* opportunity.
36 *er:* ere, before; *pace:* pass.
37 *me thynketh:* it seems to me; *acordaunt to resoun:* reasonable.
38 *condicioun:* character and circumstances.
39 *hem:* l. 31; *semed me:* seemed to me.

40 *whiche:* what kind; *degree:* rank.
41 *eek:* l. 5; *array:* dress.
42 *wol:* will.
44 *fro:* from.

To riden out, he loved chivalrye, *45*
Trouthe and honour, fredom and curteisye.
Full worthy was he in his lordes werre,
And therto hadde he riden, no man ferre,
As wel in Cristendom as in hethenesse,
And evere honoured for his worthynesse. *50*
At Alisaundre he was whan it was wonne.
Ful ofte tyme he hadde the bord bigonne
Aboven alle nacions in Pruce;
In Lettow had he reysed, and in Ruce,
No Cristen man so ofte of his degree. *55*
In Gernade at the seege eek hadde he be
Of Algezir, and riden in Belmarye.
At Lyeys was he, and at Satalye
Whan they were wonne; and in the Grete See
At many a noble armee hadde he be. *60*
At mortal batailles hadde he been fiftene,
And foughten for oure feith at Tramyssene
In lystes thries, and ay slayn his foo.
This ilke worthy knyght hadde been also
Somtyme with the lord of Palatye *65*
Agayn another hethen in Turkye.
And everemoore he hadde a sovereyn prys;
And though that he were worthy, he was wys,
And of his port as meeke as is a mayde.
He nevere yet no vileynye ne sayde *70*
In al his lyf unto no maner wight.
He was a verray, parfit, gentil knyght.
But for to tellen yow of his array,
His hors were goode, but he was nat gay.

45 *riden out:* to go on expeditions; *chivalrye:* knighthood.
46 *trouthe:* fidelity; *fredom:* liberality.
47 *lord:* the person (here the king) to whom he owed feudal homage and military service; *werre:* war.
48 *ferre:* farther.
49 *hethenesse:* heathendom.
51 *Alisaundre:* Alexandria, captured by King Peter of Cyprus in 1365.
52 *bord bigonne:* been placed at the head of the table as a mark of honor.
53 *Pruce:* he had served with the Knights of the Teutonic Order in Prussia, campaigning in Lithuania *(Lettow)* and Russia *(Ruce)*.
54 *reysed:* made a military campaign.
55 *degree:* l. 40.
56 *Gernade:* the kingdom of Granada in Spain where Henry, Earl of Derby, captured the city of Algezir in 1344; *seege:* siege; *eek:* l. 41; *be:* been.
57 *Belmarye:* Benmarin, Morocco, where there were campaigns in the 40s and 60s.
58 *Lyeys* in Armenia and *Satalye* in Asia Minor were taken by Peter of Cyprus in 1367 and 1361 respectively.
59 *Grete See:* Mediterranean.
60 *armee:* armed expedition.
62 *Tramyssene:* Tlemcen, Algeria, where there were campaigns in the 40s and 60s.
63 *lystes:* tournaments, apparently when challenged by a Saracen; *ay:* always; *foo:* foe.
64 *ilke:* same.
65 *Palatye:* Balat, Turkey. The heathen lord of Palatye was allied with Peter of Cyprus in 1365.
67 *sovereyn prys:* great reputation.
68 *worthy:* of high rank or prominence; *wys:* prudent.
69 *port:* demeanor.
70 *vileynye:* lack of courtesy; *ne:* the negative particle.
71 *no maner wight:* no kind of person.
72 *verray:* true; *parfit:* perfect.
73 *array:* l. 41.
74 *hors:* horses; *he:* i.e., the Knight; *gay:* gaily dressed.

Of fustian he wered a gypon *75*
Al bismotered with his habergeon,
For he was late ycome from his viage
And wente for to doon his pilgrymage.
With him ther was his sone, a yong Squier,
A lovere and a lusty bacheler, *80*
With lokkes crulle as they were leyd in presse.
Of twenty yeer of age he was, I gesse.
Of his stature he was of evene lengthe,
And wonderly delyvere, and of greet strengthe.
And he hadde been som tyme in chivachye *85*
In Flaundres, in Artoys, and Picardye,
And born him wel as of so litel space,
In hope to stonden in his lady grace.
Embrouded was he as it were a meede,
Al ful of fresshe floures whyte and reede. *90*
Syngynge he was, or floytynge, al the day;
He was as fressh as is the month of May.
Short was his gowne, with sleves longe and wyde.
Wel koude he sitte on hors and faire ryde;
He koude songes make and wel endite, *95*
Juste and eek daunce, and wel purtreye and write.
So hote he lovede that by nyghtertale
He slepte namoore than dooth a nyghtyngale.
Curteis he was, lowely, and servysable,
And carf biforn his fader at the table. *100*
A Yeman hadde he and servantz namo
At that tyme, for hym liste ride so,
And he was clad in cote and hood of grene.
A sheef of pecok arwes, bright and kene,

75 *fustian:* thick cotton cloth; *gypon:* a tight-fitting vest.
76 *bismotered:* stained; *habergeon:* coat of chain mail.
77 *late:* lately; *viage:* journey, expedition.
78 *doon:* do, make.
79 *Squier:* esquire, a candidate for knighthood who serves in attendance upon a knight.

80 *bacheler:* a probationer in knighthood.
81 *lokkes crulle:* locks of hair curled (as if they had been pressed in a curling iron).
82 *gesse:* guess.
83 *evene lengthe:* moderate height.
84 *wonderly delyvere:* wonderfully agile.

85 *chivachye:* a raid or expedition, especially with a body of cavalry.
86 In 1383 raids were made into Flanders, Artois, and Picardy as a part of the war between the rival popes of Rome and Avignon.
87 *as of so litel space:* considering the short time of his service.
88 *stonden:* stand; *lady:* lady's.
89 *embrouded:* embroidered; *meede:* meadow.

91 *floytynge:* playing the flute or, possibly, whistling.
92 *fressh:* fresh, bright.

94 *koude:* could.
95 *songes make:* compose music; *endite:* compose words.
96 *juste:* joust; *purtreye:* draw.
97 *hote:* hotly; *nyghtertale:* nighttime.
98 *nyghtyngale:* the nightingale, whose sweet night-song is associated with lovers.

100 *carf:* carved, a gentleman's accomplishment performed by a squire for his knight; *biforn:* in front of.
101 *Yeman:* yeoman, a servant ranking above a groom; *he:* i.e., the Knight; *namo:* no more.
102 *hym liste:* it pleased him.
104 *pecok arwes:* arrows feathered with peacock feathers.

Under his belt he bar ful thriftily; *105*
Wel koude he dresse his takel yemanly:
His arwes drouped noght with fetheres lowe.
And in his hand he bar a myghty bowe.
A not heed hadde he with a broun visage.
Of wodecraft wel koude he al the usage. *110*
Upon his arm he bar a gay bracer,
And by his syde a swerd and a bokeler,
And on that oother syde a gay daggere,
Harneised wel and sharpe as point of spere;
A Cristophre on his brest of silver sheene. *115*
An horn he bar, the bawdryk was of grene;
A forster was he soothly, as I gesse.
Ther was also a Nonne, a Prioresse,
That of hir smylyng was ful symple and coy.
Hir gretteste ooth was but by Seint Loy; *120*
And she was cleped Madame Eglentyne.
Ful wel she soong the service dyvyne,
Entuned in hir nose ful semely;
And Frenssh she spak ful faire and fetisly,
After the scole of Stratford atte Bowe, *125*
For Frenssh of Parys was to hire unknowe.
At mete wel ytaught was she with alle:
She leet no morsel from hir lippes falle,
Ne wette hir fyngres in hir sauce depe;
Wel koude she carie a morsel, and wel kepe *130*
That no drope ne fille upon hir brest.
In curteisie was set ful muchel hir lest.
Hir over-lippe wyped she so clene
That in hir coppe ther was no ferthyng sene

105 *bar:* bore; *thriftily:* carefully.
106 *koude:* could; *dresse his takel:* care for his gear.
107 *noght:* not; *fetheres lowe:* the feathers stood out firmly and uncrushed.

109 *not heed:* close-cropped head.

110 *koude:* understood; *usage:* practice.
111 *bracer:* wrist guard for archery.
112 *bokeler:* small shield.

114 *harneised:* fitted, mounted.
115 *Cristophre:* figure of St. Christopher, patron of foresters, worn for protection; *sheene:* bright.
116 *bawdryk:* a carrying strap.
117 *forster:* forester; *soothly:* truly.
118 *Prioresse:* a nun who is the superior of a priory.
119 *symple and coy:* modest and quiet; the phrase is from the language of love poetry.
120 *ooth:* oath.
121 *cleped:* called.
122 *service dyvyne:* liturgical offices set to music, including chants, etc.
123 The traditional nasal intonation in which parts of the service are chanted; *semely:* in a seemly manner.
124 *spak:* spoke; *fetisly:* elegantly.
125 *after:* according to; *scole of Stratford atte Bowe:* the manner of the Benedictine convent at Stratford near London (not on Avon).
126 *unknowe:* unknown; Parisian French was thought superior.
127 *mete:* meals; *with alle:* moreover.
128 *leet:* let.
129 *ne:* nor; *depe:* deeply.
130 *kepe:* take care.
131 *ne fille:* should not fall.
132 Literally, "on courtesy was fixed very greatly her interest"; the Prioress's table manners are those of a lady of fashion.
133 *over-lippe:* upper lip.
134 *coppe:* cup; *ferthyng:* least bit.

Of grece, whan she dronken hadde hir draughte; *135*
Ful semely after hir mete she raughte.
And sikerly she was of greet desport,
And ful plesaunt, and amyable of port,
And peyned hire to countrefete cheere
Of court, and to been estatlich of manere, *140*
And to been holden digne of reverence.
But for to speken of hir conscience,
She was so charitable and so pitous
She wolde wepe if that she sawe a mous
Caught in a trappe, if it were deed or bledde. *145*
Of smale houndes hadde she that she fedde
With rosted flessh, or milk and wastel-breed;
But soore wepte she if oon of hem were deed,
Or if men smoot it with a yerde smerte;
And al was conscience and tendre herte. *150*
Ful semely hir wympel pynched was,
Hir nose tretys, hir eyen greye as glas,
Hir mouth ful smal, and therto softe and reed;
But sikerly she hadde a fair forheed;
It was almoost a spanne brood, I trowe, *155*
For hardily, she was nat undergrowe.
Ful fetys was hir cloke, as I was war;
Of smal coral aboute hir arm she bar
A peire of bedes, gauded al with grene,
And theron heng a brooch of gold ful sheene, *160*
On which ther was first write a crowned A,
And after *Amor vincit omnia.*
Another Nonne with hire hadde she,
That was hire chapeleyne and preestes thre.

135 *grece:* grease; *draughte:* drink.
136 *mete:* food, l. 127; *raughte:* reached.
137 *sikerly:* certainly; *desport:* good cheer.
138 *port:* bearing, behavior.
139 *peyned:* took pains; *countrefete:* follow; *cheere of court:* courtly manners.
140 *been:* be; *estatlich:* stately, dignified.
141 *holden digne:* considered worthy.

143 *pitous:* merciful.
144 *mous:* mouse.

145 *deed:* dead.
146 *of:* some; *houndes:* dogs.
147 *wastel-breed:* fine white bread.
148 *soore:* sorely; *oon:* one; *hem:* them.
149 *men:* someone; *smoot:* struck; *yerde:* stick; *smerte:* smartly.

151 *semely:* seemly; *wympel:* garment covering head, sides of the facc, and neck; *pynched:* pleated.
152 *tretys:* well-shaped; *eyen:* eyes.
153 *therto:* also; *reed:* red.
154 *sikerly:* certainly.
155 *spanne:* the breadth of an extended hand from thumb to little finger; *trowe:* believe.
156 *hardily:* surely; *undergrowe:* undergrown, short.
157 *fetys:* well-made, elegant; *was war:* perceived.
158 *bar:* l. 105.
159 *peire of bedes:* rosary; *gauded:* having the larger beads (gaudees) of green.
160 *heng:* hung; *sheene:* l. 115.
162 *Amor vincit omnia:* Love conquers all.

164 *chapeleyne:* a kind of private secretary.

A Monk ther was, a fair for the maistrie, *165*
An outridere that lovede venerye,
A manly man, to been an abbot able.
Ful many a deyntee hors hadde he in stable,
And whan he rood, men myghte his brydel heere
Gynglen in a whistlynge wynd as cleere *170*
And eek as loude as dooth the chapel belle.
Ther as this lord was kepere of the celle,
The reule of Seint Maure or of Seint Beneit,
By cause that it was old and somdel streit,
This ilke Monk leet olde thynges pace, *175*
And heeld after the newe world the space.
He yaf nat of that text a pulled hen
That seith that hunters been nat holy men,
Ne that a monk, whan he is recchelees,
Is likned til a fissh that is waterlees— *180*
This is to seyn, a monk out of his cloystre.
But thilke text heeld he nat worth an oystre;
And I seyde his opinion was good.
What sholde he studie and make hymselven wood,
Upon a book in cloystre alwey to poure, *185*
Or swynken with his handes and laboure,
As Austyn bit? How shal the world be served?
Lat Austyn have his swynk to him reserved!
Therfore he was a prikasour aright.
Grehoundes he hadde as swift as fowel in flight; *190*
Of prikyng and of huntyng for the hare
Was al his lust, for no cost wolde he spare.
I seigh his sleves purfiled at the hond
With grys, and that the fyneste of a lond;

165 *fair for the maistrie:* an attractive one in the extreme.
166 *outridere:* monk charged with overseeing the monastery's estates; *venerye:* hunting.
167 *able:* worthy.
168 *deyntee:* valuable.
169 *heere:* hear.
170 *gynglen:* to jingle; *cleere:* clearly.
172 *ther as:* there where; *kepere:* head; *celle:* a small dependent monastery.
173 *reule:* the rules of monastic discipline established by St. Benedict and St. Maurus for the Benedictine order.
174 *somdel streit:* somewhat strict.
175 *ilke:* l. 64; *pace:* pass by.
176 *heeld after:* followed the customs of; *the space:* meanwhile.
177 *yaf . . .:* didn't give a plucked hen for the text.
179 *recchelees:* neglectful of duty and rules.

180 *likned:* compared; *til:* to; *waterlees:* out of water.
181 *seyn:* say; *cloystre:* cloister.
182 *thilke:* that.

184 *what:* why; *wood:* mad, crazy.
185 *poure:* pore.
186 *swynken:* work.
187 *Austyn:* St. Augustine; *bit:* commands; *How shal . . .:* "How shall the world's work be done if monks spend all their time on religious duties?" An ironic question.
189 *prikasour:* hunter on horseback.
190 *grehoundes:* greyhounds; *fowel:* bird.
191 *prikyng:* tracking the hare by its pricks, or tracks.
192 *lust:* pleasure; *cost:* expense or effort; *wolde:* would.
193 *seigh:* saw; *purfiled:* trimmed at the edges; *hond:* hand.
194 *grys:* an expensive gray fur.

And for to festne his hood under his chyn, *195*
He hadde of gold yroght a ful curious pyn;
A love-knotte in the gretter ende ther was.
His heed was balled, that shoon as any glas,
And eek his face, as he hadde been enoynt;
He was a lord ful fat and in good poynt. *200*
His eyen stepe, and rollynge in his heed,
That stemed as a forneys of a leed,
His bootes souple, his hors in greet estaat,
Now certeinly he was a fair prelaat.
He was nat pale as a forpyned goost; *205*
A fat swan loved he best of any roost.
His palfrey was as broun as is a berye.
  A Frere ther was, a wantowne and a merye,
A lymytour, a ful solempne man.
In alle the ordres foure is noon that kan *210*
So muche of daliaunce and fair langage.
He hadde maad ful many a mariage
Of yonge wommen at his owene cost.
Unto his ordre he was a noble post.
Ful wel biloved and famulier was he *215*
With frankeleyns over al in his contree,
And eek with worthy wommen of the toun;
For he hadde power of confessioun,
As seyde hymself, moore than a curat,
For of his ordre he was licenciat. *220*
Ful swetely herde he confession,
And plesaunt was his absolucion.
He was an esy man to yeve penaunce
Ther as he wiste to have a good pitaunce;

195 *festne:* fasten.
196 *of gold ywroght:* made of gold; *curious:* elaborate.
197 *love-knotte:* an ornamental knot; *gretter:* greater.
198 *balled:* bald.
199 *eek:* l. 5; *as:* as if; *enoynt:* anointed, i.e., with oil.

200 *in good poynt:* in good condition.
201 *eyen:* l. 152; *stepe:* prominent.
202 *stemed:* glowed; *forneys of a leed:* fire under a cauldron.
203 *souple:* supple; *estaat:* condition.
204 *prelaat:* prelate.

205 *forpyned:* tormented and wasted; *goost:* ghost.
206 *roost:* roast.
207 *palfrey:* saddle horse.
208 *Frere:* friar; *wantowne:* lively, wanton; *merye:* merry.
209 *lymytour:* a begging friar assigned a certain area in which to solicit alms; *solempne:* festive.

210 *ordres foure:* the four orders of friars: Dominican, Franciscan, Carmelite, Augustinian; *kan:* knows.
211 *daliaunce:* gossip, flirting; *fair langage:* flattery.
213 *owene cost:* i.e., he found husbands for young women who had been his mistresses.
214 *post:* pillar, support.
216 *frankeleyns:* see ll. 333ff. for the entertainment to be found in a franklin's house; *over al:* everywhere.
218-20 *power of confessioun:* he was licensed (a *licenciat)* by his order to hear confessions and give absolution in cases beyond the jurisdiction of a parish priest *(curat).*

221 *swetely:* sweetly; *herde:* heard.
222 *absolucion:* absolution.
223 *esy:* easy; *yeve:* give; *penaunce:* penance.
224 *ther as:* l. 172; *wiste:* knew; *pitaunce:* pittance, usually a donation of food.

For unto a povre ordre for to yive 225
Is signe that a man is wel yshryve;
For if he yaf, he dorste make avaunt
He wiste that a man was repentaunt;
For many a man so hard is of his herte,
He may nat wepe althogh hym soore smerte. 230
Therfore, instede of wepynge and prayeres,
Men moote yeve silver to the povre freres.
His typet was ay farsed ful of knyves
And pynnes, for to yeven faire wyves.
And certeinly he hadde a murye note; 235
Wel koude he synge and pleyen on a rote;
Of yeddynges he baar outrely the pris.
His nekke whit was as the flour-de-lys;
Therto he strong was as a champioun.
He knew the tavernes wel in every toun, 240
And every hostiler and tappestere,
Bet than a lazar or a beggestere.
For unto swich a worthy man as he
Acorded nat, as by his facultee,
To have with sike lazars aqueyntaunce. 245
It is nat honeste, it may nat avaunce,
For to deelen with no swich poraille,
But al with riche, and selleres of vitaille.
And over al ther as profit sholde arise,
Curteis he was, and lowely of servyse; 250
Ther nas no man nowher so vertuous.
He was the beste beggere in his hous,
For thogh a wydwe hadde noght a sho,
So plesaunt was his *In principio*

225 *povre:* poor; *yive:* give.
226 *yshryve:* shriven.
227 *he:* i.e., the penitent; *yaf:* gave; *he dorste make avaunt:* he, i.e., the friar, dared makc a boast.
228 *wiste:* knew.

230 *althogh . . .:* though it (his heart) hurts him sorely. The passage is an ironic statement of the Friar's cynical attitude toward penance.
232 *men moote:* one ought to.
233 *typet:* a loose hood used as a pocket; *farsed:* stuffed.
234 *yeven:* l. 225.
235 *murye:* merry; *note:* tune.
236 *koude:* could; *rote:* a stringed instrument.
237 *of yeddynges:* for songs; *baar . . .:* absolutely took the prize.
238 *nekke:* neck; *whit:* white; *flour-de-lys:* lily.
239 *therto:* moreover.

241 *hostiler:* innkeeper; *tappestere:* barmaid.
242 *bet:* better; *lazar:* leper; *beggestere:* female beggar.
243 *swich:* such.
244 *acorded nat:* it was not fitting; *as by . . .:* considering his position.
245 *sike:* sick.
246 *honeste:* becoming; *avaunce:* be profitable.
247 *deelen:* deal; *poraille:* poor people.
248 *selleres of vitaille:* sellers of foodstuff.
249 *over al:* l. 216; *ther as:* l. 172.

251 *vertuous:* showing moral rectitude.
253 *wydwe:* widow; *sho:* shoe.
254 *In principio (erat verbum):* "in the beginning was the word" (John 1:1), quoted as a greeting.

Yet wolde he have a ferthyng er he wente. *255*
His purchas was wel bettre than his rente.
And rage he koude as it were right a whelpe;
In love-dayes ther koude he muchel helpe,
For ther he was nat lyk a cloysterer
With a thredbare cope, as is a povre scoler, *260*
But he was lyk a maister or a pope.
Of double worstede was his semycope,
And rounded as a belle out of the presse.
Somwhat he lipsed for his wantownesse,
To make his Englissh sweete upon his tonge; *265*
And in his harpyng, whan that he hadde songe,
His eyen twynkled in his heed aryght
As doon the sterres in the frosty nyght.
This worthy lymytour was cleped Huberd.
  A Marchant was ther with a forked berd, *270*
In mottelee, and hye on horse he sat;
Upon his heed a Flaundryssh bevere hat,
His bootes clasped faire and fetisly.
His resons he spak ful solempnely,
Sownynge alway th'encrees of his wynnyng. *275*
He wolde the see were kept for any thing
Betwixen Middelburgh and Orewelle.
Wel koude he in eschaunge sheeldes selle.
This worthy man ful wel his wit besette:
Ther wiste no wight that he was in dette, *280*
So estatly was he of his governaunce,
With his bargaynes, and with his chevyssaunce.
For sothe he was a worthy man with alle,
But, sooth to seyn, I noot how men hym calle.

255 *wolde:* would; *ferthyng:* a coin = ¼ penny; *er:* ere.
256 *purchas:* proceeds of his begging; *rente:* regular income; a friar had no regular income—the line is an understatement.
257 *rage:* flirt or play amorously; *whelpe:* young dog.
258 *love-dayes:* days for settling suits out of court; *koude . . .:* could give much help (and also enrich himself).
259 *cloysterer:* a poor brother who remained in the cloister.
260 *cope:* a priest's vestment.
261 *maister:* the Master's degree had great dignity.
262 *semycope:* short robe.
263 *presse:* the round mold in which a bell is cast.
264 *lipsed:* lisped; *for wantownesse:* as an affectation.

266 *songe:* sung.

268 *doon:* do; *sterres:* stars.
269 *cleped:* l. 121.

271 *mottelee:* cloth with a figured design or mixed colors; *hye:* high.
272 *Flaundryssh:* Flemish; *bevere:* beaver.
273 *clasped:* fastened with clasps; *fetisly:* neatly.
274 *resons:* opinions; *spak:* spoke; *solempnely:* pompously.
275 *sownynge:* proclaiming; *encrees:* increase; *wynnyng:* profits.
276 *wolde:* wished; *see:* sea; *kept . . . thing:* guarded at all costs (against pirates).
277 Cities in the Netherlands and in England engaged in the wool trade.
278 *sheeld:* a French coin; it was illegal for him to profit in foreign exchange.
279 *wit besette:* employed his wit.
280 *wiste:* l. 228; *wight:* person; *dette:* debt.
281 *estatly:* dignified; *governaunce:* management.
282 *bargaynes:* bargainings; *chevyssaunce:* borrowing.
284 *sooth:* truth; *noot:* know not (his name).

A Clerk ther was of Oxenford also, *285*
That unto logyk hadde longe ygo.
As leene was his hors as is a rake,
And he nas nat right fat, I undertake,
But looked holwe, and therto sobrely.
Ful thredbare was his overeste courtepy, *290*
For he hadde geten hym yet no benefice,
Ne was so worldly for to have office.
For hym was levere have at his beddes heed
Twenty bookes, clad in blak or reed,
Of Aristotle and his philosophie, *295*
Than robes riche, or fithele, or gay sautrie.
But al be that he was a philosophre,
Yet hadde he but litel gold in cofre;
But al that he myghte of his freendes hente,
On bookes and on lernynge he it spente, *300*
And bisily gan for the soules preye
Of hem that yaf him wherwith to scoleye.
Of studie took he moost cure and moost heede.
Noght o word spak he moore than was neede,
And that was seyd in forme and reverence, *305*
And short and quyk, and ful of hy sentence;
Sownynge in moral vertu was his speche,
And gladly wolde he lerne and gladly teche.
A Sergeant of the Lawe, war and wys,
That often hadde been at the Parvys, *310*
Ther was also, ful riche of excellence.
Discreet he was, and of greet reverence—
He semed swich, his wordes weren so wise.
Justice he was ful often in assise,

285 *Clerk:* an ecclesiastical student (at Oxford).

286 *ygo:* gone; he had completed the part of his studies that included logic, which qualified him for the B.A.
287 *leene:* lean.
289 *holwe:* hollow (cheeked); *therto:* moreover.

290 *overeste courtepy:* outer cloak.
291 *benefice:* appointment to the rectorship of a parish church.
292 *office:* a secular position.
293 *hym was levere:* it was preferable to him; *heed:* head.

296 *fithele:* fiddle; *sautrie:* a kind of harp.
297 *al be:* though; *philosophre:* a pun on the secondary meaning "alchemist."
298 *cofre:* coffer, money box.
299 *freendes:* friends; *hente:* get.

301 *gan:* did.
302 *hem:* them; *yaf:* l. 227; *scoleye:* study.
303 *took cure:* gave attention.
304 *o:* one.

305 *in forme and reverence:* with propriety and modesty.
306 *quyk:* lively; *hy sentence:* elevated thought.
307 *sownynge in:* tending toward, conducing to.
308 *lerne:* learn; *teche:* teach.
309 *Sergeant:* a barrister of the highest degree, chosen from among the most eminent senior members of the bar; *war:* wary, cautious; *wys:* wise.
310 *Parvys:* a place where clients met lawyers for consultation.
313 *swich:* l. 243.
314 *assise:* assize, the regular county court, the justices of which were usually sergeants.

By patente and by pleyn commissioun. *315*
For his science and for his heigh renoun
Of fees and robes hadde he many oon.
So greet a purchasour was nowher noon;
Al was fee symple to hym in effect;
His purchasyng myghte nat been infect. *320*
Nowher so bisy a man as he ther nas,
And yet he semed bisier than he was.
In termes hadde he caas and doomes alle
That from the tyme of kyng William were falle.
Therto he koude endite and make a thyng, *325*
Ther koude no wight pynche at his writyng;
And every statut koude he pleyn by rote.
He rood but hoomly in a medlee cote,
Girt with a ceint of silk with barres smale.
Of his array telle I no lenger tale. *330*
A Frankeleyn was in his compaignye;
Whit was his berd as is the dayesye;
Of his complexion he was sangwyn.
Wel loved he by the morwe a sop in wyn;
To lyven in delit was evere his wone, *335*
For he was Epicurus owene sone,
That heeld opinion that pleyn delit
Was verraily felicitee parfit.
An housholdere, and that a greet, was he;
Saint Julian he was in his contree. *340*
His breed, his ale, was alweys after oon;
A bettre envyned man was nowher noon.
Withoute bake mete was nevere his hous,
Of fissh and flessh, and that so plentevous,

315 *patente:* letter of appointment from the king; a *pleyn commissioun* empowered justices to hear cases of all sorts.

316 *for:* on account of; *science:* knowledge.

317 Robes were commonly part of a professional man's compensation.

318 *purchasour:* buyer of land.

319 *al:* all; *fee symple:* a title without restriction.

320 *infect:* legally invalidated.

321 *ther nas:* there was not.

323 *in termes . . . he:* he could recite; *caas:* cases; *doomes:* judgments, i.e., legal precedents.

324 *were falle:* had been ruled on.

325 *therto:* l. 289; *endite . . . thyng:* compose and draw up a document.

326 *wight:* l. 280; *pynche:* find fault with.

327 *koude:* knew, l. 110; *pleyn:* fully; *by rote:* by heart.

328 *rood:* rode; *hoomly:* unpretentiously; *medlee:* motley, l. 271.

329 *ceint:* girdle; *barres:* ornamental bands.

330 *array:* l. 41.

331 Franklin, a landholder or country gentleman.

332 *dayesye:* daisy.

333 *complexion:* medicine classified men into four types, or complexions; the sanguine man was large, ruddy, lusty, bold; see l. 420.

334 *morwe:* morning; *sop in wyn:* bread soaked in wine.

335 *delit:* pleasure; *wone:* custom.

336 The philosophy of Epicurus was thought to favor luxurious living.

337 *that:* who, i.e., Epicurus; *pleyn delit:* purely sensual pleasure.

338 *verraily . . . parfit:* truly perfect felicity.

340 *St. Julian:* patron of hospitality; *contree:* region.

341 *after oon:* according to a single standard, uniformly good.

342 *envyned:* stocked with wine.

343 *bake mete:* baked food (i.e., meat pies).

It snewed in his hous of mete and drynke, 345
Of alle deyntees that men koude thynke.
After the sondry sesons of the yeer,
So chaunged he his mete and his soper.
Ful many a fat partrich hadde he in muwe,
And many a breem and many a luce in stuwe. 350
Wo was his cook but if his sauce were
Poynaunt and sharp, and redy al his geere.
His table dormant in his halle alway
Stood redy covered al the longe day.
At sessions ther was he lord and sire; 355
Ful ofte tyme he was knyght of the shire.
An anlaas and a gipser al of silk
Heeng at his girdel, whit as morne milk.
A shirreve hadde he been, and a countour.
Was nowher swich a worthy vavasour. 360
An Haberdasshere and a Carpenter,
A Webbe, a Dyere, and a Tapycer—
And they were clothed alle in o lyveree
Of a solempne and a greet fraternitee.
Ful fressh and newe hir geere apiked was; 365
Hir knyves were chaped noght with bras,
But al with silver; wroght ful clene and weel
Hire girdles and hir pouches everydeel.
Wel semed ech of hem a fair burgeys
To sitten in a yeldehalle on a deys. 370
Everich, for the wisdom that he kan,
Was shaply for to been an alderman.
For catel hadde they ynogh and rente,
And eek hir wyves wolde it wel assente—

345 *snewed:* snowed; *mete:* l. 136.

347 *after:* according to; *sondry:* l. 14.
348 It was customary to change one's dict according to the season.
349 *partrich:* partridge; *muwe:* coop.
350 *breem:* bream; *luce:* pike; *stuwe:* fish pond.
351 *wo:* woeful; *but if:* unless.
352 *poynaunt:* pungent; *redy:* ready; *geere:* gear, equipment.
353 *table dormant:* table fixed permanently in place.

355 *sessions:* meetings of the justices of the peace.
356 *knyght of the shire:* county representative in Parliament.
357 *anlaas:* short, two-edged dagger; *gipser:* a pouch or purse.
358 *heeng:* l. 160; *morne:* morning.
359 *shirreve:* sheriff, the administrative officer of a county; *countour:* auditor.
360 *vavasour:* subvassal, holding land from a tenant-in-chief.
361 Haberdasher: a seller of hats or of needles, buttons, etc.
362 *Webbe:* weaver; *Tapycer:* upholsterer or tapestry maker.
363 *o lyveree:* one (the same) livery.
364 *solempne:* distinguished; *fraternitee:* guild.

365 *hir:* their; *geere:* l. 352; *apiked:* polished.
366 *chaped:* ornamented with metal on the scabbard.

367 *weel:* well.
368 *everydeel:* every bit.
369 *ech:* each; *hem:* them; *burgeys:* burgess.
370 *yeldehalle:* guildhall; the mayor and aldermen sat on the dais.
371 *everich:* everyone; *for:* because of; *kan:* knows.
372 *shaply:* fit.
373 *catel:* property; *ynogh:* enough; *rente:* income.
374 *assente:* agree to.

And elles certeyn were they to blame. *375*
It is ful fair to been ycleped "Madame,"
And goon to vigilies al bifore,
And have a mantel roialliche ybore.
A Cook they hadde with hem for the nones,
To boille the chiknes with the marybones, *380*
And powdre-marchant tart and galyngale.
Wel koude he knowe a draughte of London ale.
He koude rooste and sethe and broille and frye,
Maken mortreux, and wel bake a pye.
But greet harm was it, as it thoughte me, *385*
That on his shyne a mormal hadde he.
For blankmanger, that made he with the beste.
A Shipman was ther, wonynge fer by weste;
For aught I woot, he was of Dertemouthe.
He rood upon a rouncy as he kouthe, *390*
In a gowne of faldyng to the knee.
A daggere hangynge on a laas hadde he
Aboute his nekke, under his arm adoun.
The hoote somer hadde maad his hewe al broun;
And certeinly he was a good felawe. *395*
Ful many a draughte of wyn hadde he ydrawe
Fro Burdeux-ward, whil that the chapman sleep;
Of nyce conscience took he no keep.
If that he faught and hadde the hyer hond,
By water he sente hem hoom to every lond. *400*
But of his craft, to rekene wel his tydes,
His stremes and his daungers hym bisides,
His herberwe and his moone, his lodemenage,
Ther nas noon swich from Hulle to Cartage.

375 *and elles:* for else; *certeyn:* certainly.
376 *ycleped:* called, 1. 269.
377 *goon:* to go; *vigilies:* ceremonies on the eve of guild festivals; *al bifore:* at the head of the procession.
378 *mantel . . .:* a mantle borne by a servant in the manner of royalty.
379 *nones:* occasion.
380 *chiknes:* chickens; *marybones:* marrowbones.
381 *powdre-marchant, galyngale:* flavorings.
382 *knowe:* distinguish; *London ale:* the best-quality ale.
383 *rooste:* roast; *sethe:* boil.
384 *mortreux:* a stew.

385 *thoughte me:* seemed to me.
386 *shyne:* shin; *mormal:* ulcer.
387 *blankmanger:* a dish of capon, rice, milk, sugar, almonds.
388 *wonynge:* dwelling; *by weste:* westward.
389 *woot:* know; Dartmouth, a port in the southwest.

390 *rouncy:* a large horse; *as he kouthe:* as well as he could.
391 *faldyng:* coarse wool cloth.
392 *laas:* lace, cord.

394 *somer:* summer (sun); *hewe:* color.
395 *good felawe:* perhaps an ironical reference to his relationship with the chapman.
396 *ydrawe:* drawn (from the cask).
397 *Burdeux-ward:* i.e., while carrying wine from Bordeaux; *chapman:* merchant; *sleep:* slept.
398 *nyce:* scrupulous; *keep:* heed.
399 *hyer hond:* upper hand.
400 i.e., made the enemy sailors walk the plank.
401 *of . . . craft:* among seamen; *rekene:* calculate.
402 *stremes:* currents; *daungers . . . bisides:* hazards near to him.
403 *herberwe:* harbor; *lodemenage:* pilotage.
404 *nas:* was not; *noon swich:* none such; Hull, in Yorkshire; Cartagena, Spain.

Hardy he was and wys to undertake; *405*
With many a tempest hadde his berd been shake;
He knew alle the havenes as they were,
Fro Gootlond to the Cape of Fynystere,
And every cryke in Britaigne and in Spayne.
His barge ycleped was the Maudelayne. *410*
With us ther was a Doctour of Phisik;
In al this world ne was ther noon hym lik,
To speke of phisik and of surgerye,
For he was grounded in astronomye.
He kepte his pacient a ful greet deel *415*
In houres by his magyk natureel.
Wel koude he fortunen the ascendent
Of his ymages for his pacient.
He knew the cause of every maladye,
Were it of hoot or cold or moyste or drye, *420*
And where engendred and of what humour;
He was a verray, parfit praktisour.
The cause yknowe, and of his harm the roote,
Anon he yaf the sike man his boote.
Ful redy hadde he his apothecaries *425*
To sende him drogges and his letuaries,
For ech of hem made oother for to wynne;
Hir frendshipe nas nat newe to bigynne.
Wel knew he the olde Esculapius,
And Deiscorides and eek Rufus, *430*
Olde Ypocras, Haly, and Galyen,
Serapion, Razis, and Avycen,
Averrois, Damascien, and Constantyn,
Bernard and Gatesden and Gilbertyn.

405 *hardy:* bold; *wys to undertake:* prudent in his enterprises.
406 *berd . . . shake:* beard been shaken.
407 *havenes:* harbors.
408 Gotland, an island near Sweden; Finisterre, westernmost cape of Spain.
409 *cryke:* inlet.
410 *barge:* ship; *ycleped:* l. 376.
411 *phisik:* medicine.
412 *noon hym lik:* none like him.
413 *to speke of:* with regard to.
414 *for:* because; *grounded:* well instructed.

415 *kepte:* cared for; *a ful greet deel:* very closely.
416 *in houres:* according to the astrological hours favorable to the treatment; *natural magic* was the use of astrology and charms, as in medicine.
417 *fortunen . . .:* determine the favorable time for using images, or talismans, in medicine.
420 *were:* whether it were; *of:* from; *hoot . . . drye:* the qualities combining in the four elements (earth, air, fire, water), and the four humors, sanguinary (blood), phlegmatic (phlegm), choleric (yellow bile), melancholy (black bile), the proportions of which in a man determined his complexion. A disturbance of one of the humors was thought to be a cause of disease. See ll. 333, 587.
422 *verray, parfit:* l. 72; *praktisour:* practitioner.
423 *yknowe:* being known; *harm:* illness.
424 *anon:* l. 32; *yaf:* l. 227; *boote:* remedy.
425 *apothecaries:* pharmacists.
426 *drogges:* drugs; *letuaries:* medicines.
427 *wynne:* profit.
428 *hir:* their; *newe . . .:* newly begun.
429-34 *Esculapius . . . Gilbertyn:* the chief medical authorities recognized in the Middle Ages.

Of his diete mesurable was he, *435*
For it was of no superfluitee,
But of greet norissyng and digestible.
His studie was but litel on the Bible.
In sangwyn and in pers he clad was al,
Lyned with taffata and with sendal; *440*
And yet he was but esy of dispence;
He kepte that he wan in pestilence.
For gold in phisik is a cordial,
Therfore he loved gold in special.
  A good Wif was ther of biside Bathe, *445*
But she was somdel deef, and that was scathe.
Of clooth-makyng she hadde swich an haunt,
She passed hem of Ypres and of Gaunt.
In al the parisshe wif ne was ther noon
That to the offrynge bifore hire sholde goon; *450*
And if ther dide, certeyn so wrooth was she,
That she was out of alle charitee.
Hir coverchiefs ful fyne were of ground;
I dorste swere they weyeden ten pound
That on a Sonday weren upon hir heed. *455*
Hir hosen weren of fyn scarlet reed,
Ful streite yteyd, and shoes ful moyste and newe.
Boold was hir face and fair and reed of hewe.
She was a worthy womman al hir lyve:
Housbondes at chirche dore she hadde fyve, *460*
Withouten oother compaignye in youthe—
But therof nedeth nat to speke as nowthe.
And thries hadde she been at Jerusalem;
She hadde passed many a straunge strem;

435 *mesurable:* moderate.
436 *superfluitee:* excess.
437 *of . . . norissyng:* greatly nourishing.
438 Physicians were commonly regarded as skeptical.
439 *sangwyn:* blood red; *pers:* bluish gray.

440 *sendal:* a rich silk.
441 *esy of dispence:* easy or slow in spending money (understatement).
442 *that . . . pestilence:* what he made during the plague.
443-44 *for . . .:* because gold was considered an excellent medicine, he specially loved it. An ironical statement.
445 *biside:* near.
446 *somdel:* somewhat; *scathe:* a pity.
447 *haunt:* practice; i.e., was so skilled.
448 *passed:* surpassed; Ypres and Gaunt were Flemish centers of clothmaking.

450 *offrynge:* the parishioners came forward in order of rank to bring offerings to the church.
451 *wrooth:* angry.
452 *out . . . charitee:* fit to be tied.
453 *coverchiefs:* kerchiefs used in the headdress; *ground:* texture.
454 *dorste:* dare; *weyeden ten pound:* the headdress was often very large and heavy.
455 *weren:* were.
456 *fyn:* fine.
457 *streite yteyd:* tightly fastened; *moyste:* soft.
458 *hewe:* hue.

460 Marriages were performed at the church door.
461 *withouten:* not counting.
462 *nedeth nat:* it is not necessary; *as nowthe:* now.
463 *thries:* thrice; *Jerusalem:* three syllables, *Jér-să-lém.*
464 *passed:* crossed; *straunge:* foreign.

At Rome she hadde been, and at Boloigne, *465*
In Galice at Seint Jame, and at Coloigne;
She koude muche of wandrynge by the weye.
Gat-tothed was she, soothly for to seye.
Upon an amblere esily she sat,
Ywympled wel, and on hir heed an hat *470*
As brood as is a bokeler or a targe;
A foot-mantel aboute hir hipes large,
And on hir feet a paire of spores sharpe.
In felaweshipe wel koude she laughe and carpe.
Of remedies of love she knew per chaunce, *475*
For she koude of that art the olde daunce.
  A good man was ther of religioun,
And was a povre Person of a toun,
But riche he was of holy thoght and werk.
He was also a lerned man, a clerk, *480*
That Cristes gospel trewely wolde preche;
His parisshens devoutly wolde he teche.
Benygne he was and wonder diligent,
And in adversitee ful pacient;
And swich he was ypreved ofte sithes. *485*
Ful looth were hym to cursen for his tithes,
But rather wolde he yeven, out of doute,
Unto his povre parisshens aboute
Of his offryng and eek of his substaunce;
He koude in litel thyng have suffisaunce. *490*
Wyd was his parisshe, and houses fer asonder,
But he ne lefte nat for reyn ne thonder,
In siknesse nor in meschief, to visite
The ferreste in his parisshe, muche and lite,

465-66 Rome, Boulogne, St. James of Compostella in Galicia, and Cologne were the sites of famous shrines.
467 *koude:* knew; *wandrynge . . . weye:* traveling.
468 *gat:* gap, i.e., between the front teeth; *soothly:* truly.
469 *amblere:* an ambling horse.

470 *ywympled:* covered with a wimple, see l. 151.
471 *brood:* broad; *bokeler, targe:* small shields.
472 *foot-mantel:* an outer skirt.
473 *spores:* spurs.
474 *felaweshipe:* company; *carpe:* talk.

475 *remedies:* cures; *per chaunce:* doubtless.
476 *koude:* l. 467; *olde daunce:* i.e., all the tricks of love.

478 *povre:* poor; *Person:* parson, parish priest.
479 *werk:* work, deeds.

482 *parisshens:* parishioners.
483 *benygne:* benign, kind; *wonder:* wonderfully.
484 *pacient:* patient.

485 *swich:* l. 243; *ypreved:* proved, i.e., by circumstances; *sithes:* times.
486 *looth were hym:* it would be displeasing to him; *cursen:* excommunicate, i.e., in order to force payment of tithes.
487 *yeven:* give; *out of doute:* without doubt.
488 *aboute:* round about.
489 *offryng:* the church offering; *substaunce:* his own income.
490 *koude:* could; *suffisaunce:* enough to live on.
491 *wyd:* wide; *fer asonder:* far apart.
492 *ne lefte nat:* ceased not (to visit).
493 *meschief:* misfortune.
494 *ferreste:* those who lived farthest away; *muche and lite:* great and small.

Upon his feet, and in his hand a staf. *495*
This noble ensample to his sheep he yaf
That first he wroghte, and afterward he taughte.
Out of the gospel he tho wordes caughte,
And this figure he added eek therto:
That if gold ruste, what shal iren do? *500*
For if a preest be foul, on whom we truste,
No wonder is a lewed man to ruste.
And shame it is, if a preest take keep:
A shiten shepherde and a clene sheep.
Wel oghte a preest ensample for to yive *505*
By his clennesse how that his sheep sholde lyve.
He sette nat his benefice to hyre,
And leet his sheep encombred in the myre,
And ran to London, unto Seinte Poules,
To seken hym a chaunterie for soules, *510*
Or with a bretherhede to been withholde;
But dwelte at hoom and kepte wel his folde,
So that the wolf ne made it nat myscarie;
He was a shepherde and noght a mercenarie.
And though he holy were and vertuous, *515*
He was to synful men nat despitous,
Ne of his speche daungerous ne digne,
But in his techyng discreet and benygne.
To drawen folk to hevene by fairnesse,
By good ensample—this was his bisynesse. *520*
But it were any persone obstinat,
What so he were, of heigh or lowe estat,
Hym wolde he snybben sharply for the nonys.
A bettre preest I trowe ther nowher noon ys.

496 *ensample:* example; *sheep:* parishioners; *yaf:* l. 227.
497 *wroghte:* practiced, i.e., he practiced what he preached.
498 *tho wordes caughte:* took those words, i.e., the above.
499 *figure:* figure of speech; *eek:* also.

500 i.e., if the highest should weaken, what can be expected of the lowest.

502 *no wonder is:* it is no wonder; *lewed:* uneducated.
503 *take keep:* (will but) take heed of it.
504 *shiten:* fouled with dung; *clene:* clean.
505 *ensample . . . yive:* to give, or set, an example.

507 *sette . . .:* did not rent out his parish appointment.
508 *and leet:* nor left; *encombred:* stuck fast (in the mire of sin).

510 *chaunterie:* chantry, a foundation employing a priest to say masses for the repose of a soul. There were numerous ones at St. Paul's in London.
511 *bretherhede . . .:* to be retained by a guild as chaplain. Both of these were regarded as easy and lucrative positions.
513 *myscarie:* go amiss.
514 *mercenarie:* a hireling.

516 *despitous:* scornful.
517 *ne of:* nor in; *daungerous ne digne:* arrogant nor haughty.
519 *fairnesse:* living a good life.
520 *bisynesse:* concern.
521 *but it were:* but if there were.
522 *what so:* whatsoever.
523 *snybben:* reprimand; *for . . . nonys:* on or for the occasion.
524 *trowe:* believe; *ys:* is.

He wayted after no pompe and reverence, 525
Ne maked him a spiced conscience,
But Cristes loore and his Apostles twelve
He taughte, but first he folwed it hymselve.
With hym ther was a Plowman, was his brother,
That hadde ylad of dong ful many a fother; 530
A trewe swynkere and a good was he,
Lyvyng in pees and parfit charitee.
God loved he best with al his hoole herte
At alle tymes, thogh him gamed or smerte,
And thanne his neighebore right as hymselve. 535
He wolde thresshe, and therto dyke and delve,
For Cristes sake, for every povre wight,
Withouten hire, if it lay in his myght.
His tithes payed he ful faire and wel,
Bothe of his propre swynk and his catel. 540
In a tabard he rood upon a mere.
Ther was also a Reve and a Millere,
A Somnour and a Pardoner also,
A Maunciple and myself—ther were namo.
The Millere was a stout carl for the nones; 545
Ful big he was of brawn and eek of bones.
That proved wel, for over al ther he cam,
At wrastlynge he wolde have alwey the ram.
He was short-sholdred, brood, a thikke knarre;
Ther was no dore that he nolde heve of harre, 550
Or breke it at a rennyng with his heed.
His berd as any sowe or fox was reed,
And therto brood, as though it were a spade.
Upon the cop right of his nose he hadde

525 *wayted after:* expected.
526 *spiced:* overscrupulous.
527 *loore:* teaching, i.e., of Christ and his apostles.

530 *ylad:* carted; *dong:* dung; *fother:* load.
531 *swynkere:* worker.
532 *pees:* peace.
533 *hoole:* whole.
534 *thogh him . . . smerte:* whether it was pleasant or unpleasant to him.
535 *thanne:* i.e., he loved God best and then (i.e., next) his neighbor just as much as himself.
536 *thresshe:* thresh; *dyke:* make ditches; *delve:* dig.
537 *povre:* poor; *wight:* person.

539 *faire:* fairly, courteously.
540 *of:* with; *propre swynk:* own labor; *catel:* property.
541 *tabard:* a loose frock; *mere:* mare.
542-44 For the Reeve, Summoner, Pardoner, Manciple, see below.
544 *namo:* no more.

545 *carl:* fellow; *for the nones:* for the occasion.
546 *brawn:* muscle; *eek:* also.
547 *proved wel:* proved well (to be true); *over al ther:* everywhere.
548 *have alwey:* always win; *ram:* a ram was the usual prize at wrestling matches.
549 *short-sholdred:* short in the upper arm; *brood:* broad; *thikke knarre:* a fellow thickly knotted with muscle.
550 *dore:* door; *nolde . . . harre:* would not heave from the hinges.
551 *breke:* break; *at a rennyng:* at one run.
552 *as . . . reed:* was as red as any sow or fox.
553 *therto:* also.
554 *cop right:* right (on the) top.

A werte, and theron stood a tuft of herys, 555
Rede as the bristles of a sowes erys;
His nosethirles blake were and wyde.
A swerd and bokeler bar he by his syde.
His mouth as greet was as a greet forneys.
He was a janglere and a goliardeys, 560
And that was moost of synne and harlotries.
Wel koude he stelen corn and tollen thries;
And yet he hadde a thombe of gold, pardee.
A whit cote and a blew hood wered he.
A baggepipe wel koude he blowe and sowne, 565
And therwithal he broghte us out of towne.
A gentil Maunciple was ther of a temple,
Of which achatours myghte take exemple
For to been wise in byyinge of vitaille;
For wheither that he payde or took by taille, 570
Algate he wayted so in his achaat,
That he was ay biforn and in good staat.
Now is nat that of God a ful fair grace,
That swich a lewed mannes wit shal pace
The wisdom of an heep of lerned men? 575
Of maistres hadde he mo than thries ten,
That were of lawe expert and curious,
Of whiche ther were a dozeyne in that hous
Worthy to been stywardes of rente and lond
Of any lord that is in Engelond, 580
To make him lyve by his propre good
In honour dettelees but if he were wood,
Or lyve as scarsly as hym list desire,
And able for to helpen al a shire

555 *werte:* wart; *herys:* hairs.
556 *rede:* red; *erys:* ears.
557 *nosethirles:* nostrils; *blake:* black.
558 *bokeler:* a small shield; *bar:* bore.
559 *forneys:* furnace.

560 *janglere:* loud talker; *goliardeys:* a teller of ribald tales.
561 *that:* i.e., his talking and his tales; *harlotries:* ribaldries.
562 *stelen:* steal; *tollen thries:* take his toll (his fee for milling, taken in grain) thrice.
563 Proverbial: "an honest miller has a golden thumb"; he was as honest as any miller; *pardee:* indeed.
565 *sowne:* sound, play upon.
566 i.e., with the music of the pipe he conducted us out of town.
567 *Maunciple:* a servant who purchased provisions for a temple, or society of lawyers.
568 *achatours:* caterers, purchasers of food; *take exemple:* take as model.
569 *vitaille:* victuals.
570 *by taille:* by tally, on credit.
571 *algate:* always; *wayted:* took precautions; *achaat:* buying.
572 *ay:* ever; *biforn:* ahead; *staat:* financial condition.

574 *swich:* such; *lewed:* unlearned; *pace:* surpass.

575 *heep:* heap.
576 *maistres:* masters; *mo:* more.
577 *curious:* skillful.

579 *styward:* manager of an estate; *rente:* income.

581 *him:* i.e., the lord; *by . . . good:* on (within) his own income.
582 *dettelees:* without debt; *but if:* unless; *wood:* mad.
583 *scarsly:* economically; *hym . . . desire:* it pleases him to wish.
584 *al a shire:* a whole shire.

In any caas that myghte falle or happe; *585*
And yet this Maunciple sette hir aller cappe!
  The Reve was a sclendre colerik man.
His berd was shave as neigh as ever he kan;
His heer was by his erys ful round yshorn;
His top was dokked lyk a preest biforn; *590*
Ful longe were his legges and ful lene,
Ylik a staf, ther was no calf ysene.
Wel koude he kepe a gerner and a bynne;
Ther was noon auditour koude on him wynne.
Wel wiste he by the droghte and by the reyn *595*
The yelding of his seed and of his greyn.
His lordes sheep, his neet, his dayerye,
His swyn, his hors, his stoor, and his pultrye
Was hoolly in this Reves governyng,
And by his covenant yaf the rekenyng, *600*
Syn that his lord was twenty yeer of age.
Ther koude no man brynge hym in arrerage.
Ther nas baillif, hierde, nor oother hyne,
That he ne knew his sleighte and his covyne;
They were adrad of hym as of the deeth. *605*
His wonyng was ful faire upon an heeth;
With grene trees yshadwed was his place.
He koude bettre than his lord purchace.
Ful riche he was astored pryvely.
His lord wel koude he plesen subtilly, *610*
To yeve and lene hym of his owene good,
And have a thank, and yet a cote and hood.
In youthe he hadde lerned a good myster:
He was a wel good wrighte, a carpenter.

585 *caas:* circumstance; *falle:* befall.
586 *sette . . . cappe:* set the caps of them all, made fools of them.
587 *Reve:* an official assisting in the management of an estate; *sclendre:* slender; *colerik:* a choleric man was slender, keen-witted, irritable, wanton (see l. 420).
588 *shave:* shaved; *neigh:* closc.
589 *erys:* ears; *yshorn:* cut.
590 *dokked:* cut short; priests had their heads shaved in front.
591 *lene:* lean.
592 *ylik:* like; *ysene:* visible.
593 *kepe:* guard; *gerner:* granary.
594 *on . . . wynne:* find him in default.
595 *wiste:* knew.
596 *yelding:* yield.
597 *neet:* cattle; *dayerye:* dairy.
598 *swyn:* swine; *stoor:* stock.
599 *hoolly:* wholly.

600 *covenant:* contract; *yaf . . . rekenyng*: he had given the accounting.
601 *syn that:* since.
602 "No one could prove him in arrears."
603 *nas:* was not; *baillif:* foreman; *hierde:* herdsman; *hyne:* hind, farm laborer.
604 *his,* i.e., of the above men; *sleighte:* trickery; *covyne:* deceit.
605 *adrad:* afraid; *the deeth:* the pestilence.
606 *wonyng:* dwelling; *heeth:* heath.

608 *purchace:* buy.
609 *astored pryvely:* stocked secretly.

610 *plesen:* please; *subtilly:* craftily.
611-12 "By giving or lending to his lord his [the lord's] own property and receive thanks and a reward besides."
613 *myster:* trade or craft.
614 *wrighte:* workman or artisan.

This Reve sat upon a ful good stot, *615*
That was a pomely grey and highte Scot.
A long surcote of pers upon he hade,
And by his syde he baar a rusty blade.
Of Northfolk was this Reve of which I telle,
Biside a toun men clepen Baldeswelle. *620*
Tukked he was as is a frere aboute,
And evere he rood the hyndreste of oure route.

A Somnour was ther with us in that place,
That hadde a fyr-reed cherubynnes face,
For sawcefleem he was, with eyen narwe. *625*
And hoot he was, and lecherous as a sparwe,
With scaled browes blake and piled berd;
Of his visage children were aferd.
Ther nas quyksilver, lytarge, ne brymstoon,
Boras, ceruce, ne oille of tartre noon, *630*
Ne oinement that wolde clense and byte,
That hym myghte helpen of his whelkes white,
Nor of the knobbes sittynge on his chekes.
Wel loved he garlek, oynons, and eek lekes,
And for to drynken strong wyn reed as blood. *635*
Thanne wolde he speke and crye as he were wood;
And whan that he wel dronken hadde the wyn,
Thanne wolde he speke no word but Latyn.
A fewe termes hadde he, two or thre,
That he had lerned out of som decree— *640*
No wonder is, he herde it al the day,
And eek ye knowen wel how that a jay
Kan clepen "Watte" as wel as kan the Pope—
But whoso koude in oother thyng hym grope,

615 *stot:* stallion.
616 *pomely:* dappled; *highte:* was named.
617 *surcote:* overcoat; *pers:* bluish gray; *upon . . . hade:* he had on.
618 *baar:* bore.
619 *Northfolk:* Norfolk.
620 *biside:* near; *men clepen:* is called.
621 His coat was tucked up around him with a belt; *frere:* friar.
622 *hyndreste:* hindmost; *route:* group.
623 Summoner, an officer who summoned offenders to appear in the ecclesiastical court, which enforced payment of tithes and disciplined such offenses as adultery, fornication, and others not coming under the common law.
624 Cherubs were proverbially red- or fiery-faced.
625 *sawcefleem:* pimply; *eyen narwe:* narrow eyes.
626 *hoot:* hot; sparrows were proverbially lecherous.
627 *scaled browes:* scabby eyebrows; *piled:* partly hairless.
628 *visage:* face; *aferd:* afraid.
629 *nas:* was no; *lytarge:* white lead.
630 *boras:* borax; *ceruce:* a cosmetic made from white lead.
631 *oinement:* ointment; these are all medicines for "saucefleem."
632 *helpen of:* rid (him) of; *whelkes:* blotches or boils.

634 *eek:* also; *lekes:* leeks, a plant something like an onion.

636 *wood:* mad.

639 *termes:* stock phrases.

641 *no wonder is:* it's no wonder; *herde:* heard.
642 *eek:* moreover; *jay:* jays were taught to say "Wat."
643 *clepen:* call.
644 *whoso koude:* if anyone should; *grope:* test.

Thanne hadde he spent al his philosophie; *645*
Ay *"Questio quid juris"* wolde he crie.
He was a gentil harlot and a kynde;
A bettre felawe sholde men noght fynde;
He wolde suffre, for a quart of wyn,
A good felawe to have his concubyn *650*
A twelf monthe, and excuse hym atte fulle.
Ful prively a fynch eek koude he pulle.
And if he foond owher a good felawe,
He wolde techen him to have noon awe
In swich caas of the Ercedekenes curs, *655*
But if a mannes soule were in his purs,
For in his purs he sholde ypunysshed be.
"Purs is the Ercedekenes helle," saide he.
But wel I woot he lyed right in dede;
Of cursyng oghte ech gilty man him drede, *660*
For curs wol slee right as assoillyng savith,
And also war him of a *Significavit.*
In daunger hadde he at his owene gise
The yonge girles of the diocise,
And knew hir conseil, and was al hir reed. *665*
A gerland hadde he set upon his heed
As greet as it were for an ale-stake;
A bokeler hadde he maad him of a cake.
With hym ther rood a gentil Pardoner
Of Rouncival, his freend and his compeer, *670*
That streight was comen fro the court of Rome.
Ful loude he soong, "Com hider, love, to me!"
This Somnour bar to hym a stif burdoun;
Was nevere trompe of half so greet a soun.

645 *philosophie:* learning.
646 *ay:* ever; *Questio . . .:* "The question is, what is the law on this point?" a common legal expression.
647 *harlot:* fellow, rascal.
648 *felawe:* comrade.
649 *suffre:* allow.
650 *have his:* keep or live with a (concubine).
651 *atte fulle:* completely; i.e., excuse him from the church court.
652 *prively:* secretly; "to pull a finch" is to have sexual relations with a woman.
653 *foond:* found; *owher:* anywhere.
654 *awe:* fear.
655 *in swich caas:* in such matters; *Ercedekenes curs:* excommunication by the archdeacon (the presiding officer of the church court).
656 *but if . . .:* unless the sinner thought his soul was in his purse.
658 i.e., the curse could be lifted upon payment of money.
659 *woot:* know.
660 *cursyng:* excommunication; *him drede:* to be afraid.
661 *slee:* slay (the soul); *right:* just; *assoillyng:* absolution.
662 "And he should also beware of a *Significavit,* the writ remanding an excommunicated person to prison."
663 *in daunger:* under his control; *gise:* disposal.
664 *girles:* youths of both sexes; *diocise:* diocese.
665 *conseil:* secrets; *al hir reed:* wholly their adviser or helper.
666 *gerland:* a hoop adorned with flowers.
667 *greet:* large; *ale-stake:* a support for a garland, which was often used as a part of the sign for an alehouse.
668 *bokeler:* shield; *cake:* a round, flat loaf of bread.
669 *Pardoner:* a man, sometimes in minor orders, authorized to sell papal indulgences.
670 *Rouncival:* a convent hospital near Charing Cross; *compeer:* comrade.
672 *soong:* sang; *com hider:* come hither.
673 *bar . . . burdoun:* bore him a strong bass accompaniment.
674 *trompe:* trumpet.

This Pardoner hadde heer as yelow as wex, *675*
But smothe it heeng as dooth a strike of flex;
By ounces henge his lokkes that he hadde,
And therwith he his shuldres overspradde;
But thynne it lay, by colpons, oon and oon.
But hood for jolitee wered he noon, *680*
For it was trussed up in his walet;
Hym thoughte he rood al of the newe jet;
Dischevelee save his cappe he rood al bare.
Swiche glarynge eyen hadde he as an hare.
A vernycle hadde he sowed upon his cappe. *685*
His walet lay biforn hym in his lappe,
Bretful of pardon, comen from Rome al hoot.
A voys he hadde as smal as hath a goot;
No berd hadde he, ne nevere sholde have;
As smothe it was as it were late yshave; *690*
I trowe he were a geldyng or a mare.
But of his craft, fro Berwyk into Ware,
Ne was ther swich another pardoner.
For in his male he hadde a pilwe-beer,
Which that he seyde was Oure Lady veyl; *695*
He seyde he hadde a gobet of the seyl
That Seint Peter hadde whan that he wente
Upon the see, til Jhesu Crist hym hente.
He hadde a croys of laton, ful of stones,
And in a glas he hadde pigges bones. *700*
But with thise relikes whan that he fond
A povre person dwellynge upon lond,
Upon a day he gat hym moore moneye
Than that the person gat in monthes tweye;

676 *heeng:* hung; *strike:* hank; *flex:* flax.
677 *ounces:* small clusters.
678 i.e., he spread his hair over his shoulders.
679 *colpons:* strands; *oon and oon:* one by one, separately.

680 *wered:* wore.
681 *walet:* a small bag or pack.
682 *hym thoughte:* it seemed to him that; *jet:* fashion.
683 *dischevelee:* with hair loose; *save:* except for.
684 *glarynge:* shining.

685 *vernycle:* small copy of St. Veronica's handkerchief, which was said to have miraculously received the imprint of Christ's face when she lent it him on his way to Calvary.
686 *biforn:* before.
687 *bretful:* brimful; *pardon:* indulgences; *hoot:* hot, fresh.
688 *smal:* thin; *goot:* goat.

690 *late yshave:* just shaved.
691 *trowe:* believe; *geldyng:* castrated horse.
692 *craft:* trade; from Berwick in the north to Ware in the south.
693 *swich:* such.
694 *male:* bag; *pilwe-beer:* pillowcase.

695 *Lady:* Lady's, i.e., Mary's veil.
696 *gobet:* a small piece.
697 *whan that:* when; *wente:* traveled, walked, sailed, etc.
698 *hente:* seized, in reference either to Jesus's recruitment of Peter, a fisherman (Matthew: 4:18), or to his rescuing of Peter after his attempt to walk on the water (Matthew: 14:29).
699 *croys:* cross; *laton:* a cheap, brassy metal.
701 *relikes:* relics; *fond:* found.
702 *povre person:* poor parson; *upon lond:* in the country.
703 *gat hym:* got for himself, i.e., by charging parishioners a fee for kissing the relics.
704 *tweye:* two.

And thus with feyned flaterye and japes, *705*
He made the person and the peple his apes.
But trewely to tellen atte laste,
He was in chirche a noble ecclesiaste;
Wel koude he rede a lesson or a storie,
But alderbest he song an offertorie; *710*
For wel he wiste whan that song was songe,
He moste preche and wel affile his tonge
To wynne silver, as he ful wel koude;
Therefore he song the murierly and loude.
Now have I told you soothly, in a clause, *715*
Th'estaat, th'array, the nombre, and eek the cause
Why that assembled was this compaignye
In Southwerk at this gentil hostelrye
That highte the Tabard, faste by the Belle.
But now is tyme to yow for to telle *720*
How that we baren us that ilke nyght,
Whan we were in that hostelrie alyght;
And after wol I telle of our viage
And al the remenaunt of oure pilgrimage.
But first I pray yow of youre curteisye, *725*
That ye n'arette it nat my vileynye,
Thogh that I pleynly speke in this matere,
To telle yow hir wordes and hir cheere,
Ne thogh I speke hir wordes proprely.
For this ye knowen al so wel as I: *730*
Who so shal telle a tale after a man,
He moot reherce, as neigh as evere he kan,
Everich a word, if it be in his charge,
Al speke he never so rudeliche and large,

705 *feyned:* feigned, false; *japes:* tricks.
706 *apes:* apes, dupes.
707 *trewely:* truly; *atte:* at the.

709 *rede:* read; *lesson:* passage from the Bible or the Fathers read in the service; *storie:* scries of lessons.

710 *alderbest:* best of all; *offertorie:* an anthem sung during the offering.
711 *wiste:* knew.
712 *moste:* must; *affile:* file, make smooth.
713 *murierly:* more merrily.

715 *in a clause:* briefly.
716 *estaat:* rank; *array:* dress, condition.

718 *gentil:* excellent.
719 *highte:* was called; *faste:* close; *Belle:* another tavern.

721 *baren:* bore, conducted ourselves; *ilke:* same.
722 *were . . . alyght:* had alighted (from our horses).
723 *wol:* will; *viage:* trip.
724 *remenaunt:* rest, remainder.

726. *n'arette it nat:* do not blame it on; *vileynye:* ill breeding.

728 *hir:* their; *cheere:* behavior.
729 *proprely:* exactly, literally.

730 *al so wel as:* as well as.
731 *who so:* whosoever; *shal telle:* has to tell.
732 *moot:* must; *reherce:* repeat; *neigh:* nearly, closely.
733 *everich a:* every; *charge:* responsibility.
734 *al speke he:* although he should speak; *never so:* however; *large:* freely.

Or ellis he moot telle his tale untrewe, *735*
Or feyne thyng, or fynde wordes newe.
He may nat spare althogh he were his brother;
He moot as wel seye o word as another.
Crist spak hymself ful brode in holy writ,
And wel ye woot no vileynye is it. *740*
Eek Plato seith, whoso kan him rede,
The wordes mote be cosyn to the dede.
Also I pray yow to foryeve it me,
Al have I nat set folk in hir degree
Here in this tale as that they sholde stonde. *745*
My wit is short, ye may wel understonde.
Greet cheere made oure Hoost us everichon,
And to the soper sette he us anon.
He served us with vitaille at the beste;
Strong was the wyn, and wel to drynke us leste. *750*
A semely man oure Hooste was withalle
For to been a marchal in an halle.
A large man he was, with eyen stepe;
A fairer burgeys was ther noon in Chepe,
Boold of his speche, and wys, and wel ytaught, *755*
And of manhood hym lakkede right naught.
Eek therto he was right a murye man,
And after soper pleyen he bigan,
And spak of myrthe amonges othere thynges,
Whan that we hadde maad oure rekenynges, *760*
And seyde thus, "Now, lordynges, trewely,
Ye been to me right welcome, hertely;
For by my trouthe, if that I shal nat lye,
I saugh nat this yeer so murye a compaignye

736 *feyne:* falsify; *fynde:* invent.
737 *spare:* spare anyone.
738 *he . . . another:* he is as bound to say one word as another.
739 *brode:* broadly, indelicately.

740 *woot:* know.
741 *whoso:* whoever; *rede:* read.
742 *mote:* must.

744 *al have I:* although I have; *degree:* order of rank.

746 *wit:* intelligence, understanding.
747 *everichon:* everyone.
748 *anon:* forthwith, at once.
749 *vitaille:* food.

750 *us leste:* it pleased us.
751 *semely . . . for to been:* fitting or suited to be.
752 *marchal:* official in charge of a feast or banquet.
753 *stepe:* prominent.
754 *fairer:* more excellent; *burgeys:* burgher; *Chepe:* Cheapside, a principal commercial center in London.
755 *ytaught:* taught, informed.
756 *hym lakkede:* there was lacking in him.

758 *pleyen:* to be entertaining or amusing.
759 *myrthe:* pleasure, amusement.

760 *maad oure rekenynges:* paid our bills.

762 *hertely:* heartily.

764 *saugh nat:* have not seen.

At ones in this herberwe as is now. *765*
Fayn wolde I doon yow myrthe, wiste I how.
And of a myrthe I am right now bythoght
To doon yow ese, and it shal coste noght.
Ye goon to Caunterbury—God yow speede;
The blisful martir quite yow youre meede. *770*
And wel I woot as ye goon by the weye,
Ye shapen yow to talen and to pleye,
For trewely, confort ne myrthe is noon
To ride by the weye domb as a stoon;
And therfore wol I maken yow disport, *775*
As I seyde erst, and doon yow som confort.
And if yow liketh alle, by oon assent,
For to stonden at my juggement,
And for to werken as I shal yow seye,
Tomorwe whan ye riden by the weye, *780*
Now by my fader soule that is deed,
But ye be murye I wol yeve yow myn heed!
Hoolde up youre hondes withouten moore speche."
Oure conseil was nat longe for to seche;
Us thoughte it was nat worth to make it wys, *785*
And graunted hym withouten moore avys,
And bad him seye his voirdit as hym leste.
"Lordynges," quod he, "now herkneth for the beste;
But taak it nought, I prey yow, in desdeyn.
This is the poynt, to speken short and pleyn, *790*
That ech of yow, to shorte with oure weye
In this viage, shal telle tales tweye—
To Caunterbury-ward, I mene it so—
And homward he shal tellen othere two,

765 *at ones:* at once, all at the same time; *herberwe:* inn.
766 *fayn:* gladly; *wolde:* would; *doon:* cause, give; *wiste I:* if I knew.
767 *am . . . bythoght:* have just now thought.
768 *doon yow ese:* give you pleasure.

770 *quite . . . meede:* pay (give) you your reward.
771 *woot:* know; *by the weye:* on your way.
772 *shapen yow:* intend; *talen:* tell tales, converse.
773 *confort:* comfort, pleasure.
774 *domb as a stoon:* dumb as a stone.

775 *disport:* diversion.
776 *erst:* first.
777 *yow liketh alle:* it pleases you all; *by oon assent:* by common assent.
778 *stonden . . . juggement:* abide by my judgment.
779 *werken:* do.

781 *fader . . . deed:* the soul of my father who is dead.
782 *but:* unless; *yeve:* give.

784 *conseil:* opinion; *seche:* seek, i.e., it was quickly seen.

785 It seemed to us not worth deliberating over.
786 *graunted:* agreed with; *avys:* deliberation.
787 *bad:* asked, ordered; *voirdit:* verdict; *hym leste:* it pleased him.
788 *herkneth:* hearken.

791 *ech:* each; *shorte . . . weye:* shorten our way with.
792 *viage:* l. 723; *tweye:* two.
793 *mene:* mean.
794 *othere:* another.

Of aventures that whilom have bifalle; *795*
And which of yow that bereth hym best of alle—
That is to seyn, that telleth in this caas
Tales of best sentence and moost solaas—
Shal have a soper at oure aller cost,
Here in this place, sittynge by this post, *800*
Whan that we come agayn fro Caunterbury.
And for to make yow the moore mury,
I wol myselven goodly with yow ryde,
Right at myn owene cost, and be youre gyde;
And who so wole my juggement withseye *805*
Shal paye al that we spenden by the weye.
And if ye vouche sauf that it be so,
Tel me anon, withouten wordes mo,
And I wol erly shape me therfore."
  This thyng was graunted and oure othes swore *810*
With ful glad herte, and preyden hym also
That he wolde vouche sauf for to do so,
And that he wolde been oure governour,
And of oure tales juge and reportour,
And sette a soper at a certeyn pris, *815*
And we wol reuled been at his devys
In heigh and lowe; and thus by oon assent
We been acorded to his juggement.
And therupon the wyn was fet anon;
We dronken and to reste wente echon, *820*
Withouten any lenger taryynge.
  Amorwe whan that day bigan to sprynge,
Up roos oure Hoost and was oure aller cok,
And gadred us togidre in a flok,

795 *whilom:* once upon a time; *bifalle:* happened, befallen.
796 *which:* whichever; *bereth hym:* performs.
797 *caas:* affair.
798 *sentence:* instruction, morality; *solaas:* amusement, delight.
799 *soper:* supper; *oure aller:* of all of us.

802 *mury:* merry.
803 *goodly:* kindly.
804 *cost:* expense; *gyde:* guide, ruler.

805 *wole:* will; *withseye:* contradict.

807 *vouche sauf:* vouchsafe.
808 *anon:* at once; *mo:* more.
809 *shape me:* prepare myself.

810 *othes swore:* (we) swore our oaths.
811 *preyden:* (we) prayed, asked.

815 *sette a soper:* arrange a supper; *pris:* price.
816 *devys:* disposal.
817 *in heigh and lowe:* in all respects; *oon assent:* l. 777.
818 *acorded:* agreed.
819 *fet:* fetched.

820 *dronken:* drank; *echon:* each one.

822 *amorwe:* in the morning.
823 *oure aller cok:* the cock for us all (i.e., to awaken us).
824 *gadred:* gathered; *togidre:* together.

And forth we riden, a litel moore than paas, 825
Unto the wateryng of Seint Thomas;
And there oure Hoost bigan his hors areste,
And seyde, "Lordynges, herkneth if yow leste.
Ye woot youre forward and I it yow recorde;
If even-song and morwe-song accorde, 830
Lat see now who shal telle the firste tale.
As evere mote I drynke wyn or ale,
Who so be rebel to my juggement
Shal paye for al that by the wey is spent.
Now draweth cut er that we ferrer twynne; 835
He which that hath the shorteste shal bigynne.
Sire Knyght," quod he, "my mayster and my lord,
Now draweth cut, for that is myn accord.
Cometh neer," quod he, "my lady Prioresse,
And ye, sire Clerk, lat be youre shamefastnesse, 840
Ne studieth noght. Ley hond to, every man!"
Anon to drawen every wight bigan,
And shortly for to tellen as it was,
Were it by aventure or sort or cas,
The sothe is this, the cut fil to the Knyght, 845
Of which ful blithe and glad was every wight,
And telle he moste his tale, as was resoun,
By forward and by composicioun,
As ye han herd. What nedeth wordes mo?
And whan this goode man saugh that it was so, 850
As he that wys was and obedient
To kepe his forward by his free assent,
He seyde, "Syn I shal begynne the game,
What, welcome be the cut, a Goddes name!

825 *riden:* rode; *paas:* a step.
826 *wateryng . . .:* a watering place for horses at the second milestone.
827 *areste:* to stop.
828 *yow leste:* it please you.
829 *woot:* know; *forward:* agreement; *yow recorde:* recall it to you.
830 *even-song . . .:* if what you say in the morning agrees with what you said last night.
832-34 i.e., as surely as I ever hope to drink wine or ale, whoever defies my rulings shall pay. . . .

835 *draweth cut:* draw lots; *er:* before; *ferrer twynne:* depart farther.
836 *which:* who.

838 *accord:* ruling.
839 *neer:* nearer.
840 *lat be:* leave off; *shamefastnesse:* modesty.
841 *ne studieth noght:* nor do not deliberate.
842 *wight:* person.
843 *shortly:* quickly.
844 *were it:* whether it was; *aventure . . .:* luck, fate, or chance.

845 *sothe:* truth; *fil:* fell.

847 *moste:* must; *resoun:* right.
848 *forward:* 1. 829; *composicioun:* arrangement.
849 *han:* have; *nedeth:* is the need for; *mo:* more.

850 *saugh:* saw.
851 *as:* since; *wys:* wise.

854 *a:* in.

Now lat us ryde, and herkneth what I seye." *855*
And with that word we ryden forth oure weye,
And he bigan with right a murye cheere
His tale anon, and seyde as ye may heere.

The tale which the Knight tells is, characteristically, an excellent example of a medieval courtly romance, a story of love and jealousy and battle in a rich setting of court and tournament, making skillful use of the language and conventions of courtly love. We may note that the Miller, in the tale which follows, seems at times almost to parody some of these features. The Knight's rival lovers and the fair Emelye are, at least, significantly paralleled on a strikingly lower—and comic—plane by the chief characters of the *Miller's Tale.*

Heere folwen the wordes bitwene the Hoost and the Millere.

Whan that the Knyght had thus his tale ytoold,
In al the route nas ther yong ne oold *3110*
That he ne seyde it was a noble storie,
And worthy for to drawen to memorie,
And namely the gentils everichon.
Oure Hooste lough and swoor, "So moot I gon,
This gooth aright; unbokeled is the male. *3115*
Lat se now who shal telle another tale;
For trewely the game is wel bigonne.
Now telleth ye, sire Monk, if that ye konne,
Somwhat to quite with the Knyghtes tale."
The Millere, that for dronken was al pale, *3120*
So that unnethe upon his hors he sat,
He nolde avalen neither hood ne hat,
Ne abyde no man for his curteisie,
But in Pilates voys he gan to crie,

857 *murye cheere:* merry countenance.

3110 *route:* company; *nas: (ne was)* was not.

3112 *drawen:* recall.
3113 *namely:* especially; *gentils:* gentlefolk; *everichon:* everyone.
3114 *lough:* laughed; *so . . . gon:* as I may walk.

3115 *gooth:* goes; *male:* pouch, peddler's pack (i.e., of stories).
3116 *lat se:* let's see.

3118 *konne:* can.
3119 *somwhat:* something; *quite:* requite, repay.

3120 *dronken:* drunkenness.
3121 *unnethe:* hardly, with difficulty.
3122 *nolde: (ne wolde)* would not; *avalen:* take off, doff.
3123 *abyde:* wait for.
3124 *Pilates:* in the mystery (Biblical) plays Pilate is often represented as ranting and tyrannical.

And swoor, "By armes and by blood and bones, *3125*
I kan a noble tale for the nones,
With which I wol now quite the Knyghtes tale."
  Oure Hooste saugh that he was dronke of ale,
And seyde, "Abyde, Robyn, my leeve brother,
Som bettre man shal telle us first another. *3130*
Abyde, and lat us werken thriftily."
  "By Goddes soule," quod he, "That wol nat I;
For I wol speke or elles go my wey."
  Oure Hoost answerde, "Tel on, a devele wey!
Thou art a fool; thy wit is overcome." *3135*
  "Now herkneth," quod the Millere, "alle and some!
But first I make a protestacioun
That I am dronke; I knowe it by my soun;
And therfore if that I mysspeke or seye,
Wyte it the ale of Southwerk, I you preye. *3140*
For I wol telle a legende and a lyf
Bothe of a carpenter and of his wyf,
How that a clerk hath set the wrightes cappe."
  The Reve answerde and seyde, "Stynt thy clappe!
Lat be thy lewed dronken harlotrye. *3145*
It is a synne and eek a greet folye
To apeyren any man, or hym defame,
And eek to bryngen wyves in swich fame.
Thou mayst ynogh of othere thynges seyn."
  This dronke Millere spak ful soone ageyn, *3150*
And seyde, "Leve brother Osewold,
Who hath no wyf, he is no cokewold.
But I sey nat therfore that thou art oon;
Ther been ful goode wyves many oon,

3125 *by armes . . .*: much earlier profanity consisted of swearing by the parts of God's (Christ's) body.
3126 *kan:* know; *for the nones:* for the occasion.

3128 *saugh:* saw.
3129 *abyde:* wait; *leeve:* dear.
3130 *bettre:* i.e., higher ranking.
3131 *thriftily:* profitably, efficiently.

3133 *elles:* else.
3134 *a devele wey:* and away to the devil.

3136 *herkneth:* listen; *alle and some:* one and all.
3137 *protestacioun:* public affirmation.
3138 *soun:* i.e., the sound of my voice.
3139 *mysspeke or seye:* speak or say amiss.

3140 *wyte it:* blame it on.
3141 *legende:* saint's life (said facetiously); *lyf:* life (story).
3143 *set (his) cappe:* made a fool of (him); *wrightes:* carpenter's
3144 *stynt:* stop; *clappe:* chatter; note that the Reeve was a carpenter himself.
3145 *lat be:* have done with; *lewed:* ignorant; *harlotrye:* obscenity.
3146 *eek:* also; *folye:* folly.
3147 *apeyren:* injure.
3148 *fame:* notoriety.
3149 *ynogh:* enough; *seyn:* say.

3151 *leve:* dear.
3152 *who:* i.e., he who; *cokewold:* cuckold.
3153 *oon:* one.
3154 *been:* are.

And evere a thousand goode ayeyns oon badde. *3155*
That knowestow wel thyself, but if thou madde.
Why artow angry with my tale now?
I have a wyf, pardee, as wel as thow;
Yet nolde I, for the oxen in my plogh,
Take upon me moore than ynogh, *3160*
As demen of myself that I were oon;
I wol bileve wel that I am noon.
An housbonde shal nat been inquisityf
Of Goddes pryvetee, nor of his wyf.
So he may fynde Goddes foyson there, *3165*
Of the remenant nedeth nat enquere."
What sholde I moore seyn, but this Millere
He nolde his wordes for no man forbere,
But tolde his cherles tale in his manere.
M'athynketh that I shal reherce it heere, *3170*
And therfore every gentil wight I preye,
For Goddes love, demeth nat that I seye
Of yvel entente, but for I moot reherce
Hir tales alle, be they bettre or werse,
Or elles falsen som of my mateere. *3175*
And therfore, whoso list it nat yheere,
Turne over the leef and chese another tale;
For he shal fynde ynowe, grete and smale,
Of storial thyng that toucheth gentillesse,
And eek moralitee and holynesse. *3180*
Blameth nat me if that ye chese amys.
The Millere is a cherl, ye knowe wel this;
So was the Reve, and othere many mo,
And harlotrie they tolden bothe two.

3155 *ayeyns:* against, for each.
3156 *knowestow:* you know; *but if:* unless; *madde:* are mad.
3157 *artow:* are you.
3158 *pardee:* par Dieu, indeed.
3159 *nolde:* would not; *plogh:* plow.

3160 *take upon me:* presume; *moore . . . ynogh:* unnecessarily.
3161 *as demen:* to judge; *oon:* i.e., a cuckold.

3163 *shal nat:* ought not.
3164 *pryvetee:* secrets.

3165 *so:* provided that; *foyson:* plenty, i.e., plenty of what he wants.
3166 *nedeth nat:* it is not desirable; *enquere:* to inquire.
3168 *forbere:* keep back.
3169 *cherl:* churl, a low-born person.

3170 *m'athynketh:* it displeases me; *shal:* must; *reherce:* repeat.
3171 *gentil wight:* person of good birth or refinement.
3172 *demeth nat:* do not conclude; *seye:* speak.
3173 *of:* from; *yvel:* evil; *for:* because; *moot:* must.
3174 *hir:* their; *be they:* whether they be.

3175 *falsen:* falsify; *mateere:* material.
3176 *whoso:* whoever; *list:* it pleases; *yheere:* to hear.
3177 *chese:* choose.
3178 *ynowe:* enough.
3179 *storial:* historical, i.e., true; *toucheth:* concerns; *gentillesse:* courtesy, good breeding.

3181 *amys:* amiss.

3183 *othere many mo:* many others more.
3184 *harlotrie:* ribaldry.

Avyseth yow, and put me out of blame; 3185
And eek men shal nat maken ernest of game.

THE MILLER'S TALE

Though, as Chaucer warns us, the following story is a churl's tale told in churl's wise, it is artistically one of the finest of Chaucer's productions. The characterization of the hende Nicholas, the winsome Alisoun, and the foppish Absalom is so efficiently devised that within the small compass of these seven hundred odd lines they come to live in imagination and memory as do few other literary creations. The narrative unfolds without a wasted word or a missed opportunity, culminating in a series of shocking and ridiculous and hilarious events that come so fast upon one another at the close that the reader is left breathless. Somewhat less obvious are the many delicate touches of humorous and lifelike detail that lie everywhere in the description, the imagery, the action, and the dialogue of the story. By such means is a conventional bawdy tale of cuckoldry raised to the level of great art. Even the carpenter, while not ceasing to be that traditional figure of fun, the slow-witted old husband of a lusty young wife, is enriched by such touches as his warm-hearted concern for Nicholas and the brilliantly pathetic and ironic stroke which makes his first thought upon learning of the flood to be for his wife:

"Allas, my wyf!
And shal she drenche? Allas, myn Alisoun!"

This tale, like most of the bawdier tales, is probably an adaptation of a medieval type of short story known as the fabliau. These stories were disseminated chiefly in oral form, and as a result relatively few have survived from medieval times. Several versions of this story are known, however, one being of the fourteenth century.

Heere bigynneth the Millere his tale.

Whilom ther was dwellynge at Oxenford
A riche gnof, that gestes heeld to bord,
And of his craft he was a carpenter.

3185 *avyseth yow:* take heed.
3186 *maken ernest:* make a serious matter; *game:* sport, joke.

3187 *whilom:* once.
3188 *gnof:* churl, fellow; *gestes:* i.e., lodgers; *heeld:* took in; *bord:* board.

With hym ther was dwellynge a poure scoler, *3190*
Hadde lerned art, but al his fantasye
Was turned for to lerne astrologye,
And koude a certeyn of conclusions,
To demen by interrogacions,
If that men asked hym in certein houres *3195*
Whan that men sholde have droghte or elles shoures,
Or if men asked hym what sholde bifalle
Of every thyng; I may nat rekene hem alle.
This clerk was cleped hende Nicholas.
Of deerne love he koude and of solas, *3200*
And therto he was sleigh and ful privee,
And lyk a mayden meke for to see.
A chambre hadde he in that hostelrye
Allone, withouten any compaignye,
Ful fetisly ydight with herbes swoote; *3205*
And he hymself as sweete as is the roote
Of lycorys, or any cetewale.
His Almageste and bookes grete and smale,
His astrelabie, longynge for his art,
His augrym stones layen faire apart *3210*
On shelves couched at his beddes heed;
His presse ycovered with a faldyng reed;
And al above ther lay a gay sautrie,
On which he made a-nyghtes melodie
So swetely that all the chambre rong, *3215*
And *Angelus ad virginem* he song,
And after that he song the kynges noote;
Ful often blessed was his myrie throte.
And thus this sweete clerk his tyme spente

3190 *poure scoler:* poor scholar.
3191 *hadde lerned art:* who had studied the (liberal) arts, i.e., grammar, logic, rhetoric, arithmetic, geometry, music, and astronomy; *fantasye:* i.e., intellectual pleasure.
3193 *koude:* knew; *certeyn:* a certain number; *conclusions:* astrological operations.
3194 *to demen:* with which to determine; *by interrogacions:* concerning questions.
3195 *houres:* answers to such questions are calculated on the basis of the position of the planets at the time *(houres)* the question is asked.
3196 *men sholde have:* i.e., there would be; *droghte:* drought.
3197 *bifalle:* happen.
3198 *of:* concerning; *may:* can; *rekene:* specify.
3199 *cleped:* called; *hende:* pleasant.
3200 *deerne:* secret; *koude:* knew, understood; *solas:* pleasures.
3201 *therto:* also; *sleigh:* sly; *privee:* secretive.
3202 *meke:* meek; *for to see:* in appearance.
3203 *hostelrye:* lodginghouse.
3204 *allone:* i.e., to himself.
3205 *fetisly:* pleasingly; *ydight:* decked; *swoote:* sweet (smelling).

3207 *lycorys:* licorice; *cetewale:* an aromatic herb.
3208 *Almageste:* a work by the Egyptian astronomer, Ptolemy; loosely, any book on astrology.
3209 *astrelabie:* astrolabe, an astronomical instrument; *longynge for:* belonging to, used in.
3210 *augrym stones:* counters marked with Arabic numerals, used for calculation; *faire:* neatly.
3211 *couched:* placed.
3212 *presse:* a chest with shelves; *faldyng:* a woolen cloth.
3213 *sautrie:* psaltery, a stringed musical instrument.
3214 *a-nyghtes:* at night.

3216 *Angelus . . .:* a hymn, "The angel [said] to the Virgin."
3217 *the kynges noote:* the title of a song.
3218 *blessed:* i.e., praised by his audience.

After his freendes fyndyng and his rente. *3220*
This carpenter hadde wedded newe a wyf,
Which that he lovede moore than his lyf;
Of eighteteene yeer she was of age.
Jalous he was, and heeld hire narwe in cage,
For she was wylde and yong and he was old, *3225*
And demed hymself been lik a cokewold.
He knew nat Catoun, for his wit was rude,
That bad man sholde wedde his simylitude;
Men sholde wedden after hire estaat,
For youthe and elde is often at debaat. *3230*
But sith that he was fallen in the snare,
He moste endure, as oother folk, his care.
Fair was this yonge wyf, and therwithal
As any wezele hir body gent and smal.
A ceynt she werede, barred al of silk, *3235*
A barmclooth eek as whit as morne milk
Upon hir lendes, ful of many a goore.
Whit was hir smok, and broyden al bifoore
And eek bihynde, on hir coler aboute,
Of col-blak silk, withinne and eek withoute. *3240*
The tapes of hir white voluper
Were of the same suyte of hir coler;
Hir filet brood of silk, and set ful hye.
And sikerly she hadde a likerous yë.
Ful smale ypulled were hire browes two, *3245*
And tho were bent and blake as any sloo.
She was ful moore blisful on to see
Than is the newe pere-jonette tree,
And softer than the wolle is of a wether.

3220 *after:* depending on; *fyndyng:* support (by providing him money); *rente:* income.

3221 *newe:* newly, recently.

3224 *narwe:* closely, strictly.

3226 *demed:* judged; *been lik:* i.e., likely to be; *cokewold:* cuckold.

3227 *Catoun:* Dionysius Cato, the supposed author of a book of maxims used in the grammar schools; *wit:* mind; *rude:* untutored.

3228 *that:* who, i.e., Cato; *bad man sholde:* said that a man ought (to); *simylitude:* one like himself.

3229 *after:* in keeping with; *hire:* their; *estaat:* condition.

3230 *elde:* age; *at debaat:* in strife.

3231 *sith:* since.

3232 *moste:* must.

3233 *therwithal:* in addition.

3234 *wezele:* weasel; *gent:* graceful; *smal:* slender.

3235 *ceynt:* girdle; *werede:* wore; *barred:* with bars or stripes.

3236 *barmclooth:* apron; *whit:* white.

3237 *lendes:* loins; *goore:* gore, a triangular piece of cloth inserted to make the skirt flare.

3238 *smok:* undergarment; *broyden:* embroidered.

3239 *on her coler aboute:* around her collar.

3240 *of:* with; *withinne . . .:* inside and out.

3241 *tapes:* ribbons; *voluper:* cap.

3242 *same suyte:* i.e., they matched the embroidery on her collar.

3243 *filet:* headband; *hye:* high (on her head).

3244 *sikerly:* certainly; *likerous:* wanton; *yë:* eye.

3245 *smale:* delicately; *ypulled:* plucked.

3246 *tho:* they; *bent:* arched; *sloo:* sloe.

3247 *on to see:* to look on.

3248 *newe:* newly leafed; *pere-jonette:* the early-ripe pear.

3249 *wolle:* wool.

And by hir girdel heeng a purs of lether, *3250*
Tasseled with silk and perled with latoun.
In al this world, to seken up and doun,
There nys no man so wys that koude thenche
So gay a popelote or swich a wenche.
Ful brighter was the shynyng of hir hewe *3255*
Than in the tour the noble yforged newe.
But of hir song, it was as loude and yerne
As any swalwe sittynge on a berne.
Therto she koude skippe and make game,
As any kyde or calf folwynge his dame. *3260*
Hir mouth was sweete as bragot or the meeth,
Or hoord of apples leyd in hey or heeth.
Wynsynge she was as is a joly colt,
Long as a mast and upright as a bolt.
A brooch she baar upon hir lowe coler, *3265*
As brood as is the boos of a bokeler.
Hir shoes were laced on hir legges hye.
She was a prymerole, a piggesnye,
For any lord to leggen in his bedde,
Or yet for any good yeman to wedde. *3270*
  Now, sire, and eft sire, so bifel the cas,
That on a day this hende Nicholas
Fil with this yonge wyf to rage and pleye,
Whil that hir housbonde was at Oseneye,
As clerkes ben ful subtile and ful queynte; *3275*
And prively he caughte hire by the queynte,
And seyde, "Ywis, but if ich have my wille,
For deerne love of thee, lemman, I spille."
And heeld hire harde by the haunchebones,

3250 *heeng:* hung.
3251 *perled:* with pearl-shaped ornaments; *latoun:* a brassy metal.
3252 *to seken:* seeking.
3253 *nys:* is not; *thenche:* imagine.
3254 *popelote:* poppet, a term of endearment; *swich:* such; *wenche:* girl.
3255 *hewe:* hue, complexion.
3256 *noble:* a gold coin; *yforged newe:* newly forged (in the Tower of London).
3257 *of:* as for; *yerne:* lively.
3258 *swalwe:* swallow; *berne:* barn.
3259 *therto:* also; *make game:* frolic.
3260 *kyde:* kid; *dame:* dam.
3261 *bragot, meeth:* fermented drinks made with honey.
3262 *hoord:* store; *heeth:* heather.
3263 *wynsynge:* skittish, frisky.
3264 *upright:* straight; *bolt:* a crossbow bolt, or arrow.

3265 *baar:* bore, wore.
3266 *boos:* boss; *bokeler:* shield.
3267 *hye:* high (up on her legs).
3268 *prymerole:* primrose or cowslip; *piggesnye:* a pig's eye, a kind of wild flower.
3269 *leggen:* lay.
3270 *yeman:* yeoman.
3271 *eft:* again; *bifel:* happened; *cas:* circumstance.

3273 *fil:* began; *rage:* flirt.
3274 *Oseneye:* a town near Oxford.

3275 *ben:* are; *subtile:* sly; *queynte:* artful.
3276 *prively:* secretly, furtively; *queynte:* pudendum.
3277 *ywis:* indeed; *but if:* unless.
3278 *deerne:* secret; *lemman:* sweetheart; *spille:* die.

And seyde, "Lemman, love me al atones, *3280*
Or I wol dyen, also God me save!"
And she sproong as a colt dooth in the trave,
And with hir heed she wryed faste awey,
And seyde, "I wol nat kisse thee, by my fey!
Why, lat be," quod she, "lat be, Nicholas! *3285*
Or I wol crie 'out, harrow!' and 'allas!'
Do wey youre handes, for youre curteisye!"
  This Nicholas gan mercy for to crye,
And spak so faire, and profred him so faste,
That she hir love hym graunted atte laste, *3290*
And swoor hir ooth by seint Thomas of Kent,
That she wol been at his comandement,
Whan that she may hir leyser wel espie.
"Myn housbonde is so ful of jalousie
That but ye wayte wel and been privee, *3295*
I woot right wel I nam but deed," quod she.
"Ye moste been ful deerne, as in this cas."
  "Nay therof care thee noght," quod Nicholas.
"A clerk hadde litherly biset his whyle,
But if he koude a carpenter bigyle." *3300*
And thus they been accorded and ysworn
To wayte a tyme, as I have told biforn.
  Whan Nicholas had doon thus everideel,
And thakked hire aboute the lendes weel,
He kiste hire sweete and taketh his sawtrie, *3305*
And pleyeth faste, and maketh melodie.
  Thanne fil it thus, that to the paryssh chirche,
Cristes owene werkes for to wirche,
This goode wyf went on an haliday.

3280 *al atones:* at once, right away.
3281 *also . . . save:* may God save me!
3282 *sproong:* sprang; *trave:* a frame for holding unruly horses.
3283 *wryed:* twisted; *faste:* quickly.
3284 *fey:* faith.

3286 *out, harrow:* cries of distress.
3287 *do wey:* take away.
3288 *gan:* began.
3289 *profred him:* offered his love; *faste:* eagerly.

3291 *Thomas:* St. Thomas Becket.
3292 *comandement:* command.
3293 *leyser:* opportunity; *espie:* see.

3295 *but:* unless; *wayte:* take care; *privee:* discreet.
3296 *woot:* know; *nam but deed:* am as good as dead.
3297 *moste:* must; *deerne:* secret; *as in:* in; *cas:* affair.
3298 *care:* worry.
3299 *litherly biset:* ill employed; *whyle:* time.

3300 *but if:* unless; *bigyle:* beguile, deceive.
3301 *accorded:* agreed.

3303 *thus everideel:* all this.
3304 *thakked:* stroked; *lendes:* loins.

3305 *sawtrie:* l. 3213.

3307 *fil:* befell; *paryssh:* parish.
3308 *werkes:* works; *wirche:* perform.
3309 *haliday:* holy day.

Hir forheed shoon as bright as any day, 3310
So was it wasshen whan she leet hir werk.
  Now was ther of that chirche a parissh clerk,
The which that was ycleped Absolon.
Crul was his heer, and as the gold it shoon,
And strouted as a fanne large and brode; 3315
Ful streight and evene lay his joly shode.
His rode was reed, his eyen greye as goos.
With Poules wyndow corven on his shoos,
In hoses rede he wente fetisly.
Yclad he was ful smal and proprely 3320
Al in a kirtel of a lyght waget;
Ful faire and thikke been the poyntes set.
And therupon he hadde a gay surplys
As whit as is the blosme upon the rys.
A myrie child he was, so God me save. 3325
Wel koude he laten blood and clippe and shave,
And maken a chartre of lond or acquitaunce.
In twenty manere koude he trippe and daunce
After the scole of Oxenforde tho,
And with his legges casten to and fro, 3330
And pleyen songes on a smal rubible;
Therto he song som tyme a loud quynyble;
And as wel koude he pleye on a giterne.
In al the toun nas brewhous ne taverne
That he ne visited with his solas, 3335
Ther any gaylard tappestere was.
But sooth to seyn, he was somdeel squaymous
Of fartyng, and of speche daungerous.
  This Absolon, that jolif was and gay,

3311 *wasshen:* washed; *leet:* left off.
3312 *parissh clerk:* an official, often a layman, who assisted the priest in conducting the services.
3313 *ycleped:* called.
3314 *crul:* curly.
3315 *strouted:* spread out; *fanne:* fan, or perhaps a shovel-shaped basket used in winnowing grain.
3316 *joly:* pretty; *shode:* parting of his hair.
3317 *rode:* complexion; *goos:* goose.
3318 *Poules . . .:* the uppers of his shoes were carved with open-work designs resembling a window at St. Paul's.
3319 *hoses:* hose covering the whole leg; *fetisly:* elegantly.
3320 *smal:* with fine textures; *proprely:* handsomely.
3321 *kirtel:* jacket; *waget:* blue.
3322 *poyntes:* laces or ties for fastening the jacket.
3323 *therupon:* over that; *surplys:* surplice.
3324 *blosme:* blossom; *rys:* bough.
3325 *child:* young man.
3326 *laten blood:* let blood (barbers usually performed such minor surgery).
3327 *chartre:* i.e., a legal document; *acquitaunce:* deed of release.
3329 *after:* according to (the Oxford style); *tho:* then.
3330 *casten:* kick, prance.
3331 *rubible:* rebec, a kind of lute.
3332 *quynyble:* a part sung in a very high or falsetto voice.
3333 *giterne:* guitar.
3334 *nas:* there was not.
3335 *solas:* entertainment.
3336 *ther:* where; *gaylard:* lively; *tappestere:* barmaid.
3337 *sooth:* truth; *somdeel:* somewhat; *squaymous:* squeamish.
3338 *daungerous:* fastidious.
3339 *jolif:* pretty.

Gooth with a sencer on the haliday, 3340
Sensynge the wyves of the parisshe faste;
And many a lovely look on hem he caste,
And namely on this carpenteris wyf.
To look on hire hym thoughte a myrie lyf,
She was so propre and sweete and likerous. 3345
I dar wel seyn, if she hadde been a mous,
And he a cat, he wolde hire hente anon.
This parissh clerk, this joly Absolon,
Hath in his herte swich a love-longynge
That of no wyf ne took he noon offrynge; 3350
For curteisie, he seyde, he wolde noon.
The moone, whan it was nyght, ful brighte shoon,
And Absolon his gyterne hath ytake,
For paramours he thoghte for to wake.
And forth he gooth, jolif and amorous, 3355
Til he cam to the carpenteres hous,
A litel after cokkes hadde ycrowe,
And dressed hym up by a shot-wyndowe
That was upon the carpenteris wal.
He syngeth in his voys gentil and smal, 3360
"Now, deere lady, if thy wille be,
I praye yow that ye wole rewe on me,"
Ful wel acordaunt to his gyternynge.
This carpenter awook and herde him synge,
And spak unto his wyf, and seyde anon, 3365
"What! Alison! herestow nat Absolon,
That chaunteth thus under oure boures wal?"
And she answerde hir housbonde therwithal,
"Yis, God woot, John, I heere it every deel."

3340 *sencer:* censer; *haliday:* holy day.

3341 *sensynge:* i.e., perfuming as he carried the censer about the church; *faste:* closely.

3343 *namely:* especially.

3344 *hym thoughte:* seemed to him.

3345 *propre:* comely; *likerous:* wanton.

3347 *hente:* have seized; *anon:* at once.

3349 *love-longynge:* love-sickness.

3350 *of:* from; *offrynge:* offering.

3351 *wolde noon:* would take none.

3353 *gyterne:* guitar; *ytake:* taken.

3354 *for paramours:* for love's sake; *thoghte:* intended; *wake:* stay awake.

3355 *gooth:* goes; *jolif:* pretty.

3357 *cokkes:* the cocks; *ycrowe:* crowed.

3358 *dressed hym up:* placed himself; *shot-wyndowe:* a hinged window.

3360 *smal:* high.

3361 *if . . . be:* if it be thy will; these are the elegant phrases of conventional love poetry.

3362 *rewe:* have pity.

3363 *acordaunt to:* in harmony with.

3366 *herestow:* do you (not) hear.

3367 *boures:* chamber's.

3368 *therwithal:* thereupon.

3369 *yis:* yes, indeed; *woot:* knows; *deel:* bit.

This passeth forth; what wol ye bet than weel? *3370*
Fro day to day this joly Absolon
So woweth hire that hym is wo bigon.
He waketh al the nyght and al the day;
He kembeth his lokkes brode, and made hym gay;
He woweth hire by meenes and brocage, *3375*
And swoor he wolde been hir owene page;
He syngeth, brokkynge as a nyghtyngale;
He sente hire pyment, meeth, and spiced ale,
And wafres pipyng hoot out of the gleede;
And, for she was of towne, he profred meede. *3380*
For som folk wol ben wonnen for richesse,
And somme for strokes, and somme for gentillesse.
Somtyme, to shewe his lightnesse and maistrye,
He pleyeth Herodes upon a scaffold hye.
But what availleth hym as in this cas? *3385*
She loveth so this hende Nicholas
That Absolon may blowe the bukkes horn;
He ne hadde for his labour but a scorn.
And thus she maketh Absolon hire ape,
And al his ernest turneth til a jape. *3390*
Ful sooth is this proverbe, it is no lye,
Men seyn right thus: "Alwey the nye slye
Maketh the ferre leeve to be looth."
For though that Absolon be wood or wrooth,
By cause that he fer was from hire sight, *3395*
This nye Nicholas stood in his light.
Now ber thee wel, thou hende Nicholas,
For Absolon may waille and synge "allas."
And so bifel it on a Saterday

3370 *passeth . . .:* so it went; *what . . . weel:* what more need I say.
3372 *woweth:* woos; *that:* so intensely that; *wo bigon:* wretched.
3373 *waketh:* lies awake.
3374 *kembeth:* combs; *brode:* extravagantly wide; *gay:* gaily dressed.

3375 *meenes:* intermediaries; *brocage:* go-betweens.
3376 *page:* servant.
3377 *brokkynge:* trilling and quavering.
3378 *pyment:* spiced wine; *meeth:* mead.
3379 *wafres:* cakes; *gleede:* coals.

3380 *for:* because; *of towne:* a town woman; *profred:* offered; *meede:* money gifts.
3381 *ben wonnen:* be won; *for:* by.
3382 *strokes:* blows; *gentillesse:* courtesy.
3383 *lightnesse:* agility; *maistrye:* skill.
3384 He plays the part of Herod in the mystery plays.
3385 *availleth hym:* does it avail him; *as in:* in; *cas:* case.

3387 *blowe . . . horn:* go unrewarded.

3389 *ape:* fool.

3390 *ernest:* earnest effort; *jape:* joke.
3391 *sooth:* true.
3392 *alwey:* always; *nye slye:* the sly one near at hand.
3393 *ferre leeve:* dear one far away; *looth:* hateful.
3394 *wood:* mad; *wrooth:* angry.

3395 *by cause that:* because; *fer:* far.
3396 *nye:* near.
3397 *ber thee:* bear yourself.

This carpenter was goon til Osenay, *3400*
And hende Nicholas and Alisoun
Acorded been to this conclusioun,
That Nicholas shal shapen hym a wyle
This sely jalous housbonde to bigyle;
And if so be the game wente aright, *3405*
She sholde slepen in his arm al nyght,
For this was his desir and hire also.
And right anon, withouten wordes mo,
This Nicholas no lenger wolde tarie,
But dooth ful softe unto his chambre carie *3410*
Bothe mete and drynke for a day or tweye,
And to hire housbonde bad hire for to seye,
If that he axed after Nicholas,
She sholde seye she nyste where he was,
Of al that day she saugh hym nat with yë; *3415*
She trowed that he was in maladye,
For for no cry hir mayde koude hym calle,
He nolde answere for thyng that myghte falle.
  This passeth forth al thilke Saterday
That Nicholas stille in his chambre lay, *3420*
And eet and sleep, or dide what hym leste,
Til Sonday that the sonne gooth to reste.
This sely carpenter hath greet merveyle
Of Nicholas, or what thyng myghte hym eyle,
And seyde, "I am adrad, by Seint Thomas, *3425*
It stondeth nat aright with Nicholas.
God shilde that he deyde sodeynly!
This world is now ful tikel, sikerly;
I saugh to-day a cors yborn to chirche

3402 *acorded:* agreed.
3403 *shapen hym:* arrange; *wyle:* trick.
3404 *sely:* foolish; *bigyle:* deceive.

3407 *hire:* hers.
3408 *anon:* at once; *mo:* more.
3409 *tarie:* tarry.

3410 *softe:* softly.
3411 *mete:* food.
3412 *bad:* told.
3413 *axed:* asked.
3414 *nyste: (ne wiste)* knew not.

3415 *of:* in; *saugh:* saw; *yë:* eye.
3416 *trowed:* believed; *in maladye:* ill.
3417 *for:* because; *for no cry:* i.e., no matter how she shouted she couldn't call him.
3418 *nolde:* would not; *thyng:* anything; *falle:* i.e., be done.
3419 *passeth forth:* goes on; *thilke:* that.

3421 *hym leste:* pleased him.

3423 *sely:* innocent, poor; *hath . . . merveyle:* marvels much.
3424 *of:* about; *hym eyle:* ail him.

3425 *adrad:* afraid (that).
3426 *stondeth nat aright:* goes not well.
3427 *shilde:* forbid; *deyde:* should die.
3428 *tikel:* unstable, changeable; *sikerly:* certainly.
3429 *cors:* corpse; *yborn:* borne.

That now, on Monday last, I saugh hym wirche. *3430*
  "Go up," quod he unto his knave anoon,
"Clepe at his dore, or knokke with a stoon.
Looke how it is, and tel me boldely."
  This knave gooth hym up ful sturdily,
And at the chambre dore whil that he stood *3435*
He cride and knokked as that he were wood,
"What! how! what do ye, maister Nicholay?
How may ye slepen al the longe day?"
  But al for noght, he herde nat a word.
An hole he foond, ful lowe upon a bord, *3440*
Ther as the cat was wont in for to crepe,
And at that hole he looked in ful depe,
And at the laste he hadde of hym a sight.
This Nicholas sat capyng evere upright,
As he had kiked on the newe moone. *3445*
Adoun he gooth and tolde his maister soone
In what array he saugh this ilke man.
  This carpenter to blessen hym bigan,
And seyde, "Help us, seinte Frydeswyde!
A man woot litel what hym shal bityde. *3450*
This man is falle, with his astromye,
In som woodnesse or in som agonye.
I thoghte ay wel how that it sholde be!
Men sholde nat knowe of Goddes pryvetee.
Ye, blessed be alwey a lewed man *3455*
That noght but oonly his bileve kan!
So ferde another clerk with astromye;
He walked in the feeldes for to prye
Upon the sterres, what ther sholde bifalle,

3430 *now:* just now; *hym:* i.e., the dead man; *wirche:* working.
3431 *knave:* servant boy; *anoon:* at once, straightway.
3432 *clepe:* call; *stoon:* stone.
3433 *looke:* see; *boldely:* i.e., without delay.
3434 *gooth hym:* goes; *sturdily:* straightway.

3436 *wood:* mad.

3439 *noght:* nothing.

3440 *foond:* found.
3441 *ther as:* where; *wont:* accustomed; *crepe:* creep.
3442 *depe:* deeply, far.
3443 *hym:* i.e., Nicholas.
3444 *capyng:* gaping, staring; *evere:* steadily, fixedly; *upright:* up in the air.
3445 *as:* as if; *had kiked:* was gazing.

3447 *array:* condition; *ilke:* same.
3448 *blessen hym:* cross himself.

3450 *woot:* knows; *hym . . . bityde:* will happen to him.
3451 *falle:* fallen; *with:* as a result of; *astromye:* the carpenter's mistake for "astronomy."
3452 *woodnesse:* madness; *agonye:* i.e., a fit.
3453 *thoghte ay:* always thought, or knew.
3454 *pryvetee:* secrets.
3455 *lewed:* ignorant.
3456 *bileve:* creed; *kan:* knows.
3457 *ferde:* fared.
3458 *feeldes:* fields; *prye:* peer, gaze.
3459 *sterres:* stars; *what . . .:* i.e., to find out from them what was going to happen in the future.

Til he was in a marle-pit yfalle; *3460*
He saugh nat that. But yet, by seint Thomas,
Me reweth soore of hende Nicholas.
He shal be rated of his studiyng,
If that I may, by Jhesus, hevene kyng!
Get me a staf that I may underspore, *3465*
Whil that thou, Robyn, hevest up the dore.
He shal out of his studiyng, as I gesse."
  And to the chambre dore he gan hym dresse.
His knave was a strong carl for the nones,
And by the haspe he haaf it of atones; *3470*
Into the floor the dore fil anon.
This Nicholas sat ay as stille as stoon,
And evere caped upward into the eir.
This carpenter wende he were in despeir,
And hente hym by the sholdres myghtily, *3475*
And shook hym harde, and cride spitously,
"What! Nicholay! what, how! what, looke adoun!
Awak, and thenk on Cristes passioun!
I crouche thee from elves and fro wightes."
Therwith the nyght-spel seyde he anonrightes *3480*
On foure halves of the hous aboute,
And on the thresshfold of the dore withoute:
"Jhesu Crist and seinte Benedight,
Blesse this hous from every wikked wight;
For nyghtes verye, the white *paternoster!* *3485*
Where wentestow, seint Petres soster?"
  And atte laste this hende Nicholas
Gan for to sike soore, and seyde, "Allas!
Shal al the world be lost eftsoones now?"

3460 *marle-pit:* a pit from which fertilizing clay is dug; *was yfalle:* had fallen.
3461 *that:* i.e., that he would fall in a pit.
3462 *me reweth of:* I pity; *soore:* sorely; *hende:* gentle.
3463 *rated of:* scolded for.

3465 *staf:* staff; *underspore:* push under (so as to pry up).
3466 *Robyn:* the servant; *hevest:* heave (off the hinges).
3467 *shal out:* shall come out.
3468 *to:* at; *gan hym dresse:* placed himself.
3469 *carl:* fellow; n.b. the line echoes I:545.

3470 *haaf:* heaved; *of:* off; *atones:* at once.
3471 *into:* onto; *fil:* fell.

3474 *wende:* thought.

3475 *hente:* seized.
3476 *spitously:* vehemently.

3478 *passioun:* suffering.
3479 *crouche:* mark with the sign of the cross (for protection); *wightes:* creatures.
3480 *nyght-spel:* charm spoken at night to ward off evil spirits; *anonrightes:* right away.
3481 *halves:* sides; *aboute:* around.
3482 *thresshfold:* threshold.
3483 *Benedight:* Benedict.

3485 *for:* against; *verye:* evil spirits (?); *white paternoster:* a prayer, regarded as a source of protection.
3486 *wentestow:* did you go; *soster:* sister; this "night-spell" is made up of scraps of various charms and makes only partial sense.
3488 *gan:* began; *sike:* sigh; *soore:* sorely.
3489 *eftsoones:* very soon.

This carpenter answerde, "What seystow? *3490*
What! thynk on God, as we doon, men that swynke."
This Nicholas answerde, "Fecche me drynke,
And after wol I speke in pryvetee
Of certeyn thyng that toucheth me and thee.
I wol telle it noon oother man, certeyn." *3495*
This carpenter goth doun and comth ageyn,
And broghte of myghty ale a large quart;
And whan that ech of hem had dronke his part,
This Nicholas his dore faste shette,
And doun the carpenter by hym he sette. *3500*
He seyde, "John, myn hooste, lief and deere,
Thou shalt upon thy trouthe swere me heere
That to no wight thou shalt this conseil wreye;
For it is Cristes conseil that I seye,
And if thou telle it man, thou art forlore; *3505*
For this vengeaunce thou shalt han therfore,
That if thou wreye me, thou shalt be wood."
"Nay, Crist forbede it, for his holy blood!"
Quod tho this sely man, "I nam no labbe;
Ne, though I seye, I nam nat lief to gabbe. *3510*
Sey what thou wolt, I shal it nevere telle
To child ne wyf, by hym that harwed helle!"
"Now John," quod Nicholas, "I wol nat lye;
I have yfounde in myn astrologye,
As I have looked in the moone bright, *3515*
That now a Monday next, at quarter nyght,
Shal falle a reyn, and that so wilde and wood,
That half so greet was never Noees flood.
This world," he seyde, "in lasse than an hour

3490 *seystow:* do you say.
3491 *doon:* do; *swynke:* work, i.e., workingmen.

3493 *pryvetee:* secrecy, privacy.
3494 *toucheth:* concerns.

3499 *faste:* securely; *shette:* shut.

3500 *by hym he sette:* he seated (the carpenter) beside him.
3501 *lief:* beloved.
3502 *trouthe:* honor.
3503 *wight:* person; *conseil:* secret; *wreye:* reveal.

3505 *man:* i.e., to any man; *forlore:* lost.
3506 *vengeaunce:* punishment; *han:* have; *therfore:* for that.
3507 *wreye:* betray; *wood:* mad.

3509 *tho:* then; *sely:* simple; *nam:* am not; *labbe:* telltale.

3510 *seye:* i.e., say it myself; *lief:* fond of; *to gabbe:* gossiping.
3511 *wolt:* will, wish.
3512 *ne:* nor; *hym:* i.e., Christ; the popular story of the harrowing of hell, based on the Apocryphal Gospel of Nicodemus, tells of Christ's delivery, after the Crucifixion, of the souls of the patriarchs whom he takes with him to paradise.
3514 *yfounde:* learned.
3516 *a:* on; *quarter nyght:* 9 P.M., the end of the night's first quarter.
3517 *reyn:* rain; *wood:* violent.
3518 *Noees:* Noah's.
3519 *lasse:* less.

Shal al be dreynt, so hidous is the shour. *3520*
Thus shal mankynde drenche, and lese hir lyf."
 This carpenter answerde, "Allas, my wyf!
And shal she drenche? Allas, myn Alisoun!"
For sorwe of this he fil almoost adoun,
And seyde, "Is ther no remedie in this cas?" *3525*
 "Why, yis, for Gode," quod hende Nicholas,
"If thou wolt werken after loore and reed.
Thou mayst nat werken after thyn owene heed;
For thus seith Salomon, that was ful trewe,
'Werk al by conseil, and thou shalt nat rewe.' *3530*
And if thou werken wolt by good conseil,
I undertake, withouten mast and seyl,
Yet shal I saven hire and thee and me.
Hastow nat herd hou saved was Noe,
Whan that oure Lord hadde warned hym biforn *3535*
That al the world with water sholde be lorn?"
 "Yis," quod this Carpenter, "ful yoore ago."
 "Hastou nat herd," quod Nicholas, "also
The sorwe of Noe with his felaweshipe,
Er that he myghte gete his wyf to shipe? *3540*
Hym had be levere, I dar wel undertake,
At thilke tyme, than alle hise wetheres blake
That she hadde had a ship hirself allone.
And therfore, woostow what is best to doone?
This asketh haste, and of an hastif thyng *3545*
Men may nat preche or maken tariyng.
 Anon go gete us faste into this in
A knedyng trogh or ellis a kymelyn
For ech of us, but looke that they be large,

3520 *dreynt:* drowned; *hidous:* hideous.
3521 *drenche:* drown; *lese:* lose; *hir:* their.

3524 *fil almoost:* almost fell.

3526 *yis:* yes; *for:* by.
3527 *wolt werken:* will act; *after:* according to; *loore:* instruction; *reed:* advice.
3528 *heed:* head, i.e., ideas.
3529 *trewe:* honest.
3530 *conseil:* advice; *rewe:* regret; see Ecclesiasticus 32:19, (also III:651).

3532 *undertake:* i.e., promise; *seyl:* sail.

3534 *Noe:* Noah, the form of the name in the Vulgate.
3535 *biforn:* beforehand.
3536 *with:* by; *lorn:* lost, destroyed.
3537 *ful . . . ago:* very long ago.

3539 *sorwe:* trouble; *with:* and; *felaweshipe:* company; the allusion is to a broadly comic episode in the mystery plays in which Noah has trouble getting his wife to board the ark.
3541 *hym levere:* preferable to him, i.e., he would rather have had; *dar undertake:* daresay.
3542 *thilke:* that; *wetheres blake:* black rams.
3544 *woostow:* do you know; *doone:* do.

3545 *asketh:* requires; *hastif:* urgent.
3546 *preche:* preach, talk at length; *tariyng:* delay.
3547 *anon:* at once; *in:* dwelling.
3548 *knedyng trogh:* kneading trough (for bread); *kymelyn:* tub used for brewing.

In which we mowe swymme as in a barge, *3550*
And han therinne vitaille suffisant
But for a day,—fy on the remenant!
The water shal aslake and goon away
Aboute pryme upon the nexte day.
But Robyn may nat wite of this, thy knave, *3555*
Ne eek thy mayde Gille I may nat save;
Axe nat why, for though thou aske me,
I wol nat tellen Goddes pryvetee.
Suffiseth thee, but if thy wittes madde,
To han as greet a grace as Noe hadde. *3560*
Thy wyf shal I wel saven, out of doute.
Go now thy wey, and speed thee heeraboute.
  But whan thou hast for hire and thee and me
Ygeten us thise knedyng tubbes thre,
Thanne shaltow hange hem in the roof ful hye, *3565*
That no man of oure purveiaunce spye.
And whan thou thus hast doon as I have seyd,
And hast oure vitaille faire in hem yleyd,
And eek an ax to smyte the corde atwo,
Whan that the water comth, that we may go, *3570*
And broke an hole an heigh upon the gable,
Unto the gardyn-ward over the stable,
That we may frely passen forth oure way,
Whan that the grete shour is goon away,
Thanne shaltou swymme as myrie, I undertake, *3575*
As dooth the white doke after hire drake.
Thanne wol I clepe, 'How, Alison! how, John!
Be myrie, for the flood wol passe anon.'
And thou wolt seyn, 'Hayl, maister Nicholay!

3550 *mowe:* may; *swymme:* float; *barge:* ship, vessel.
3551 *han:* have; *vitaille:* food; *suffisant:* enough.
3552 *but:* only; *fy:* fie; *remenant:* rest.
3553 *aslake:* diminish.
3554 *pryme:* 9 A.M., see VI:662.

3555 *wite:* know; *knave:* servant boy.
3556 *eek:* also; *mayde:* maidservant.
3557 *axe:* ask.
3558 *pryvetee:* secret.
3559 *suffiseth thee:* let it suffice you; *but if:* unless; *madde:* are mad.
3560 *han:* have.
3561 *out of doute:* doubtless.
3562 *speed thee:* make haste; *heeraboute:* about it.

3564 *ygeten:* got.

3565 *thanne:* then; *shaltow:* must you; *roof:* the hall is open to the roof with crossbeams or joists.
3566 *that:* so that; *purveiaunce:* preparations; *spye:* will see.
3568 *faire:* properly; *yleyd:* placed.
3569 *smyte:* i.e., cut; *atwo:* in two.

3570 *whan that:* when; *that:* so that; *go:* i.e., float away.
3571 *an heigh:* high up; *upon:* in.
3572 *gardyn-ward:* toward the garden, on the garden side.
3573 *that:* so that; *frely:* easily; *oure way:* on our way.

3575 *swymme:* float; *myrie:* merrily; *undertake:* promise.
3576 *doke:* duck; *drake:* a male duck.
3577 *clepe:* call.

3579 *hayl:* hail.

Good morwe, I se thee wel, for it is day.' 3580
And thanne shul we be lordes al oure lyf
Of al the world, as Noe and his wyf.
But of o thyng I warne thee ful right:
Be wel avysed on that ilke nyght
That we ben entred into shippes bord, 3585
That noon of us ne speke nat a word,
Ne clepe, ne crie, but been in his preyere;
For it is Goddes owene heeste deere.
Thy wyf and thou moote hange fer atwynne;
For that bitwixe yow shal be no synne, 3590
Namoore in lookyng than ther shal in deede,
This ordinance is seyd. Go, God thee speede!
Tomorwe at nyght whan men ben alle aslepe,
Into oure knedyng-tubbes wol we crepe,
And sitten there, abidyng Goddes grace. 3595
Go now thy wey, I have no lenger space
To make of this no lenger sermonyng.
Men seyn thus, 'sende the wise, and sey no thyng';
Thou art so wys, it needeth thee nat teche.
Go, save oure lyf, and that I the biseche." 3600
This sely carpenter goth forth his wey.
Ful ofte he seide "allas" and "weylawey,"
And to his wyf he tolde his pryvetee,
And she was war, and knew it bet than he,
What al this queynte cast was for to seye. 3605
But nathelees she ferde as she wolde deye,
And seyde, "Allas! go forth thy wey anon,
Help us to scape, or we been dede echon!
I am thy trewe, verray wedded wyf;

3580 *morwe:* morning; *se:* see.

3582 *as:* like.
3583 *o:* one.
3584 *avysed:* careful; *ilke:* same.

3585 *that:* on which; *ben entred:* enter; *into bord:* on board.

3587 *clepe:* call out; *been . . . preyere:* be saying his prayers.
3588 *it:* i.e., this; *heeste deere:* blessed command.
3589 *moote:* must; *fer:* far; *atwynne:* apart.

3590 *for that:* so that; *bitwixe:* between; *synne:* sinful act.

3592 *ordinance:* command; *seyd:* spoken; *speede:* give (you) speed.

3595 *abidyng:* waiting upon.
3596 *space:* time.
3597 *of:* concerning; *sermonyng:* i.e., talking.
3598 *wise:* i.e., wise man (on your errand); *no thyng:* nothing; i.e., a word to the wise is sufficient.
3599 *it needeth nat:* it is not necessary; *teche:* to instruct.
3600 *the biseche:* beseech thee.
3601 *sely:* simple.

3603 *pryvetee:* secret.
3604 *war:* aware; *bet:* better.

3605 *queynte:* artful; *cast:* plan; *was . . . seye:* meant.
3606 *nathelees:* nevertheless; *ferde:* behaved; *wolde deye:* was about to die.

3608 *scape:* escape; *dede:* dead; *echon:* each one.
3609 *trewe:* faithful; *verray:* true.

Go, deere spouse, and help to save oure lyf." 3610
Lo, which a greet thyng is affeccion!
Men may dye of ymaginacion,
So depe may impression be take.
This sely carpenter bigynneth quake;
Hym thynketh verraily that he may see 3615
Noees flood come walwynge as the see
To drenchen Alisoun, his hony deere.
He wepeth, weyleth, maketh sory cheere;
He siketh with ful many a sory swogh;
He gooth and geteth hym a knedyng trogh, 3620
And after that a tubbe and a kymelyn,
And pryvely he sente hem to his in,
And heng hem in the roof in pryvetee.
His owene hand he made laddres thre,
To clymben by the ronges and the stalkes 3625
Unto the tubbes hangynge in the balkes,
And hem vitailled, bothe trogh and tubbe,
With breed and chese and good ale in a jubbe,
Suffisynge right ynogh as for a day.
But er that he hadde maad al this array, 3630
He sente his knave, and eek his wenche also,
Upon his nede to London for to go.
And on the Monday whan it drow to nyght,
He shette his dore withoute candel-lyght,
And dressed alle thyng as it sholde be. 3635
And shortly, up they clomben alle thre;
They seten stille wel a furlong way.
"Now, *Pater-noster,* clom!" seyde Nicholay,
And "clom," quod John, and "clom," seyde Alisoun.

3611 *which a:* what a; *affeccion:* emotion.

3613 *depe:* deeply; *be take:* be made, i.e., by the imagination.
3614 *quake:* to tremble.

3615 *hym thynketh:* it seems to him; *verraily:* truly.
3616 *walwynge:* rolling.
3617 *drenchen:* drown.
3618 *weyleth:* wails; *sory:* sorrowful; *cheere:* face.
3619 *siketh:* sighs; *swogh:* groan, sigh.

3622 *pryvely:* secretly; *in:* house.
3623 *heng:* hung.
3624 *his owene:* with his own.

3625 *ronges:* rungs; *stalkes:* uprights.
3626 *balkes:* beams.
3627 *vitailled:* victualed, provisioned.
3628 *jubbe:* jug.
3629 *ynogh:* enough.

3630 *er:* before; *maad:* made; *array:* arrangement.
3631 *wenche:* girl.
3632 *nede:* business.
3633 *drow to:* drew toward.
3634 *shette:* shut.

3635 *dressed:* arranged.
3636 *shortly:* in short; *clomben:* climbed.
3637 *seten:* sat; *wel:* fully; *furlong way:* two or three minutes, literally, the time it takes to go a furlong.
3638 *Pater-noster:* i.e., say a paternoster; *clom:* mum, be silent.

This carpenter seyde his devocioun, *3640*
And stille he sit and biddeth his preyere,
Awaitynge on the reyn, if he it heere.
  The dede sleep, for wery bisynesse,
Fil on this carpenter right, as I gesse,
Aboute corfew-tyme, or litel moore; *3645*
For travaille of his goost he groneth soore,
And eft he routeth, for his heed myslay.
Doun of the laddre stalketh Nicholay,
And Alisoun ful softe adoun she spedde;
Withouten wordes mo they goon to bedde, *3650*
Ther as the carpenter is wont to lye.
Ther was the revel and the melodye;
And thus lith Alison and Nicholas,
In bisynesse of myrthe and of solas,
Til that the belle of laudes gan to rynge, *3655*
And freres in the chauncel gonne synge.
  This parissh clerk, this amorous Absolon,
That is for love alwey so wo bigon,
Upon the Monday was at Oseneye
With compaignye, hym to disporte and pleye, *3660*
And axed upon cas a cloisterer
Ful prively after John the carpenter;
And he drough hym apart out of the chirche,
And seyde, "I noot; I saugh hym heere nat wirche
Syn Saterday; I trow that he be went *3665*
For tymber, ther oure abbot hath hym sent;
For he is wont for tymber for to go,
And dwellen at the grange a day or two;
Or elles he is at his hous, certeyn.

3640 *devocioun:* i.e., he said his paternoster.
3641 *sit:* sits; *biddeth:* says.
3642 *heere:* might hear.
3643 *dede:* dead, i.e., deep; *for:* as a result of; *wery:* weary; *bisynesse:* labor.
3644 *fil:* fell; *right:* just.

3645 *corfew-tyme:* about 8 P.M.
3646 *travaille:* affliction; *goost:* spirit; *groneth:* groans.
3647 *eft:* then; *routeth:* snores; *for:* because; *myslay:* lay askew.
3648 *of:* from; *stalketh:* creeps.
3649 *spedde:* hurried.

3651 *ther as:* there where; *wont:* accustomed.
3652 *revel:* revelry.
3653 *lith:* lies.
3654 *bisynesse:* work; *myrthe:* pleasure; *solas:* entertainment.

3655 *laudes:* the service following nocturns, here shortly before daybreak.
3656 *freres:* friars; *chauncel:* chancel; *gonne:* began.
3657 *wo bigon:* woebegone.

3660 *compaignye:* companions; *hym to disporte:* to amuse himself.
3661 *axed:* asked; *upon cas:* by chance; *cloisterer:* resident of a monastery.
3662 *prively:* privately.
3663 *drough:* drew; *apart:* aside.
3664 *noot:* know not; *saugh:* i.e., have seen; *wirche:* working.
3665 *syn:* since; *trow:* believe.
3666 *ther:* where.
3667 *wont:* accustomed.
3668 *grange:* an outlying farm belonging to the monastery.

Where that he be, I kan nat soothly seyn." *3670*
  This Absolon ful joly was and light,
And thoghte, "Now is tyme to wake al nyght;
For sikirly I saugh hym nat stirynge
Aboute his dore syn day bigan to sprynge.
So moot I thryve, I shal, at cokkes crowe, *3675*
Ful pryvely knokken at his wyndowe
That stant ful lowe upon his boures wal.
To Alison now wol I tellen al
My love-longynge, for yet I shal nat mysse
That at the leeste wey I shal hire kisse. *3680*
Som maner confort shal I have, parfay.
My mouth hath icched al this longe day;
That is a signe of kissyng atte leeste.
Al nyght me mette eek I was at a feeste.
Therfore I wol go slepe an houre or tweye, *3685*
And al the nyght thanne wol I wake and pleye."
  Whan that the firste cok hath crowe, anon
Up rist this joly lovere Absolon,
And hym arraieth gay at poynt-devys.
But first he cheweth greyn and lycorys, *3690*
To smellen sweete, er he hadde kembd his heer.
Under his tonge a trewe-love he beer,
For therby wende he to ben gracious.
He rometh to the carpenteres hous,
And stille he stant under the shot-wyndowe— *3695*
Unto his brest it raughte, it was so lowe—
And softe he cougheth with a semysoun:
"What do ye, hony-comb, sweete Alisoun,
My faire bryd, my sweete cynamome?

3670 *soothly:* truly.
3671 *joly:* joyous; *light:* lighthearted.
3672 *wake:* stay awake.
3673 *sikirly:* surely; *stirynge:* stirring.
3674 *about:* i.e., outside; *sprynge:* dawn, i.e., on Monday.

3675 *so . . . thryve:* as I may prosper; *cokkes crowe:* traditionally, the cock crows at about midnight, at three, and just before dawn; this is "first cock."

3677 *stant:* is set; *bour:* bedroom.
3679 *love-longynge:* lovesickness; *mysse:* fail.
3680 *at the leeste wey:* at least.
3681 *maner:* kind of; *parfay:* in faith.

3684 *mette:* dreamed; *eek:* also.

3688 *rist:* rises.
3689 *hym arraieth:* dresses himself; *at . . . devys:* with great care.

3690 *greyn:* grain of paradise, cardamom; *lycorys:* licorice.
3691 *er:* before; *kembd:* combed.
3692 *trewe-love:* a leaf of herb Paris, supposedly lucky for lovers.
3693 *wende:* thought; *gracious:* pleasing.
3694 *rometh:* goes, walks.

3695 *stant:* stands; *shot-wyndowe:* hinged window.
3694 *raughte:* reached.
3697 *semysoun:* half-sound, small sound.
3698 *what do ye:* what are you doing.
3699 *bryd:* bird; *cynamome:* cinnamon.

Awaketh, lemman myn, and speketh to me! *3700*
Wel litel thynken ye upon my wo,
That for youre love I swete ther I go.
No wonder is thogh that I swelte and swete;
I moorne as dooth a lamb after the tete.
Ywis, lemman, I have swich love-longynge, *3705*
That lik a turtel trewe is my moornynge.
I may nat ete na moore than a mayde."
"Go fro the wyndow, Jakke fool," she sayde;
"As help me God, it wol nat be 'com pa me.'
I love another—and elles I were to blame— *3710*
Wel bet than thee, by Jhesu, Absolon.
Go forth thy wey or I wol caste a ston,
And lat me slepe, a twenty devel wey!"
"Allas," quod Absolon, "and weylawey,
That trewe love was evere so yvel biset! *3715*
Thanne kysse me, syn it may be no bet,
For Jhesus love, and for the love of me."
"Wiltow thanne go thy wey therwith?" quod she.
"Ye, certes, lemman," quod this Absolon.
"Thanne make thee redy," quod she. "I come anon." *3720*
And unto Nicholas she seyde stille,
"Now hust, and thou shalt laughen al thy fille."
This Absolon doun sette hym on his knees,
And seyde, "I am a lord at alle degrees;
For after this I hope ther cometh moore. *3725*
Lemman, thy grace, and sweete bryd, thyn oore!"
The wyndow she undoth, and that in haste.
"Have do," quod she, "com of, and speed the faste,
Lest that oure neighebores thee espie."

3700 *lemman:* sweetheart; n.b. the rhyme cynamome/to me.

3702 *swete:* sweat; *ther:* wherever.
3703 *swelte:* die, languish.
3704 *moorne:* mourn; *tete:* teat.

3705 *ywis:* indeed; *swich:* such.
3706 *turtel:* turtledove, a bird commonly associated with true love.
3707 *may:* can; *ete:* eat; *na moore:* no more.
3708 *Jakke:* Jack, used contemptuously.
3709 *com pa me:* come kiss me, probably words from a popular song.
3710 *elles:* else, i.e., if I didn't; *to blame:* i.e., a fool.
3711 *bet:* better.
3712 *forth:* on.
3713 *a . . . wey:* away to twenty devils!

3715 *yvel biset:* ill bestowed.
3716 *syn:* since; *bet:* better.

3718 *wiltow:* will you.

3721 *stille:* quietly.
3722 *hust:* hush.
3723 *on his knees:* i.e., at the low window.
3724 *at alle degrees:* in every way.

3726 *bryd:* bird; *oore:* favor.

3728 *have do:* have done; *com of:* be quick; *speed the:* hurry.
3729 *espie:* spy.

This Absolon gan wipe his mouth ful drie. *3730*
Derk was the nyght as pich or as the cole,
And at the wyndow out she putte hir hole,
And Absolon, hym fil no bet ne wers,
But with his mouth he kiste hir naked ers
Ful savourly, er he were war of this. *3735*
Abak he stirte, and thoughte it was amys,
For wel he wiste a womman hath no berd.
He felte a thyng al rough and long yherd,
And seyde, "Fy! allas! what have I do?"
"Tehee!" quod she, and clapte the wyndow to, *3740*
And Absolon gooth forth a sory pas.
"A berd! a berd!" quod hende Nicholas,
"By Goddes corpus, this goth faire and weel."
This sely Absolon herde every deel,
And on his lippe he gan for anger byte, *3745*
And to hymself he seyde, "I shal thee quyte."
Who rubbeth now, who froteth now his lippes
With dust, with sond, with straw, with clooth, with chippes,
But Absolon, that seith ful ofte, "Allas!
My soule bitake I unto Sathanas, *3750*
But me were levere than al this toun," quod he,
"Of this despit awroken for to be.
Allas," quod he, "allas, I ne hadde ybleynt!"
His hoote love was coold and al yqueynt;
For fro that tyme that he hadde kist hir ers, *3755*
Of paramours he sette nat a kers;
For he was heeled of his maladie.
Ful ofte paramours he gan deffie,
And weep as dooth a child that is ybete.

3730 *gan:* began.
3731 *pich:* pitch; *cole:* coal.

3733 *hym fil:* it befell him; *bet ne wers:* better nor worse.

3735 *savourly:* with relish; *er:* before; *war:* aware.
3736 *abak:* back; *stirte:* started, jumped; *amys:* something wrong.
3737 *wiste:* knew; *berd:* beard.
3738 *yherd:* haired.
3739 *fy:* fie; *do:* done.

3741 *gooth forth:* walks on; *a sory pas:* miserably.

3743 *corpus:* body; *faire:* excellently.
3744 *sely:* poor; *deel:* bit.

3745 *gan:* did.
3746 *quyte:* repay.
3747 *froteth:* wipes.

3750 *bitake I:* do I commit; *Sathanas:* Satan.
3751 *but . . . toun:* but I would give all this town.
3752 *despit:* insult; *awroken:* revenged.
3753 *ybleynt:* turned aside.
3754 *yqueynt:* quenched.

3755 *fro:* from.
3756 *paramours:* lovers; *sette . . . kers:* didn't give a cress, i.e., a worthless thing.
3757 *heeled:* cured; *maladie:* the malady of love.
3758 *gan deffie:* renounced.
3759 *weep:* wept; *ybete:* beaten.

A softe paas he wente over the strete 3760
Until a smyth men cleped daun Gerveys,
That in his forge smythed plough harneys;
He sharpeth shaar and kultour bisily.
This Absolon knokketh al esily,
And seyde, "Undo, Gerveys, and that anon." 3765
"What, who artow?" "It am I, Absolon."
"What, Absolon! For Cristes swete tree,
Why rise ye so rathe? Ey, *benedicitee!*
What eyleth yow? Som gay gerl, God it woot,
Hath broght yow thus upon the viritoot. 3770
By seinte Note, ye woot wel what I mene."
This Absolon ne roghte nat a bene
Of al his pley; no word agayn he yaf;
He hadde moore tow on his distaf
Than Gerveys knew, and seyde, "Freend so deere, 3775
That hoote kultour in the chymenee heere,
As lene it me; I have therwith to doone;
And I wol brynge it thee agayn ful soone."
Gerveys answerde, "Certes, were it gold,
Or in a poke nobles alle untold, 3780
Thou sholdest have, as I am trewe smyth.
Ey, Cristes foo! What wol ye do therwith?"
"Therof," quod Absolon, "be as be may.
I shal wel telle it thee to-morwe day,"
And caughte the kultour by the colde stele. 3785
Ful softe out at the dore he gan to stele,
And wente unto the carpenteris wal.
He cogheth first, and knokketh therwithal
Upon the wyndowe, right as he dide er.

3760 *a softe paas:* a few quiet steps; *over:* across.
3761 *until:* to; *smyth:* blacksmith; *cleped:* called; *daun:* master.
3762 *smythed:* smithied, made in a forge; *harneys:* fittings.
3763 *sharpeth:* sharpens; *shaar:* plowshare; *kultour:* colter, a cutting blade on a plow.
3764 *esily:* gently.

3767 *tree:* cross.
3768 *rathe:* early; *benedicitee:* bless me.
3769 *eyleth:* ails; *gay:* wanton; *woot:* knows.

3770 *viritoot:* move, prowl (?).
3771 *Note:* Neot, a ninth-century English saint; *mene:* mean.
3772 *roghte:* cared; *bene:* bean.
3773 *of:* for; *pley:* joking; *word agayn:* reply; *yaf:* gave.
3774 *tow:* flax fibers for spinning, held on a distaff, i.e., he had more on his mind.

3776 *hoote:* hot; *chymenee:* fireplace.
3777 *as* with imperatives = "please"; *lene:* lend; *have to doone:* have something to do.

3779 *were it:* if it were.
3780 *poke:* bag; *nobles:* gold coins; *alle untold:* countless.

3782 *foo:* foe, i.e., Satan.
3783 *be as be may:* be as it may.
3784 *it:* i.e., about it.

3785 *stele:* handle.
3786 *softe:* softly; *gan to stele:* did steal.

3789 *right:* just; *er:* before.

This Alison answerde, "Who is ther *3790*
That knokketh so? I warante it a theef."
"Why, nay," quod he, "God woot, my sweete leef,
I am thyn Absolon, my deerelyng.
Of gold," quod he, "I have thee broght a ryng.
My moder yaf it me, so God me save; *3795*
Ful fyn it is, and therto wel ygrave.
This wol I yeve thee if thou me kisse."
This Nicholas was risen for to pisse,
And thoughte he wolde amenden al the jape;
He sholde kisse his ers er that he scape. *3800*
And up the wyndowe dide he hastily,
And out his ers he putteth pryvely
Over the buttok, to the haunche-bon;
And therwith spak this clerk, this Absolon,
"Spek, sweete bryd, I noot nat where thou art." *3805*
This Nicholas anon leet fle a fart
As greet as it had been a thonder-dent,
That with the strook he was almoost yblent;
And he was redy with his iren hoot,
And Nicholas amydde the ers he smoot. *3810*
Of gooth the skyn an hande-brede aboute,
The hoote kultour brende so his toute,
And for the smert he wende for to dye.
As he were wood, for wo he gan to crye,
"Help! water! water! help, for Goddes herte!" *3815*
This carpenter out of his slomber sterte,
And herde oon crien "water" as he were wood,
And thoughte, "Allas, now comth Nowelis flood!"
He sit hym up withouten wordes mo,

3791 *warante:* warrant, i.e., it must be.
3792 *woot:* knows; *leef:* dear.
3793 *deerelyng:* darling.

3795 *yaf:* gave; *so . . . save:* as God saves me.
3796 *fyn:* pure; *therto:* also; *ygrave:* engraved.
3797 *yeve:* give.

3799 *amenden:* improve on; *jape:* joke.

3800 *scape:* escape.
3801 *dide he:* i.e., he raised.
3802 *pryvely:* quietly.
3803 *over:* past; *haunche-bon:* thighbone.

3805 *spek:* speak; *bryd:* bird; *noot:* know not.
3806 *leet fle:* let fly.
3807 *as:* as if; *thonder-dent:* thunderclap.
3808 *strook:* blast; *he:* i.e., Absolon; *yblent:* blinded.

3810 *amydde:* in the middle of; *smoot:* smote.
3811 *of:* off; *gooth:* goes; *hande-brede:* handbreadth.
3812 *brende:* burned; *toute:* buttocks.
3813 *smert:* pain; *wende for to:* thought (he) would.
3814 *wood:* mad.

3815 *herte:* heart.
3816 *sterte:* started, jumped.
3817 *oon:* someone.
3818 *comth:* comes; *Nowelis:* Noah's, the carpenter has confused Noah and Nowel (Noel).
3819 *sit hym:* sits.

And with his ax he smoot the corde atwo, *3820*
And doun gooth al; he foond neither to selle
Ne breed ne ale til he cam to the celle
Upon the floor, and ther aswowne he lay.
  Up stirte hire Alison and Nicholay,
And criden, "out" and "harrow" in the strete. *3825*
The neighebores, bothe smale and grete,
In ronnen for to gauren on this man
That yet aswowne lay bothe pale and wan,
For with the fal he brosten hadde his arm.
But stonde he moste unto his owene harm; *3830*
For whan he spak, he was anon bore doun
With hende Nicholas and Alisoun.
They tolden every man that he was wood,
He was agast so of Nowelis flood
Thurgh fantasie, that of his vanytee *3835*
He hadde yboght hym knedyng tubbes thre,
And hadde hem hanged in the roof above;
And that he preyed hem, for Goddes love,
To sitten in the roof, *par compaignye*.
  The folk gan laughen at his fantasye; *3840*
Into the roof they kiken and they cape,
And turned al his harm unto a jape.
For what so that this carpenter answerde,
It was for noght; no man his reson herde.
With othes grete he was so sworn adoun *3845*
That he was holde wood in al the toun;
For every clerk anonright heeld with oother;
They seyde, "The man is wood, my leeve brother";
And every wight gan laughen at this stryf.

3820 *smoot:* smote; *atwo:* in two.
3821 *foond:* found (time).
3822 *celle:* floor boarding; i.e., he didn't stop to do business on the way down.
3823 *aswowne:* in a swoon.
3824 *stirte:* jumped.
3825 *criden:* cried.

3827 *ronnen:* ran; *gauren:* stare.

3829 *brosten:* broken.

3830 *stonde unto:* endure; *harm:* injury.
3831 *spak:* spoke; *bore doun:* overcome (in argument).
3832 *with:* by.
3833 *he:* i.e., the carpenter; *wood:* mad.
3834 *agast:* afraid.

3835 *thurgh:* through; *fantasie:* imagination; *of:* in; *vanytee:* folly.
3836 *yboght hym:* bought himself.

3839 *par compaignye:* for company.
3840 *gan:* did.
3841 *kiken:* peer; *cape:* gape.
3842 *jape:* joke.
3843 *what so:* whatever.
3844 *noght:* nothing; *reson:* explanation.

3845 *sworn adoun:* outstripped in swearing (that his story was true).
3846 *holde:* considered.
3847 *clerk:* student; *anonright:* immediately; *heeld:* sided with; *oother:* i.e., Nicholas.
3848 *leeve:* dear.
3849 *wight:* person; *gan laughen:* did laugh; *stryf:* strife.

Thus swyved was this carpenteris wyf, *3850*
For al his kepyng and his jalousye;
And Absolon hath kist hir nether yë;
And Nicholas is scalded in the towte.
This tale is doon, and God save al the rowte!

Heere endeth the Millere his tale.

Following this, the Reeve counters with another fabliau of the same type as the Miller's, concerning, of course, the humiliation of a miller. The *Cook's Tale,* another fabliau, follows but breaks off unfinished, ending Fragment I. Fragment II consists entirely of the tale of the Sergeant of the Law, a moral account of a falsely accused wife. Fragment III begins abruptly with the words of the Wife of Bath. An introductory passage linking this to an earlier tale was presumably never completed by the poet.

THE WIFE OF BATH'S PROLOGUE

The Wife's prologue is the longest and fullest of the character studies in the *Canterbury Tales,* and the Wife is the most completely realized character of all the pilgrims. She is, in fact, so remarkable an individual that she would be almost unbelievable if she were not so undeniably real. Her prologue is a triumphant confession as well as an apologia for marriage, or better, for multiple marriage; and its chief proposition is the superior marital contentment that results from the sovereignty of the wife over the husband.

Most of all, she is an ardent feminist. She is created out of many materials, not the least being the facts of life, but most important in her genesis are the authorities of the great medieval anti-

3850 *swyved:* lain with.
3851 *for:* in spite of; *kepyng:* guarding.
3852 *nether:* lower; *yë:* eye.

3854 *rowte:* company.

feminist literature. She knows these authorities well—having been thoroughly coached in them by her fifth husband—but she defies them. And her wit and her learning and her strength are equal to the needs of her defense. She can cap argument with argument, meet authority with authority, and give blow for blow.

Her advocacy is all callous, earthy, grossly humorous, but as is so common in Chaucer, also rich in irony. For in her defense of women and in the details of her triumphs she richly, and to some extent inadvertently, exemplifies the vices of women and of wives even as she does not fail to hit shrewdly the follies of men and husbands. Even as she defies the traditional concept of woman as "the los of al mankynde," she shows forth in her own rich biography the very characteristics which medieval (and modern?) critics so often attack. Yet somehow the portrait is more sympathetic than otherwise, for her intelligence and her earthy gusto are so irresistible that, for once, we cannot favor the underdogs, the vain, gullible, jealous, pedantic husbands.

FRAGMENT III

THE PROLOGE OF THE WYVES TALE OF BATHE

"Experience, though noon auctoritee *1*
Were in this world, is right ynogh for me
To speke of wo that is in mariage;
For lordynges, sith I twelf yeer was of age—
Thonked be God that is eterne on lyve— *5*
Housbondes at chirche dore I have had fyve
(If I so ofte myghte han wedded be),
And alle were worthy men in hir degree.
But me was told, certeyn, nat longe agon is,
That sith that Crist ne wente nevere but ones *10*
To weddyng in the Cane of Galilee,
That by the same ensample taughte he me
That I ne sholde wedded be but ones.
Herke eek, lo, which a sharp word for the nones,
Biside a welle, Jhesus, God and man, *15*
Spak in repreeve of the Samaritan:
'Thou hast yhad fyve housbondes,' quod he,
'And that ilke man that now hath thee
Is nat thyn housbonde.' Thus seyde he certeyn.
What that he mente therby I kan nat seyn; *20*
But that I axe why that the fifthe man
Was noon housbonde to the Samaritan?
How manye myghte she have in mariage?
Yet herde I nevere tellen in myn age

1 *though . . . were:* though there were no quotable authority (on marriage).
2 *right ynogh:* certainly enough; *for me:* to enable me.
3 *wo:* woe.
4 *lordynges:* gentlemen; *sith:* since; *twelf:* by canon law the legal age for the marriage of girls was twelve.
5 *eterne on lyve:* eternal in life.
6 *chirche dore:* cf. I:460.
7 i.e., if so many marriages can be valid; *han:* have.
8 *degree:* social rank.
9 *me was told:* it was told to me; *agon:* ago; *is:* it is.
10 *sith:* l. 4; *Crist ne wente:* i.e., attended as a guest; *ones:* once.
11 *Cane:* Cana, see John 2:1.
12 i.e., taught me by his example.
14 *herke . . . which a:* hear, too, what a; *for the nones:* to this purpose.

16 *repreeve:* reproof, see John 4:6ff.

18 *ilke:* same.

21 *axe:* ask.

24 *in myn age:* in my life.

Upon this nombre diffinicioun. 25
Men may devyne and glosen up and doun,
But wel I woot, expres, withouten lye,
God bad us for to wexe and multiplye;
That gentil text kan I wel understonde.
Eek wel I woot he seyde myn housbonde 30
Sholde lete fader and moder and take to me;
But of no nombre mencion made he
Of bigamye or of octogamye;
Why sholde men thanne speke of it vileynye?
Lo, here the wise kyng, daun Salomon; 35
I trowe he hadde wyves mo than oon.
As wolde God it leveful were to me
To be refresshed half so ofte as he!
Which yifte of God hadde he for alle hise wyves!
No man hath swich that in this world alyve is. 40
God woot this noble king, as to my wit,
The firste nyght hadde many a murye fit
With ech of hem, so wel was hym on lyve.
Blessed be God that I have wedded fyve,
Of whiche I have pyked out the beste, *44a*
Bothe of here nether purs and of here cheste. *44b*
Diverse scoles maken parfyt clerkes, *44c*
And diverse practyk in many sondry werkes *44d*
Maken the werkman parfit sekirly: *44e*
Of fyve husbondes scoleying am I. *44f*
Welcome the sixte whan that evere he shal! 45
For sith I wol nat kepe me chaast in al,
Whan myn housbonde is fro the world ygon,
Som Cristen man shal wedde me anon;
For thanne, th'apostle seith that I am free

25 *diffinicioun:* a clear explanation.
26 *devyne:* guess; *glosen:* interpret, explain.
27 *woot:* know; *expres:* expressly.
28 *wexe:* wax, increase.

31 *lete:* leave; *take:* betake himself.

33 *bigamye:* canon law applied this term to successive marriages.
34 *speke vileynye:* speak despiteful language.
35 *here:* i.e., for instance; *daun:* master; Solomon had seven hundred wives and three hundred concubines (I Kings 11:3).
36 *trowe:* believe; *wyves mo than oon:* of wives more than one.
37 *as:* an expletive used with statements of wishing or asking = "please"; *leveful:* permissible.

39 *which yifte:* what a gift!
40 *that in . . .:* i.e., no man that is alive, etc., has such a gift.
41 *God woot:* God knows; *as . . . wit:* in my judgment.
42 *murye:* merry; *fit:* bout.
43 *so wel:* i.e., so well it was for him in life.

44a *of whiche:* i.e., in picking whom I have selected the best.
44b *of:* in respect to; *here:* their; *nether purse:* i.e., scrotum; *cheste:* money box.
44c *diverse scoles:* a variety of schools; *parfyt clerkes:* perfect scholars.
44d *practyk:* practical experiences; *sondry:* various.
44e *sekirly:* certainly.
44f *of:* from; *scoleying am I:* I have studied.
45 *shal:* i.e., shall come.
46 *sith:* l. 4; *chaast:* chaste.
47 *ygon:* gone.
48 *anon:* at once.
49 *apostle:* Paul, see I Corinthians 7:9.

To wedde, a Goddes half, where it liketh me. *50*
He seith that to be wedded is no synne;
Bet is to be wedded than to brynne.
What rekketh me thogh folk seye vileynye
Of shrewed Lameth and his bigamye?
I woot wel Abraham was an holy man, *55*
And Jacob eek, as fer as evere I kan,
And ech of hem hadde wyves mo than two,
And many another holy man also.
Where kan ye seye in any manere age
That hye God defended mariage *60*
By expres word? I pray you, telleth me!
Or where comanded he virginitee?
I woot as wel as ye, it is no drede,
Th'apostle, whan he speketh of maydenhede,
He seyde that precept therof hadde he noon. *65*
Men may conseille a womman to be oon,
But conseillyng is no comandement.
He put it in oure owene juggement.
For hadde God comanded maydenhede,
Thanne hadde he dampned weddyng with the dede; *70*
And certes, if ther were no seed ysowe,
Virginitee, thanne wherof sholde it growe?
Poul dorste nat comanden at the leeste
A thyng of which his maister yaf noon heeste.
The dart is set up for virginitee: *75*
Cacche whoso may, who renneth best lat see.
  But this word is nat take of every wight,
But ther as God list yeve it of his myght.
I woot wel that th'apostle was a mayde;

50 *a Goddes half:* in God's name; *liketh:* pleases.
51 *seith:* says.
52 *bet:* better; *brynne:* burn.
53 *rekketh me:* does it matter to me.
54 *shrewed:* cursed; *Lameth:* Genesis 4:19ff., the first man mentioned in the Bible as having two wives.

56 *kan:* know.

59 *manere:* kind of.

60 *hye:* high; *defended:* forbade.

63 *woot:* know; *it is no drede:* there is no fear, i.e., doubt.
64 *maydenhede:* virginity.
65 *precept:* commandment, i.e., from Jesus, see I Corinthians 7:6ff.
66 *conseille:* advise; *oon:* one, i.e., unmarried.

68 *put . . .:* left it to our own decision.
69 *for hadde:* for if (God) had.
70 Then he would have condemned marriage at the same time.
71 *certes:* certainly; *ysowe:* sown.

73 *dorste:* dared; *comanden:* order, demand; *at the leeste:* at least.
74 *of which:* concerning which; *yaf:* gave; *heeste:* command.
75 *dart:* prize in a race (i.e., the race of life).
76 *cacche:* catch, win; *renneth:* runs; *lat:* let's.
77 *take of:* applicable to; *wight:* person.
78 *but ther as:* only there where; *list:* it pleases (God); *yeve:* to give, apply.

But natheless, thogh that he wroot and sayde 80
He wolde that every wight were swich as he,
Al nys but conseil to virginitee;
And for to been a wyf he yaf me leve
Of indulgence; so is it no repreve
To wedde me if that my make dye, 85
Withoute excepcion of bigamye;
Al were it good no womman for to touche—
He mente as in his bed or in his couche,
For peril is bothe fyr and tow t'assemble;
Ye knowe what this ensample may resemble. 90
This al and som, he heeld virginitee
Moore parfit than weddyng in freletee.
(Freletee clepe I but if that he and she
Wolde leden al hir lyf in chastitee.)
I graunte it wel, I have noon envye, 95
Thogh maydenhede preferre bigamye;
It liketh hem to be clene body and goost.
Of myn estaat I nyl nat make no boost;
For wel ye knowe, a lord in his houshold
Ne hath nat every vessel al of gold; 100
Somme been of tree, and doon hir lord servyse.
God clepeth folk to hym in sondry wyse,
And everich hath of God a propre yifte,
Som this, som that, as hym lyketh shifte.
Virginitee is greet perfeccion, 105
And continence eek with devocion,
But Crist, that of perfeccion is welle,
Bad nat every wight he sholde go selle
Al that he hadde and yeve it to the poore

80 *natheless:* nevertheless; *wroot:* wrote.
81 *wolde:* would, wished; *swich:* such, the same.
82 *al nys but:* all (that) is only; *conseil:* recommendation.
83 *yaf . . . indulgence:* gave me permission.
84 *repreve:* disgrace, sin.

85 *make:* mate.
86 *withoute . . . bigamye:* not even excepting that (sin) of bigamy.
87 *al were it:* although it would be.
88 *mente:* meant.
89 *peril is:* it is dangerous; *fyr . . . tow:* fire and tow (a highly inflammable substance); *t'assemble:* to bring together.
90 *ensample:* metaphor; *resemble:* i.e., apply to.
91 *al . . . som:* the whole of it.
92 *parfit:* perfect; *freletee:* frailty.
93 *clepe I:* I call it; *but if:* unless.
94 *leden:* lead.

96 *preferre:* be preferable to; *bigamye:* remarriage.
97 *liketh:* pleases; *clene:* pure; *goost:* spirit.
98 *estaat:* condition; *nyl:* will not; *boost:* boast.

100 *vessel:* utensil.
101 *tree:* wood; *and doon:* and yet do.
102 *clepeth:* summons; *sondry wyse:* various ways.
103 *everich:* each; *propre:* own, suitable; *yifte:* gift.
104 *hym lyketh:* it pleases him; *shifte:* to ordain.

107 *welle:* fountain, source.
108 *bad:* bade; *wight:* person.
109 *yeve:* give.

And in swich wise folwe hym and his foore. *110*
He spak to hem that wolde lyve parfitly—
And lordynges, by youre leve, that am nat I!
I wol bistowe the flour of al myn age
In th'actes and in fruyt of mariage.
Telle me also, to what conclusion *115*
Were membres maad of generacion,
And of so parfit wys a wight ywroght?
Trusteth right wel, they were nat maad for noght.
Glose whoso wole, and seye bothe up and doun
That they were maked for purgacioun *120*
Of uryne, and oure bothe thynges smale
Were eek to knowe a femele from a male,
And for noon oother cause—sey ye no?
Th'experience woot wel it is noght so.
So that the clerkes be nat with me wrothe, *125*
I sey this, that they maked been for bothe,
That is to seye, for office and for ese
Of engendrure, ther we nat God displese.
Why sholde men elles in hir bookes sette
That man shal yelde to his wyf hir dette? *130*
Now wherwith sholde he make his paiement,
If he ne used his sely instrument?
Thanne were they maad upon a creature
To purge uryne, and eek for engendrure.
But I seye noght that every wight is holde, *135*
That hath swich harneys as I to yow tolde,
To goon and usen hem in engendrure;
Thanne sholde men take of chastitee no cure.
Crist was a mayde and shapen as a man,

110 *swich wise:* such a manner; *foore:* path, footsteps.
111 *spak:* spoke; *wolde:* wished.
112 *leve:* leave.
113 *wol:* will; *bistowe:* bestow; *flour:* flower.
114 *fruyt:* fruit, rewards.

115 *conclusion:* end, purpose.
116 *membres . . .:* members of generation (sexual organs) made.
117 *of . . . wys:* in such a perfect manner; *ywroght:* made.

119 *glose:* interpret; *whoso:* whoever; *seye . . .:* cf. "swear up and down."

120 *purgacioun:* purging.

122 *were . . . knowe:* exist in order that we may distinguish.

124 *woot:* knows, i.e., tells us.

125 *so that:* in order that; *clerkes:* scholars; *wrothe:* angry.

127 *office:* function, i.e., excretion; *ese:* ease.
128 *engendrure:* generation; *ther:* wherein.
129 *elles:* else; *sette:* set down.
130 *shal yelde:* must pay; *hir dette:* her debt, see I Corinthians 7:3.

132 *sely:* innocent, good.
133 *maad:* made.

135 *holde:* bound.
136 *harneys:* equipment.

138 *thanne:* then; *sholde:* would; *cure:* heed.
139 *mayde:* virgin; *shapen:* made, i.e., equipped.

And many a seint sith that the world bigan; *140*
Yet lyved they evere in parfit chastitee.
I nyl envye no virginitee;
Lat hem be breed of pured whete seed,
And lat us wyves hote barly breed;
And yet with barly breed, Mark telle kan, *145*
Oure Lord Jhesu refresshed many a man.
In swich estaat as God hath cleped us
I wol persevere; I nam nat precius.
In wyfhode wol I use myn instrument
As frely as my Makere hath it sent. *150*
If I be daungerous, God yeve me sorwe!
Myn housbonde shal it have bothe eve and morwe,
Whan that hym list come forth and paye his dette.
An housbonde wol I have, I wol nat lette,
Which shal be bothe my dettour and my thral, *155*
And have his tribulacion withal
Upon his flessh while that I am his wyf.
I have the power duryng al my lyf
Upon his propre body, and nat he:
Right thus th'Apostle tolde it unto me; *160*
And bad oure housbondes for to love us weel.
Al this sentence me liketh every deel."
Up stirte the Pardoner and that anon:
"Now dame," quod he, "by God and by Seint John,
Ye been a noble prechour in this cas! *165*
I was aboute to wedde a wyf; allas,
What sholde I bye it on my flessh so deere?
Yet hadde I levere wedde no wyf to yeere!"
"Abyde," quod she, "my tale is nat bigonne.

142 *nyl:* will not.
143 *lat hem:* let them; *breed:* bread; *pured:* refined.
144 *hote:* be called.

147 *estaat:* estate, condition; *cleped:* called, placed.
148 *nam nat:* am not; *precius:* fastidious.

151 *daungerous:* sparing, stingy; *yeve:* give; *sorwe:* sorrow.
152 *morwe:* morning.
153 *hym list:* it pleases him.
154 *lette:* cease or desist from.

155 *which:* who; *thral:* slave.
156 *tribulacion:* tribulation, affliction.

159 *propre:* own.
160 See I Corinthians 7:4.

162 *sentence:* judgment, opinion; *me liketh:* pleases me; *every deel:* every bit.
163 *stirte:* started; *anon:* at once.

165 *prechour:* preacher; *cas:* matter, subject.
166 cf. I:691.
167 *what:* why; *bye it . . . so deere:* pay so dearly for it. . . .
168 *levere:* rather; *to yeere:* this year.
169 *abyde:* wait.

Nay, thow shalt drynken of another tonne, *170*
Er that I go, shal savoure wors than ale.
And whan that I have toold thee forth my tale
Of tribulacion in mariage,
Of which I am expert in al myn age—
This is to seye, myself hath been the whippe— *175*
Thanne maystow chese wheither thou wolt sippe
Of thilke tonne that I shal abroche.
Be war of it, er thou too neigh approche;
For I shal telle ensamples mo than ten.
'Whoso that nyl be war by othere men, *180*
By hym shal othere men corrected be.'
Thise same wordes writeth Ptholomee;
Rede in his Almageste and take it there."
"Dame, I wolde praye yow, if youre wyl it were,"
Seyde this Pardoner, "as ye bigan, *185*
Telle forth youre tale; spareth for no man,
And teche us yonge men of youre praktike."
"Gladly," quod she, "sith it may you like;
But that I praye to al this compaignye,
If that I speke after my fantasye, *190*
As taketh nat agrief of that I seye,
For myn entente nys but for to pleye.
Now sire, thanne wol I telle yow forth my tale.
As evere moote I drynke wyn or ale,
I shal seye sooth: tho housbondes that I hadde, *195*
As three of hem were goode, and two were badde.
The thre were goode men, and riche, and olde;
Unnethe myghte they the statut holde
In which that they were bounden unto me—

170 *tonne:* tun, a large wine barrel.
171 *er:* ere; *savoure:* taste.

174 *age:* time.

176 *maystow:* may you; *chese:* choose, decide.
177 *thilke:* this; *abroche:* broach, tap, open.
178 *er:* before; *neigh:* near.

180-81 "Whoever will not be warned by others will become an example [of disaster] to others."
182 Ptolemy's *Almagest;* the aphorism is actually found in another work incorrectly attributed to Ptolemy.

184 *wyl:* will, desire.

187 *praktike:* l. 44d.
188 *sith:* since; *you like:* please you.

190 *after:* according to; *fantasye:* fancy, imagination.
191 *as:* an expletive used with imperatives = "please"; *agrief:* amiss.
192 *entente:* intent; *nys but:* is only.

194 *as . . . I:* as ever I hope to.
195 *sooth:* truth; *tho:* those.

198 *unnethe:* hardly; *statut holde:* obey the statute (see l. 130).
199 *in which:* by which.

Ye woot wel what I mene of this, pardee! 200
As help me God, I laughe whan I thynke
How pitously anyght I made hem swynke!
And by my fey, I tolde of it no stoor.
They hadde me yeven hir land and hir tresoor;
Me neded nat do lenger diligence 205
To wynne hir love or doon hem reverence.
They loved me so wel, by God above,
That I ne tolde no deyntee of hir love.
A wys womman wol bisye hire evere in oon
To gete hir love, ye, ther as she hath noon. 210
But sith I hadde hem hoolly in myn hond,
And sith they hadde yeven me al hir lond,
What sholde I take kepe hem for to plese,
But it were for my profit and myn ese?
I sette hem so awerke, by my fey, 215
That many a nyght they songen 'weilaway!'
The bacon was nat fet for hem, I trowe,
That som men han in Essexe at Dunmowe.
I governed hem so wel after my lawe,
That ech of hem ful blisful was and fawe 220
To brynge me gaye thynges fro the fayre;
They were ful glad whan I spak to hem faire,
For God it woot, I chidde hem spitously.
  Now herkneth how I bar me proprely,
Ye wise wyves, that kan understonde, 225
Thus sholde ye speke and bere hem wrong on honde;
For half so boldely kan ther no man
Swere and lyen as a woman kan.
I sey nat this by wyves that been wyse,

200 *woot:* know; *mene of:* mean by; *pardee:* indeed.

202 *anyght:* at night; *swynke:* work.
203 *fey:* faith; *tolde . . . stoor:* accounted it of no value.
204 *yeven:* given; *hir:* their; *tresoor:* wealth.

205 *me neded nat:* it was not necessary to me; *do diligence:* to be diligent.

208 *tolde . . . deyntee:* set no value.
209 *bisye hire:* busy herself; *evere in oon:* constantly.

210 *hir:* their; *ye:* yes; *ther as:* there where.
211 *hond:* hand.

213 *take kepe:* take pains; *hem:* them.
214 *but:* unless; *ese:* ease.

215 *awerke:* to work; *fey:* faith.
216 *songen 'weilaway':* cried "woe is me!"
217 *fet:* fetched, brought back; *trowe:* believe.
218 At Dunmow a bacon was offered to any married couple who lived a year without quarreling; *han:* have.
219 *after:* according.

220 *fawe:* glad.
221 *fayre:* fair.

223 *chidde:* chided; *spitously:* spitefully, cruelly.
224 *herkneth:* hearken; *bar me:* behaved; *proprely:* suitably.

226 *bere hem . . . on honde:* accuse them falsely.

229 *by:* for; *wyse:* discreet.

But if it be whan they hem mysavyse. *230*
A wys wyf shal, if that she kan hir good,
Bere hym on honde that the cow is wood,
And take witnesse of hir owene mayde
Of hir assent. But herkneth how I sayde:
'Sire olde kaynard, is this thyn array? *235*
Why is my neighebores wyf so gay?
She is honoured over al ther she gooth;
I sitte at hoom; I have no thrifty cloth.
What dostow at my neighebores hous?
Is she so fair? Artow so amorous? *240*
What rowne ye with oure mayde, *benedicite?*
Sire olde lechour, lat thy japes be!
And if I have a gossib or a freend,
Withouten gilt thou chidest as a feend,
If that I walke or pleye unto his hous. *245*
Thou comest hoom as dronken as a mous,
And prechest on thy bench, with yvel preef!
Thou seist to me, it is a greet mescheef
To wedde a povre womman for costage;
And if that she be riche, of heigh parage, *250*
Thanne seistow that it is a tormentrye
To suffre hir pride and hir malencolye.
And if that she be fair, thou verray knave,
Thou seist that every holour wol hire have;
She may no while in chastitee abyde *255*
That is assailled upon ech a syde.
Thou seyst som folk desire us for richesse,
Some for oure shape, and somme for oure fairnesse,
And som for she kan outher synge or daunce,

230 *but if:* unless; *hem mysavyse:* act ill-advisedly, make a mistake.
231 *kan . . . good:* knows what is best for her.
232 *bere . . . wood:* "make him believe the chough *(cow)* is mad," alluding to the bird [chough] that tells the husband of the wife's unfaithfulness; the wife persuades him the bird is lying.
233 "And bring her own maid to bear witness of her agreement."
235 *kaynard:* dotard; *array:* arrangement.
236 *gay:* gaily dressed.
237 *over al ther:* everywhere that; *gooth:* goes.
238 *thrifty cloth:* serviceable clothes.
239 *dostow:* do you; are you doing.
240 *artow:* art thou.
241 *rowne:* whisper; *benedicite:* bless you; in three syllables: *bén-sĭ-té.*
242 *lechour:* lecher; *japes:* tricks.
243 *gossib:* confidant.
244 *withouten gilt:* though (I am) guiltless; *chidest:* scold; *feend:* fiend, devil.

247 *with yvel preef:* bad luck to you.
248 *mescheef:* misfortune.
249 *povre:* poor; *for costage:* on account of the expense.
250 *heigh parage:* high birth.
251 *seistow:* sayest thou.
252 *malencolye:* melancholy, dark moods.
253 *verray:* true.
254 *holour:* lecher, ribald.

256 *ech a:* every.
257 *us:* i.e., us women; *richesse:* wealth.

259 *outher:* either.

And som for gentilesse and daliaunce, 260
Som for hir handes and hir armes smale:
Thus goth al to the devel by thy tale!
Thou seyst men may nat kepe a castel wal,
It may so longe assailled been over al.
And if that she be foul, thou seist that she 265
Coveiteth every man that she may se,
For as a spanyel she wol on hym lepe,
Til that she fynde som man hire to chepe.
Ne noon so grey goos gooth ther in the lake,
As, seistow, wol be withoute make; 270
And seyst it is an hard thyng for to welde
A thyng that no man wol, his thankes, helde.
Thus seistow, lorel, whan thow goost to bedde;
And that no wys man nedeth for to wedde,
Ne no man that entendeth unto hevene— 275
With wilde thonder-dynt and firy levene
Moote thy welked nekke be tobroke!
Thou seyst that droppyng houses and eek smoke
And chidyng wyves maken men to flee
Out of hir owene houses. A, *benedicite!* 280
What eyleth swich an old man for to chide?
Thow seyst we wyves wil oure vices hide
Til we be fast, and thanne we wol hem shewe—
Wel may that be a proverbe of a shrewe!
Thou seist that oxen, asses, hors, and houndes, 285
They been assayed at diverse stoundes,
Bacyns, lavours, er that men hem bye,
Spoones and stooles, and al swich housbondrye,
And so be pottes, clothes, and array;

260 *gentilesse:* good breeding; *daliaunce:* courtly flirtation.

262 *goth:* goes; *by thy tale:* according to your story.
263 *kepe:* defend.
264 i.e., when it is long assailed on all sides.
265 *foul:* ugly.
266 *coveiteth:* covets, wants.
267 *lepe:* leap.
268 *chepe:* buy, i.e., take.
269 *ne noon so:* not a; *gooth:* goes, i.e., swims.

270 *make:* mate.
271 *welde:* control.
272 *thyng:* i.e., a woman; *wol:* wants; *his thankes:* willingly; *helde:* to hold, have.
273 *lorel:* wretch.

275 *entendeth:* aims.
276 *dynt:* bolt; *levene:* lightning.
277 *moote:* may; *welked:* withered; *tobroke:* broken to bits.
278 *droppyng:* dripping, leaky.
279 *chidyng:* scolding.

281 *eyleth:* ails; *swich:* such; *for to chide:* to scold so.

283 *fast:* secure, i.e., married; *shewe:* show.
284 *wel:* indeed; *shrewe:* scoundrel.
285 *hors:* horses.
286 *assayed:* tested, evaluated; *diverse stoundes:* different, i.e., several different, times.
287 *bacyns:* basins; *lavours:* washbowls; *er:* before; *bye:* buy.
288 *housbondrye:* household goods.
289 *be:* are; *array:* garments.

But folk of wyves maken noon assay 290
Til they be wedded—olde dotard shrewe!
And thanne, seistow, we wil oure vices shewe.
Thou seist also that it displeseth me
But if that thou wolt preise my beautee,
And but thou poure alwey upon my face, 295
And clepe me "Faire Dame" in every place;
And but thou make a feeste on thilke day
That I was born, and make me fressh and gay;
And but thou do to my norice honour,
And to my chamberere withinne my bour, 300
And to my fadres folk, and his allyes—
Thus seistow, olde barel-ful of lyes!
And yet of oure apprentice Janekyn,
For his crispe heer, shynyng as gold so fyn,
And for he squiereth me bothe up and doun, 305
Yet hastow caught a fals suspecioun.
I wil hym nat thogh thou were deed tomorwe!
But tel me this, why hydestow, with sorwe,
The keyes of thy cheste away fro me?
It is my good as wel as thyn, pardee! 310
What, wenestow make an ydiot of oure dame?
Now by that lord that called is Seint Jame,
Thou shalt nat bothe, thogh that thow were wood,
Be maister of my body and of my good;
That oon thou shalt forgo, maugree thyne eyen. 315
What helpeth it of me to enquere and spyen?
I trowe thou woldest loke me in thy chiste!
Thou sholdest seye, "Wyf, go wher thee liste;
Taak youre disport, I wol nat leve no talys.

290 i.e., make no test of their wives.

294 *but if:* unless; *wolt:* will.

295 *but:* unless; *poure:* gaze.
296 *clepe:* call.
297 *feeste:* celebration; *thilke:* that.
298 *gay:* brightly dressed.
299 *norice:* nurse.

300 *chamberere:* chambermaid, lady's maid; *bour:* a private room.
301 *fadres:* father's; *allyes:* relatives.

304 *crispe heer:* curly hair.

305 *for:* because; *squiereth:* escorts.
306 *hastow:* have you; *fals:* false.
307 *wil:* want; *deed:* dead.
308 *hydestow:* do you hide; *with sorwe:* ill luck to you.
309 *cheste:* money box.

310 *good:* goods, wealth.
311 *wenestow:* do you think to.

313 *wood:* mad.

315 *that oon:* i.e., one or the other; *maugree . . .:* despite your eyes, i.e, despite anything you can do about it.
316 *what . . .:* what does it help to inquire about and spy on me.
317 *trowe:* believe; *woldest:* would like to; *loke:* lock.
318 *thee liste:* it pleases you.
319 *taak:* take; *disport:* pleasure; *leve:* believe; *talys:* tales.

I knowe yow for a trewe wyf, dame Alys." 320
We love no man that taketh kepe or charge
Wher that we goon; we wol been at oure large.
Of alle men yblessed moot he be,
The wise astrologen daun Ptholomee,
That seith this proverbe in his Almageste: 325
"Of alle men his wisdom is hyeste
That rekketh nat who hath the world in honde."
By this proverbe thow shalt understonde,
Have thow ynogh, what thar thee rekke or care
How myrily that othere folkes fare? 330
For certes, olde dotard, by youre leve,
Ye shal have queynte right ynogh at eve.
He is too greet a nygard that wil werne
A man to lighte a candle at his lanterne;
He shal have never the lasse lighte, pardee. 335
Have thou ynogh, thee thar nat pleyne thee.
Thou seist also that if we make us gay
With clothyng and with precious array,
That it is peril of oure chastitee;
And yet, with sorwe, thou most enforce thee, 340
And seye thise wordes in th'Apostles name:
"In habit maad with chastitee and shame
Ye wommen shal apparaille yow," quod he,
"And nat in tressed heer and gay perree,
As perles, ne with gold, ne clothes riche." 345
After thy text, ne after thy rubriche,
I wol nat werke as muchel as a gnat.
Thou seydest this, that I was lyk a cat;
For whoso wolde senge a cattes skyn,

321 *taketh kepe:* takes heed; *charge:* notice.
322 *at oure large:* at large, free.
323 *moot:* may.
324 *astrologen:* astronomer; *daun:* master; *Ptholomee:* l. 182.

326 *hyeste:* highest.

327 *rekketh:* recks, cares; *hath . . . in honde:* has great wealth.

329 *have thow ynogh:* if you have enough; *thar:* need; *rekke:* care; *care:* worry.

331 *dotard:* foolish one.
332 *queynte:* pudendum.
333 *nygard:* niggard; *werne:* refuse, deny.

335 *never the lasse:* nonethelcss.
336 *thee thar nat:* it is not needful for you; *pleyne thee:* to complain.

338 *array:* l. 289.
339 *peril of:* perilous for.
340 *with sorwe:* l. 308; *enforce thee:* strengthen (your position).
341 See I Timothy 2:9.
342 *habit:* dress; *maad:* made; *shame:* modesty.
343 *apparaille yow:* dress yourselves.
344 *tressed heer:* elaborately dressed hair; *perree:* jewelry.

346 *after:* according to; *ne:* nor; *rubriche:* rubric, the directions, heading, or comment printed with a text.
347 *werke:* i.e., live, conduct myself; *as muchel as:* i.e., any more than (a gnat would).

349 *whoso:* whoever, i.e., whenever anyone; *senge:* singe; *skyn:* fur.

Thanne wolde the cat wel dwellen in his in; 350
And if the cattes skyn be slyk and gay,
She wol nat dwelle in house half a day,
But forth she wole, er any day be dawed,
To shewe her skyn and goon a-caterwawed.
This is to seye, if I be gay, sire shrewe, 355
I wol renne out, my borel for to shewe.
Sire olde fool, what helpeth thee t'espyen?
Thogh thow preye Argus with his hundred eyen
To be my warde-cors, as he kan best,
In feith, he shal nat kepe me but me lest; 360
Yet koude I make his berd, so mote I thee.
Thou seydest eek that ther been thynges three,
The whiche thynges troublen al this erthe,
And that no wight may endure the ferthe.
O leeve sire shrewe, Jhesu shorte thy lyf! 365
Yet prechestow and seist an hateful wyf
Yrekened is for oon of thise myschaunces.
Been ther none othere maner resemblaunces
That ye may likne youre parables to,
But if a sely wyf be oon of tho? 370
Thou liknest eek wommanes love to helle,
To bareyne land ther water may nat dwelle;
Thow liknest it also to wilde fyr;
The moore it brenneth, the moore it hath desir
To consume every thyng that brent wol be. 375
Thow seist right as wormes shende a tree,
Right so a wyf destroyeth hir housbonde;
This knowen they that been to wyves bonde.'
Lordinges, right thus, as ye have understonde,

350 *wolde:* will, will want to; *in:* dwelling.
351 *slyk:* sleek.

353 *wole:* will (go); *er:* before; *dawed:* dawned.
354 *a-caterwawed:* caterwauling.

356 *renne:* run; *borel:* clothing.
357 *helpeth thee:* does it help thee; *t'espyen:* to watch.
358 *preye:* beg; *Argus:* a monster with a hundred eyes, some of which were always awake.
359 *warde-cors:* bodyguard.
360 *kepe:* guard; *but me lest:* unless it pleases me.
361 *make his berd:* outwit him; *so:* as; *thee:* thrive.

364 *wight:* person; *ferthe:* fourth.
365 *leeve:* dear; *shorte:* shorten.
366 *prechestow:* you preach.
367 *yrekened is for:* is reckoned as; *myschaunces:* misfortunes.
368-69 *been:* are; *maner:* kind of; *resemblaunces . . .:* subjects that you can apply your comparisons to.

370 *but if:* unless; *sely:* innocent, good; *oon:* one; *tho:* those.
371 *liknest:* compare.
372 *bareyne:* barren.
373 *wilde fyr:* an inflammable substance, like Greek fire, unquenchable by water.
374 *brenneth:* burns.
375 *brent wol be:* can be burnt.
376 *seist right:* say (that) just; *shende:* destroy.

378 *bonde:* bound.
379 *understonde:* understood, learned.

Bar I stifly myne olde housbondes on honde *380*
That thus they seyden in hir dronkenesse;
And al was fals, but that I took witnesse
On Janekyn and on my nece also.
O Lord, the peyne I dide hem and the wo,
Ful giltelees, by Goddes sweete pyne! *385*
For as an hors I koude byte and whyne;
I koude pleyne thogh I were in the gilt,
Or elles often tyme I hadde been spilt.
Whoso that first to mille comth, first grynt;
I pleyned first, so was oure werre stynt. *390*
They were ful glad to excusen hem ful blyve
Of thyng of which they nevere agilte hir lyve.
  Of wenches wolde I beren hem on honde,
Whan that for syk they myghte unnethe stonde;
Yet tikled it his herte for that he *395*
Wende that I hadde of hym so greet chiertee.
I swoor that al my walkyng out by nyghte
Was for to espye wenches that he dighte;
Under that colour hadde I many a myrthe.
For al swich wit is yeven us in oure birthe;
Deceite, wepyng, spynnyng God hath yive
To wommen kyndely whil they may lyve.
And thus of o thyng I avaunte me:
Atte ende I hadde the bet in ech degree,
By sleighte or force, or by som maner thyng, *405*
As by continuel murmur or grucchyng.
Namely abedde hadden they meschaunce:
Ther wolde I chide and do hem no plesaunce;
I wolde no lenger in the bed abyde

380 *bar on honde:* accused; *stifly:* boldly.
381 That they spoke thus while drunk.
382 *fals:* false; *but that . . .:* but I called as witnesses.

384 *dide:* caused; *wo:* woe.

385 *pyne:* suffering.

387 *pleyne:* complain.
388 *spilt:* ruined.
389 Whosoever comes first to the mill, grinds first.

390 *werre:* warfare; *stynt:* brought to an end.
391 *excusen hem:* excuse themselves; *ful blyve:* right quickly.
392 *agilte:* were guilty of; *hir lyve:* in their lives.
393 *beren on honde:* l. 380.
394 *syk:* illness; *unnethe:* hardly.

395 *tikled:* tickled, pleased; *for that:* because.
396 *wende:* thought; *of hym:* for him; *chiertee:* fondness.

398 *espye:* spy out; *dighte:* lay with.
399 *colour:* pretense.

400 *yeven:* given; *in:* at.
401 *wepyng:* weeping; *yive:* given.
402 *kyndely:* by their nature.
403 *o:* one; *avaunte me:* boast.
404 *bet:* better; *ech degree:* every way.

405 *sleighte:* trick; *maner:* kind of.
406 *murmur:* complaining; *grucchyng:* grumbling.
407 *namely:* especially; *abedde:* in bed; *meschaunce:* misfortune.
408 *chide:* scold; *do:* give.
409 *abyde:* remain.

If that I felte his arm over my syde, 410
Til he had maad his raunson unto me;
Thanne wolde I suffre hym do his nycetee.
And therfore every man this tale I telle:
Wynne whoso may, for al is for to selle;
With empty hand men may none haukes lure. 415
For wynnyng wolde I al his lust endure,
And make me a feyned appetit—
And yet in bacon hadde I nevere delit.
That made me that evere I wolde hem chide;
For thogh the Pope hadde seten hem biside, 420
I wolde nat spare hem at hir owene bord,
For by my trouthe, I quitte hem word for word.
As help me verray God omnipotent,
Though I right now sholde make my testament,
I ne owe hem nat a word that it nys quit. 425
I broghte it so aboute by my wit
That they moste yeve it up as for the beste,
Or elles hadde we nevere been in reste;
For thogh he looked as a wood leon,
Yet sholde he faille of his conclusion. 430
Thanne wolde I seye, 'Goode lief, taak keep,
How mekely looketh Wilkyn, oure sheep!
Com neer, my spouse, lat me ba thy cheke.
Ye sholde be al pacient and meke,
And han a sweete-spiced conscience, 435
Sith ye so preche of Jobes pacience;
Suffreth alway, syn ye so wel kan preche;
And but ye do, certeyn, we shal yow teche
That it is fair to have a wyf in pees.

411 *maad his raunson:* paid his ransom.
412 *suffre:* allow; *nycetee:* lust.

414 Let him get it who can, for it is all for sale.

415 *lure:* i.e., lure hawks to be caught.
416 *wynnyng:* profit.
417 *feyned:* feigned.
418 *bacon:* i.e., old meat.
419 *that made me:* i.e., that is why.

420 *seten hem biside:* sat beside them.
421 *bord:* table.
422 *trouthe:* troth; *quitte:* repaid.
423 *as help:* as (God) may help.
424 *testament:* will.

425 *nys:* is not; *quit:* paid back.

427 *yeve it up:* surrender; *as . . . beste:* as the best they could do.
428 *in reste:* at peace.
429 *wood leon:* furious lion.
430 *of . . . conclusion:* in his purpose.
431 *goode lief:* good friend; *taak keep:* take notice.
432 *mekely:* meekly.
433 *ba:* kiss.

435 *sweete-spiced:* delicate; *conscience:* feeling.
436 *sith:* since.
437 *suffreth:* be patient; *syn:* since.
438 *but:* unless; *teche:* teach.
439 *fair:* good; *in pees:* at peace.

Oon of us two moste bowen, doutelees, 440
And sith a man is moore resonable
Than womman is, ye mosten been suffrable.
What eyleth yow to grucche thus and grone?
Is it for ye wolde have my queynte allone?
Wy, taak it al! Lo, have it every deel! 445
Peter, I shrewe yow but ye love it weel!
For if I wolde selle my *bele chose,*
I koude walke as fressh as is a rose;
But I wol kepe it for youre owene tooth.
Ye be to blame! By God, I sey yow sooth!' 450
Swiche manere wordes hadde we on honde.
Now wol I speken of my fourthe housbonde.
My fourthe housbonde was a revelour;
This is to seyn, he hadde a paramour;
And I was yong and ful of ragerye, 455
Stibourne and strong and joly as a pie.
How koude I daunce to an harpe smale,
And synge, ywis, as any nyghtyngale,
Whan I had dronke a draughte of sweete wyn!
Metellius, the foule cherl, the swyn, 460
That with a staf birafte his wyf hir lyf
For she drank wyn, though I hadde been his wyf,
He sholde nat han daunted me fro drynke!
And after wyn on Venus moste I thynke,
For al so siker as cold engendreth hayl, 465
A likerous mouth moste han a likerous tayl;
In womman vinolent is no defence—
This knowen lechours by experience.
But Lord Crist! whan that it remembreth me

440 *bowen:* bow, give way.

442 *suffrable:* patient.
443 *eyleth:* ails; *grucche:* grumble.
444 *for:* because; *queynte:* pudendum; *allone:* all to yourself.

445 *wy:* why; *every deel:* every bit.
446 *shrewe:* curse; *weel:* well.
447 *bele chose:* pretty thing.
448 i.e., I could dress well on the proceeds.
449 *tooth:* taste.

450 *sooth:* truth.
451 *swiche manere:* such kind of; *on honde:* between us.

453 *revelour:* rake.
454 *paramour:* mistress.

455 *ragerye:* wantonness, passion.
456 *stibourne:* stubborn; *joly . . . pie:* merry as a magpie.

460 *cherl:* churl, lout; *swyn:* swine; *Metellius:* a story from a Latin writer.
461 *staf:* staff; *birafte:* took from; *lyf:* life.
462 *for:* because; *though:* if.
463 *he . . . daunted:* he should not have frightened.
464 *moste:* must.
465 *al so siker:* just as sure; *engendreth:* engenders.
466 *likerous:* greedy, lecherous; *moste han:* must have, i.e., goes with.
467 *vinolent:* full of wine.
468 Lechers know this.
469 *remembreth me:* comes to my mind.

Upon my youthe and on my jolitee, *470*
It tikleth me aboute myn herte roote;
Unto this day it dooth myn herte boote
That I have had my world as in my tyme.
But age, allas, that al wole envenyme,
Hath me biraft my beautee and my pith. *475*
Lat go, farewel, the devel go therwith!
The flour is goon, ther is namoore to telle;
The bren, as I best kan, now moste I selle;
But yet to be right murye wol I fonde.
Now wol I tellen of my fourthe housbonde. *480*
I saye I hadde in herte greet despit
That he of any oother had delit.
But he was quit, by God and by Seint Joce!
I made hym of the same wode a croce—
Nat of my body in no foul manere— *485*
But, certeinly, I made folk swich cheere
That in his owene grece I made hym frye
For angre and for verray jalousye.
By god, in erthe I was his purgatorie,
For which I hope his soule be in glorie. *490*
For, God it woot, he sat ful ofte and song
Whan that his shoo ful bitterly hym wrong.
Ther was no wight, save God and he, that wiste
In many wise how soore I hym twiste.
He deyde whan I cam fro Jerusalem, *495*
And lith ygrave under the roode-beem,
Al is his tombe noght so curyous
As was the sepulcre of hym Daryus,
Which that Appelles wroghte subtilly;

471 *herte roote:* root of my heart.
472 *dooth . . . boote:* does my heart good.
473 *as* is redundant here; i.e., enjoyed myself while I could.
474 *al wole envenyme:* will envenom all.

475 *biraft:* robbed of; *pith:* strength, vigor.

477 *flour:* flour.
478 Now I must sell the bran as best I can.
479 *murye:* merry; *fonde:* try.

481 *despit:* resentment.
482 *of:* from; *had delit:* might have delight.
483 *quit:* paid back; *Joce:* the Breton saint, Judocus.
484 *same . . . croce:* a cross of the same wood; i.e., paid him in his own coin.

486 *cheere:* hospitality.
487 Made him fry in his own grease.

491 *God it woot:* God knows; *song:* i.e., sang a sorry tune.
492 *shoo:* shoe; *hym wrong:* pinched him.
493 *wight:* person; *wiste:* knew.
494 *wise:* ways; *soore:* sorely; *twiste:* tortured.

495 *deyde:* died; *Jerusalem:* i.e., from her pilgrimage (n.b., three syllables).
496 *lith:* lies; *ygrave:* buried; *roode-beem:* a beam (in the church) between nave and chancel.
497 *al:* although; *curyous:* elaborate.
498-99 The sepulchre of Darius was said to have been made by a Jewish artist named Apelles.

It nys but wast to burye hym preciously. *500*
Lat hym fare wel, God yeve his soule reste;
He is now in his grave and in his cheste.
Now of my fifthe housbonde wol I telle.
God lete his soule nevere come in helle!
And yet he was to me the mooste shrewe; *505*
That feele I on my ribbes al by rewe,
And evere shal unto myn endyng day.
But in oure bed he was so fressh and gay,
And therwithal so wel koude he me glose
Whan that he wolde han my *bele chose,* *510*
That thogh he hadde me bet on every bon,
He koude wynne agayn my love anon.
I trowe I loved hym best for that he
Was of his love daungerous to me.
We wommen han, if that I shal nat lye, *515*
In this matere a queynte fantasye:
Wayte what thyng we may nat lightly have,
Therafter wol we crye al day and crave.
Forbede us thyng, and that desiren we;
Preesse on us faste, and thanne wol we fle. *520*
With daunger oute we al oure chaffare;
Greet prees at market maketh deere ware,
And too greet chepe is holde at litel prys;
This knoweth every womman that is wys.
My fifthe housbonde—God his soule blesse!— *525*
Which that I took for love, and no richesse,
He som tyme was a clerk of Oxenford,
And hadde left scole and wente at hom to bord
With my gossib, dwellyng in oure toun—

500 *nys but wast:* would have been nothing but waste: *preciously:* expensively.

502 *cheste:* coffin.

505 *mooste shrewe:* worst scoundrel.
506 *al by rewe:* one after the other.

509 *therwithal:* in addition; *glose:* flatter.
510 *han:* have; *bele chose:* pretty thing.
511 *bet:* beaten; *bon:* bone.
512 *anon:* at once.
513 *trowe:* think; *for that:* because.
514 *daungerous:* standoffish, disdainful.

516 *queynte fantasye:* curious fancy.
517 *wayte what thyng:* observe whatever thing; *lightly:* easily.
518 *therafter:* after that.
519 *forbede us thyng:* deny us a thing.

520 *preesse:* urge.
521 *daunger:* caution, coyness; *oute we:* we set forth; *chaffare:* merchandise.
522 *prees:* crowd; *deere:* expensive; *ware:* goods.
523 *chepe:* bargain; *prys:* value.

527 *som tyme:* in former time; *clerk:* student.
528 *at hom to bord:* to room and board.
529 *gossib:* friend.

God have hir soule!—hir name was Alisoun. 530
She knew myn herte and eek my privetee
Bet than oure parisshe preest, so mote I thee!
To hire biwreyed I my conseil al;
For hadde myn housbonde pissed on a wal,
Or doon a thyng that sholde have cost his lyf, 535
To hire, and to another worthy wyf,
And to my nece which that I loved weel,
I wolde han toold his conseil every deel.
And so I dide ful often, God it woot,
That made his face often reed and hoot 540
For verray shame, and blamed hymself for he
Had toold to me so greet a pryvetee.
And so bifel that ones in a Lente—
So often tymes I to my gossyb wente,
For evere yet I loved to be gay, 545
And for to walke in March, Averill, and May,
From hous to hous, to heere sondry tales—
That Jankyn clerk and my gossyb dame Alys
And I myself into the feeldes wente.
Myn housbonde was at Londoun al that Lente; 550
I hadde the bettre leyser for to pleye,
And for to se, and eek for to be seye
Of lusty folk. What wiste I wher my grace
Was shapen for to be, or in what place?
Therfore I made my visitacions 555
To vigilies and to processions,
To prechyng eek, and to thise pilgrimages,
To pleyes of myracles, and to mariages,
And wered upon my gaye scarlet gytes.

531 *herte:* inmost thoughts; *privetee:* secrets.
532 *bet:* better; *so . . . thee:* as I may thrive.
533 *biwreyed:* disclosed; *conseil:* secrets.
534 *hadde:* if (my husband) had; *wal:* wall.

536 *wyf:* woman.
537 *nece:* niece.
538 *conseil:* l. 533; *every deel:* every bit.

540 *reed and hoot:* red and hot.
541 *for he:* because he.
542 *pryvetee:* l. 531.
543 *ones:* once.

547 *heere:* hear; *sondry:* various.
548 *Jankyn:* diminutive of John, a stock name for a clerk.
549 *feeldes:* fields.

551 *leyser:* leisure.
552 i.e., to see and to be seen.
553 *of lusty folk:* by joyous folk; *what wiste I:* how did I know; *grace:* favor.
554 *shapen . . . be:* destined to be bestowed.

556 *vigilies:* feasts on the eves of saints' days.
557 *eek:* also.
558 The miracle (or mystery) plays were based on religious subjects, such as Bible stories.
559 *wered upon:* wore; *gytes:* gowns.

Thise wormes ne thise motthes ne thise mytes, *560*
Upon my peril, frete hem never a deel;
And wostow why? For they were used weel.
  Now wol I tellen forth what happed me.
I seye that in the feeldes walked we,
Til trewely we hadde swich daliance, *565*
This clerk and I, that of my purveiance
I spak to hym and seyde hym how that he,
If I were wydwe, sholde wedde me.
For certeinly, I sey for no bobance,
Yet was I nevere withouten purveiance *570*
Of mariage n'of othere thynges eek.
I holde a mouses herte nat worth a leek
That hath but oon hole for to sterte to,
And if that faille, thanne is al ydo.
I bar hym on honde he hadde enchanted me *575*
(My dame taughte me that subtiltee);
And eek I seyde I mette of hym al nyght,
He wolde han slayn me as I lay upright,
And al my bed was ful of verray blood—
'But yet I hope that ye shal do me good; *580*
For blood bitokeneth gold, as me was taught.'
And al was fals; I dremed of it right naught,
But as I folwed ay my dames loore,
As wel of that as of othere thynges moore.
But now sire—lat me se, what shal I seyn? *585*
Aha, by God, I have my tale ageyn.
  Whan that my fourthe housbonde was on beere,
I weep algate, and made sory cheere,
As wyves mooten, for it is usage,

560 *mytes:* mites.
561 *frete . . .:* ate them not a bit, i.e., because she wore them so often.
562 *wostow:* do you know.
563 *happed me:* happened to me.

565 *daliance:* flirtation.
566 *purveiance:* prudent foresight.
567 *seyde:* told.

569 *bobance:* boast.

571 *n'of:* nor for.
572 *leek:* a vegetable resembling an onion.
573 *sterte:* run.
574 *faille:* should fail him; *al ydo:* all over.
575 *bar hym on honde:* made him believe.
576 *dame:* mother; *subtiltee:* trick.
577 *mette:* dreamed.
578 *he wolde han:* that he was about to have; *upright:* supine.

581 *bitokeneth:* betokens, i.e., signifies in dreams.

583 *ay:* ever; *loore:* teaching.
584 *of:* in.
585 *what . . . seyn:* where was I?
587 *beere:* bier.
588 *weep:* wept; *algate:* anyhow; *cheere:* looks, appearance.
589 *mooten:* must.

And with my coverchief covered my visage; 590
But for that I was purveyed of a make,
I wepte but smal, and that I undertake.
To chirche was myn housbonde born amorwe
With neighebores that for hym maden sorwe;
And Jankyn oure clerk was oon of tho. 595
As help me God, whan that I saw hym go
After the beere, me thoughte he hadde a paire
Of legges and of feet so clene and faire
That al myn herte I yaf unto his hoold.
He was, I trowe, twenty wynter oold, 600
And I was fourty, if I shal seye sooth;
But yet I hadde alwey a coltes tooth.
Gat-tothed I was, and that bicam me weel;
I hadde the prente of Seint Venus seel.
As help me God, I was a lusty oon, 605
And faire, and riche, and yong, and wel bigoon,
And trewely, as myne housbondes tolde me,
I hadde the beste *quonyam* myghte be.
For certes, I am al Venerien
In feelyng, and myn herte is Marcien. 610
Venus me yaf my lust, my likerousnesse,
And Mars yaf me my sturdy hardynesse;
Myn ascendent was Taur and Mars ther inne—
Allas, allas, that evere love was synne!
I folwed ay myn inclinacion 615
By vertu of my constellacion;
That made me I koude noght withdrawe
My chambre of Venus from a good felawe.
Yet have I Martes mark upon my face,

591 *for that:* because; *purveyed:* provided; *make:* mate.

593 *born:* carried; *amorwe:* in the morning.

595 *oon of tho:* one of those.
596 *go:* walk.

599 *yaf:* gave.
600 *trowe:* believe.
601 *sooth:* truth.
602 *coltes tooth:* youthful desires.
603 *gat-tothed:* with a gap between the front teeth, thought to be a mark of lechery; *bicam:* became, suited.
604 *prente:* prlnt; *Seint . . . seel:* the seal of Saint Venus.
605 *as . . . God:* may God help me.
606 *wel bigoon:* well provided.

608 *quonyam:* i.e., pudendum.
609 *certes:* certainly; *Venerien:* influenced by Venus.
610 *herte:* spirit; *Marcien:* influenced by Mars.
611 *yaf:* gave; *likerousnesse:* lecherousness.
612 *hardynesse:* boldness; the passage reflects the doctrine that the position of the planets at a person's birth determines his character.
613 *myn ascendent:* the zodiacal sign just rising in the east at my birth; Taurus was called the mansion of Venus. Mars seen in this sign showed influence of Mars on Venus.
615 *ay:* ever; *inclinacion:* inclination.
616 *by vertu . . .:* controlled by the position of the planets at my birth.
617 *withdrawe:* withhold.
619 *Martes mark:* Mars' mark, a birthmark.

And also in another privee place. *620*
For God so wys be my savacion,
I loved nevere by no discrecion,
But evere folwede myn appetit,
Al were he short or long or blak or whit;
I took no kepe, so that he liked me, *625*
How poore he was, ne eek of what degree.
What sholde I seye but at the monthes ende,
This joly clerk Jankyn that was so hende
Hath wedded me with greet solempnytee;
And to him yaf I al the lond and fee *630*
That evere was me yeven therbifore—
But afterward repented me ful sore;
He nolde suffre no thyng of my list.
By God, he smoot me ones on the lyst,
For that I rente out of his book a leef, *635*
That of the strook myn ere wax al deef.
Stibourne I was as is a leonesse,
And of my tonge a verray jangleresse,
And walke I wolde, as I had doon biforn,
From hous to hous, although he had it sworn; *640*
For which he often tymes wolde preche,
And me of olde Romayn gestes teche;
How he Symplicius Gallus lefte his wif,
And hire forsook for terme of al his lif,
Noght but for open-heveded he hir say *645*
Lokyng out at his dore upon a day.
Another Romayn tolde he me by name,
That, for his wyf was at a someres game
Withouten his wityng, he forsook hire eke.

621 *wys:* surely; *be:* i.e., as (God) may be; *savacion:* salvation.
622 *by no:* according to no.

624 *al:* whether; *blak or whit:* dark or light.
625 *took . . . kepe:* cared not; *he liked me:* he pleased me.
626 *degree:* rank.

628 *hende:* courteous, pleasant.

630 *fee:* property.
631 *me yeven:* given to me.
632 *sore:* sorely.
633 *nolde suffre:* would not allow; *list:* wish, pleasure.
634 *smoot:* struck; *ones:* once; *lyst:* ear.

635 *rente:* tore.
636 *of:* from; *ere:* ear; *wax:* became.
637 *stibourne:* stubborn.
638 *verray jangleresse:* real chatterbox.
639 *wolde:* would, was determined to.

640 *it:* the contrary.

642 *Romayn gestes:* Roman stories; *teche:* teach.
643 *he* is redundant.
644 *terme:* the space.

645 *noght but for:* for nothing but that; *open-heveded:* bareheaded; *say:* saw.

647 *another:* of another.
648 *for:* because; *someres game:* the games and revels on Midsummer Eve.
649 *wityng:* knowing; *eke:* also.

And thanne wolde he upon his Bible seke *650*
That ilke proverbe of Ecclesiaste
Where he comandeth and forbedeth faste
Man shal nat suffre his wyf go roule aboute.
Thanne wolde he seye right thus withouten doute:
'Whoso that buyldeth his hous al of salwes, *655*
And priketh his blynde hors over the falwes,
And suffreth his wyf to go seken halwes,
Is worthy to been hanged on the galwes!'
But al for noght, I sette noght an hawe
Of his proverbes n'of his olde sawe; *660*
Ne I wolde nat of hym corrected be.
I hate hym that my vices telleth me,
And so doo mo, God woot, of us than I.
This made hym with me wood al outrely;
I nolde noght forbere hym in no cas. *665*
Now wol I seye yow sooth, by Seint Thomas,
Why that I rente out of his book a leef,
For which he smoot me so that I was deef.
He hadde a book that gladly, nyght and day,
For his disport he wolde rede alway; *670*
He cleped it Valerie and Theofraste,
At which book he lough alwey ful faste.
And eek ther was somtyme a clerk at Rome,
A cardinal, that highte Seint Jerome,
That made a book agayn Jovinian; *675*
In which book eek ther was Tertulan,
Crysippus, Trotula, and Helowys,
That was abbesse nat fer fro Parys;
And eek the Parables of Salomon,

650 *he:* i.e., Jankyn; *seke:* look for.

651 *ilke:* same; Ecclesiasticus, a book of the Old Testament Apocrypha.

652 *faste:* firmly.

653 *man:* one; *roule:* roam.

655 *salwes:* willow twigs.

656 *priketh:* rides; *falwes:* plowed land.

657 *halwes:* holy shrines, i.e., go on pilgrimages.

658 *is worthy:* deserves; *galwes:* gallows.

659 *sette . . . hawe:* rated not at the value of a hawthorn berry.

660 *n'of:* nor of; *sawe:* sayings.

661 *of hym:* by him.

663 *doo mo:* do more; *of us:* i.e., of us women.

664 *with me wood:* furious with me; *al outrely:* entirely.

665 *nolde:* would not; *noght:* by no means; *forbere hym:* let him alone.

666 *sooth:* truth.

667 *leef:* leaf.

668 *smoot:* struck.

670 *disport:* amusement.

671ff *cleped:* called; *Valerie etc.:* this book is an anthology of the best-known medieval satires on women and marriage.

672 *lough:* laughed.

673 *eek:* also, i.e., also in his anthology; *somtyme a clerk:* a clerk once (at Rome).

674 *highte:* was called.

675 *agayn:* against.

677 Héloïse, wife of Abelard, spent her last years in a convent, of which she became prioress.

678 *nat fer:* not far.

Ovides Art, and bookes many oon— *680*
And alle thise were bounden in o volume.
And every nyght and day was his custume,
Whan he hadde leyser and vacacion
From oother worldly occupacion,
To reden in this book of wikked wyves. *685*
He knew of hem mo legendes and lyves
Than been of goode wyves in the Bible.
For trusteth wel, it is an impossible
That any clerk wol speke good of wyves,
But if it be of holy seintes lyves, *690*
Ne of noon oother womman never the mo.
Who peynted the leon, tel me who?
By God, if wommen hadde writen stories,
As clerkes han withinne hir oratories,
They wolde han writen of men moore wikkednesse *695*
Than al the mark of Adam may redresse.
The children of Mercurie and of Venus
Been in hir wirkyng ful contrarius;
Mercurie loveth wysdam and science,
And Venus loveth riot and dispence; *700*
And for hir diverse disposicion,
Ech falleth in otheres exaltacion.
And thus, God woot, Mercurie is desolat
In Pisces, wher Venus is exaltat;
And Venus falleth ther Mercurie is reysed; *705*
Therfore no womman of no clerk is preysed.
The clerk, whan he is old and may noght do
Of Venus werkes worth his olde sho,
Thanne sit he doun and writ in his dotage

680 *Ovides Art:* Ovid's *Art of Love; many oon:* many a one.
681 *o:* one.

683 *leyser:* leisure; *vacacion:* spare time.

686 *of hem:* concerning them; *lyves:* biographies.

688 *impossible:* impossibility.
689 *clerk:* cleric.
690 *but:* unless.
691 *ne:* nor, and not; *never the mo:* never the more, not a one.
692 cf. the Aesopian fable of the lion looking at a painting of a hunter slaying a lion. The lion says, "Yes, but who painted the picture? A lion might have done it differently."
694 *han:* have; *oratorie:* a study or closet for prayers.

696 *mark:* race, sex; *redresse:* redress.
697 Clerks are children of Mercury and women children of Venus.
698 *wirkyng:* operations, i.e., all they do; *contrarius:* opposed.
699 *science:* knowledge.
700 *riot:* revelry; *dispence:* expenditure.
701 *for:* because of; *diverse disposicion:* different natures.
702 *falleth:* declines, loses his power; *exaltacion:* dominant position; each of these planets is astrologically in its weakest position when the other is dominant.
703 *desolat:* powerless.
704 *Pisces:* in the zodiac the sign of the fish.
705 *ther:* where.
707 *may noght do:* is able to do nothing.
708 *werkes:* work, acts; *sho:* i.e., his performance is not worth an old shoe.
709 *thanne . . .:* then he sits down and writes.

That wommen kan nat kepe hir mariage! 710
  But now to purpos why I tolde thee
That I was beten for a book, pardee!
Upon a nyght Jankyn, that was oure sire,
Redde on his book, as he sat by the fire,
Of Eva first, that for hir wikkednesse 715
Was al mankynde broght to wrecchednesse,
For which that Jhesu Crist hymself was slayn,
That boghte us with his herte blood agayn.
Lo, heere expres of wommen may ye fynde,
That womman was the los of al mankynde. 720
  Tho redde he me how Sampson loste his heres:
Slepynge, his lemman kitte it with hir sheres;
Thurgh which treson loste he bothe his eyen.
  Tho redde he me, if that I shal nat lyen,
Of Hercules and of his Dianyre, 725
That caused hym to sette hymself afyre.
  No thyng forgat he the care and the wo
That Socrates hadde with his wyves two;
How Xantippa caste pisse upon his heed.
This sely man sat stille as he were deed; 730
He wiped his heed, namoore dorste he seyn
But 'Er that thonder stynte, comth a reyn.'
  Of Phasipha that was the queene of Crete,
For shrewednesse hym thoughte the tale swete;
Fy, speke namoore—it is a grisly thyng— 735
Of hire horrible lust and hir likyng.
  Of Clitermystra for hir lecherye
That falsly made hir housbonde for to dye,
He redde it with ful good devocion.

710 *kepe:* be faithful to; *hir:* their.
711 *to purpos:* to the subject.

713 *oure sire:* my husband.

715 *that for hir:* for whose.

718 *boghte:* redeemed.
719 *heere expres:* here expressly (stated).
720 *los:* ruin.
721 *tho redde he me:* then he read to me; *heres:* hair.
722 *slepynge:* i.e., while he was sleeping; *lemman:* lover.

724 *lyen:* lie.
725 Deianeira gave unknowingly to Hercules a shirt that burned him so that he had himself killed.

727 *no thyng:* he did not by any means.

729 Xantippe, the wife of Socrates and a famous shrew.
730 *sely:* poor.
731 *namoore . . . seyn:* he dared say no more.
732 *er that:* before; *stynte:* stops; *comth:* comes.
733 Pasiphaë, wife of Minos, who loved a bull and was the mother of the Minotaur.
734 *shrewednesse:* malice; *hym thoughte:* seemed to him.
735 *speke:* speak.
737 Clytemnestra, wife of Agamemnon, who took a lover and murdered her husband when he returned from Troy.

He tolde me eek for what occasion *740*
Amphiorax at Thebes loste his lyf.
Myn housbonde hadde a legende of his wyf
Eriphilem, that for an ouche of gold
Hath prively unto the Grekes told
Wher that hir housbonde hidde hym in a place, *745*
For which he hadde at Thebes sory grace.
Of Lyvia tolde he me and of Lucye:
They bothe made hir housbondes for to dye,
That oon for love, that oother was for hate.
Lyvia hir housbonde, on an even late, *750*
Empoysoned hath, for that she was his fo;
Lucia, likerous, loved hir housbonde so
That, for he sholde alwey upon hire thynke,
She yaf hym swich a manere love-drynke
That he was deed er it were by the morwe. *755*
And thus algates housbondes han sorwe.
Thanne tolde he me how oon Latumyus
Compleyned unto his felawe Arrius
That in his gardyn growed swich a tree,
On which he seyde how that his wyves thre *760*
Hanged hemself for herte despitus.
'O leeve brother,' quod this Arrius,
'Yif me a plante of thilke blessed tree,
And in my gardyn planted shal it be.'
Of latter date of wyves hath he red *765*
That somme han slayn hir housbondes in hir bed
And lete hir lechour dighte hire al the nyght,
Whan that the corps lay in the floor upright;
And somme han dryven nayles in hir brayn

741 Amphiaraus, betrayed by his wife Eriphyle, was forced to go to the siege of Thebes, where he was killed.
743 *ouche:* a jeweled ornament.
744 *prively:* secretly.

745 *hidde hym:* had hidden himself.
746 *sory grace:* wretched fate.
747 Livia murdered her husband for her lover Sejanus; Lucilia, wife of the poet Lucretius, killed her husband accidentally with a love potion.

750 *even late:* late in an evening.

752 *likerous:* lustful.
753 *for:* so that.
754 *yaf:* gave; *manere:* kind of.
755 *er:* before; *by the morwe:* early morning.
756 *algates:* always.
757 *Latumyus . . .:* a favorite medieval story appearing in numerous works using various names.

759 *swich:* such.

761 *hemself:* themselves; *for herte despitus:* out of spite.
762 *leeve:* dear; *quod:* said.
763 *yif:* give; *plante:* cutting; *thilke:* this.

765 *of latter date:* i.e., of wives of a later time.

767 *lechour:* lover; *dighte:* have intercourse with.
768 *whan that:* while; *in:* on; *upright:* supine.
769 *hir:* their, i.e., their husbands'.

Whil that they slepte, and thus they han hem slayn; *770*
Somme han hem yeven poysoun in hir drynke;
He spak moore harm than herte may bithynke;
And therwithal he knew of mo proverbes
Than in this world ther growen gras or herbes.
'Bet is,' quod he, 'thyn habitacioun *775*
Be with a leon or a foul dragoun,
Than with a womman usyng for to chide.'
'Bet is,' quod he, 'hye in the roof abyde,
Than with an angry wyf doun in the hous;
They been so wikked and contrarious, *780*
They haten that hir housbondes loven ay.'
He seyde, 'A womman cast hir shame away
Whan she cast of hir smok,' and forthermo,
'A fair womman, but she be chaast also,
Is lyk a gold ryng in a sowes nose.' *785*
Who wolde wene, or who wolde suppose
The wo that in myn herte was and pyne?
  And whan I saugh he wolde nevere fyne
To reden on this cursed book al nyght,
Al sodeynly thre leves have I plyght *790*
Out of his book right as he radde, and eke
I with my fist so took hym on the cheke
That in oure fyr he fil bakward adoun.
And he up stirte as dooth a wood leoun,
And with his fest he smoot me on the heed *795*
That in the floor I lay as I were deed.
And whan he saugh how stille that I lay,
He was agast, and wolde han fled his way,
Til atte laste out of my swogh I brayde.

773 *therwithal:* in addition; *mo:* more.

775 *bet is:* it is better; *habitacioun:* habitation, dwelling.

777 *usyng:* accustomed; *chide:* scold.
778 *hye:* high; *abyde:* to dwell.

781 *haten that:* hate that which; *ay:* ever.
782 *cast:* casts.
783 *of:* off; *smok:* undergarment.
784 *but:* unless; *chaast:* chaste.

786 *wene:* think; *suppose:* imagine.
787 *pyne:* torment.
788 *saugh:* saw; *fyne:* end, stop.
789 *reden:* read.

790 *al sodeynly:* suddenly; *leves:* leaves; *plyght:* plucked.
791 *radde:* read.

793 *fyr:* fire; *fil:* fell.
794 *stirte:* started, jumped; *wood:* mad.
795 *smoot:* smote; *heed:* head.
796 *in:* on.

798 *agast:* aghast, frightened; *his way:* away.
799 *swogh:* swoon, faint; *brayde:* awoke.

'O hastow slayn me, false theef?' I sayde, *800*
'And for my land thus hastow mordred me?
Er I be deed, yet wol I kisse thee.'
And neer he cam and kneled faire adoun,
And seyde, 'Deere suster Alisoun,
As help me God, I shal thee nevere smyte. *805*
That I have doon, it is thyself to wyte.
Foryeve it me, and that I thee biseke.'
And yet eftsoones I hitte hym on the cheke,
And seyde, 'Theef, thus muchel am I wreke;
Now wol I dye; I may no lenger speke.' *810*
But at the laste, with muchel care and wo,
We fille acorded by us selven two.
He yaf me al the bridel in myn hond,
To han the governance of hous and lond,
And of his tonge and of his hond also; *815*
And made hym brenne his book anon right tho.
And whan that I hadde geten unto me,
By maistrye, al the soveraynetee,
And that he seyde, 'Myn owene trewe wyf,
Do as thee lust the terme of al thy lyf; *820*
Keep thyn honour, and keep eek myn estaat,'
After that day we hadden never debaat.
God help me so, I was to hym as kynde
As any wyf from Denmark unto Inde,
And also trewe, and so was he to me. *825*
I pray to God that sit in magestee,
So blesse his soule for his mercy deere.
Now wol I seye my tale, if ye wol heere."
The Frere lough whan he hadde herd al this;

800 *hastow:* have you.

802 *er:* before.
803 *neer:* nearer; *faire:* gently.
804 *suster:* sister.
805 *smyte:* smite.
806 *doon:* done so; *wyte:* blame.
807 *foryeve:* forgive; *biseke:* beseech.
808 *eftsoones:* once again.
809 *wreke:* avenged.

810 *speke:* speak.

812 *fille:* became, came to; *acorded:* agreed; *by:* between.
813 *yaf:* gave; *bridel:* bridle, authority.

815 *of . . .:* i.e., control over his word and deed.
816 *brenne:* burn; *anon right:* right at once; *tho:* then.
817 *unto me:* to myself.
818 *maistrye:* superiority; *soveraynetee:* sovereignty, control.
819 *that:* i.e., when that.

820 *thee lust:* it pleases thee: *terme:* span.
821 *keep:* guard, take care of; *estaat:* estate, property.
822 *debaat:* argument, strife.

824 *Inde:* India.
825 *also trewe:* just as true.
826 *sit:* sits.
827 *his:* Jankyn's; *his:* God's.

829 *Frere:* Friar; *lough:* laughed.

"Now dame," quod he, "so have I joye or blis, *830*
This is a long preamble of a tale."
And whan the Somnour herde the Frere gale,
"Lo," quod the Somnour, "Goddes armes two!
A frere wol entremette him everemo!
Lo, goode men, a flye and eek a frere *835*
Wol falle in every dyssh and eek matere.
What spekestow of preambulacioun?
What, amble or trotte or pees or go sit doun!
Thou lettest oure disport in this manere."
"Ye, woltow so, sire Somnour?" quod the Frere; *840*
"Now by my feith, I shal, er that I go,
Telle of a somnour swich a tale or two
That al the folk shal laughen in this place."
"Now elles, Frere, I bishrewe thy face,"
Quod this Somnour, "and I bishrewe me, *845*
But if I telle tales two or thre
Of freres, er I come to Sidyngborne,
That I shal make thyn herte for to morne,
For wel I woot thy pacience is gon."
Oure Hooste cride, "Pees, and that anon!" *850*
And seyde, "Lat the womman telle hir tale.
Ye fare as folk that dronken ben of ale.
Do, dame, tel forth youre tale, and that is best."
"Al redy, sire," quod she, "right as yow lest,
If I have licence of this worthy Frere." *855*
"Yis, dame," quod he, "tel forth, and I wol heere."

Heere endeth the Wyf of Bathe hir Prologe.

830 *so have I:* as I may have.
831 *preamble:* preamble, prologue.
832 *Somnour:* Summoner; *gale:* exclaim.

834 *entremette him:* interfere; *everemo:* always.

836 *eek matere:* also (into every) matter.
837 *what spekestow:* why do you speak; *preambulacioun:* see l. 831.
838 *pees:* peace! i.e., shut up!
839 *lettest:* prevent, obstruct; *disport:* sport.
840 *woltow so:* do you say so? is that the way you want it?

844 *elles:* unless—connected to l. 846, i.e., "unless I tell"; *bishrewe:* curse.

846 *but if:* unless.
847 *of:* about; *Sidyngborne:* Sittingbourne, about 40 mi. from London.
848 *herte:* spirit; *morne:* grieve.
849 *woot:* know.

852 *fare:* behave; *dronken:* drunk.

854 *yow lest:* it pleases you.
855 *licence:* permission.

THE WIFE OF BATH'S TALE

The *Wife of Bath's Tale* is an adaptation of a well-known folk tale to the special purposes of the teller. It is the familiar story of the "loathly lady" here given an Arthurian setting and cleverly modified to illustrate the proposition of the Wife's prologue: when a wife acquires "maistrie" over her husband, "they live unto their lives' end in perfect joy."

Some of the more interesting features of the story are those which seem to tell us more about the teller than she perhaps intends. We may recall from her prologue the mingled pleasure and sadness with which she remembers her youthful joys and her stout-hearted defiance of the age which creeps upon her.

> *But Lord Crist! whan that it remembreth me*
> *Upon my youthe and on my jolitee,*
> *It tikleth me aboute myn herte roote . . .*
> *That I have had my world as in my tyme.*
> *But age, allas, that al wole envenyme,*
> *Hath me biraft my beautee and my pith.*
> *Lat go, farewel, the devel go therwith! . . .*
> *But yet to be right murye wol I fonde.* (469-79)

In view of this aspect of the Wife's personality, it is interesting to observe that the heroine of her story is an old woman who has valuable knowledge of the ways of men and women and who is able at will to make herself young and beautiful again. It is not hard to guess that this is the Wife herself, both as she sees herself to be and as she would be.

We may note further of the loathly lady of the story that, like her creator, she is adept at learned argument. But her lecture on the respect due to age, to poverty, and to *gentilesse* has an ironic and perhaps unsuspected appropriateness to the Wife's present situation. Though the latter in her youth had so little fondness for poverty that she married three rich old husbands, though she showed little respect for age in her treatment of them, and though *gentilesse* seems nowhere an aspect of her own character, yet now that she is herself grown old and rich and secure, these conservative sentiments seem to have acquired an attraction that was not always apparent to her.

Heere bigynneth the Tale of the Wyf of Bathe.

In th'olde dayes of the kyng Arthour,
Of which that Britons speken greet honour,
Al was this land fulfild of fayerye.
The elf-queene, with hir joly compaignye, 860
Daunced ful ofte in many a grene mede.
This was the olde opinion, as I rede;
I speke of many hundred yeres ago.
But now kan no man se none elves mo,
For now the grete charitee and prayeres 865
Of lymytours and othere holy freres,
That serchen every lond and every streem,
As thikke as motes in the sonne-beem,
Blessynge halles, chambres, kichenes, boures,
Citees, burghes, castels, hye toures, 870
Thropes, bernes, shipnes, dayeryes—
This maketh that ther been no fayeryes.
For ther as wont to walken was an elf,
Ther walketh now the lymytour hymself,
In undermeles and in morwenynges, 875
And seith his matyns and his holy thynges
As he gooth in his lymytacioun.
Wommen may go now saufly up and doun;
In every bussh or under every tree
Ther is noon oother incubus but he, 880
And he ne wol doon hem but dishonour.

And so bifel it that this kyng Arthour
Hadde in his hous a lusty bacheler,
That on a day cam ridynge fro ryver.

858 *of which:* of whom; *Britons:* Bretons.
859 *fulfild:* filled full; *fayerye:* fairy folk.

861 *mede:* meadow.
862 *rede:* read, understand.

864 *se:* see; *mo:* more.

865 *charitee:* scanned as if two syllables, *chár-tĕe.*
866 *lymytours:* see I:209; *freres:* friars.
867 *serchen:* search, i.e., haunt, frequent.
868 *motes . . .:* the dust particles floating in a sunbeam.
869 *halles, boures:* see VII:2832.

870 *burghes:* boroughs; *hye:* high.
871 *thropes . . .:* villages, barns, stables, dairies.

873 *ther as:* there where; *wont . . . was:* was accustomed.

875 *undermeles:* afternoons; *morwenynges:* mornings.
876 *matyns:* matins; *thynges:* i.e., prayers.
877 *gooth:* walks; *lymytacioun:* the area assigned to him.
878 *saufly:* safely.

880 *incubus:* an evil spirit that lies with women in their sleep.
881 *ne wol doon . . .:* will only dishonor them, whereas the incubus was thought responsible for the conception of semi-demons.
882 *bifel it:* it happened.
883 *bacheler:* see I:80.
884 *fro ryver:* from hawking by the river.

And happed that, allone as she was born, 885
He saugh a mayde walkynge hym biforn;
Of which mayde anon, maugree hir heed,
By verray force, he rafte hir maydenhed;
For which oppression was swich clamour
And swich pursute unto the kyng Arthour, 890
That dampned was this knyght for to be deed,
By cours of lawe, and sholde han lost his heed—
Paraventure swich was the statut tho—
But that the queene and othere ladyes mo
So longe preyeden the kyng of grace, 895
Til he his lyf hym graunted in the place,
And yaf hym to the queene, al at hir wille,
To chese wheither she wolde hym save or spille.
The queene thanked the kyng with al hir myght,
And after this thus spak she to the knyght, 900
Whan that she saugh hir tyme upon a day:
"Thou standest yet," quod she, "in swich array
That of thy lyf yet hastow no suretee.
I grante thee lyf, if thou kanst tellen me
What thyng is it that wommen moost desiren. 905
Be war, and keep thy nekke-boon from iren!
And if thou kanst nat tellen it anon,
Yet shal I yeve thee leve for to gon
A twelf-month and a day, to seche and lere
An answere suffisant in this matere; 910
And suretee wol I han, er that thou pace,
Thy body for to yelden in this place."
Wo was this knyght, and sorwefully he siketh;
But what! he may nat do al as hym liketh,

886 *saugh:* saw; *hym biforn:* before him.
887 *of:* from; *maugree . . .:* in spite of her head, i.e., anything she could do.
888 *rafte:* took; *maydenhed:* virginity.
889 *for:* on account of; *swich:* such.
890 *pursute:* petitioning.
891 *dampned:* condemned; *deed:* dead.
892 *sholde han:* was to have.
893 *paraventure:* perchance; *statut:* law; *tho:* then.
894 *but:* except; *mo:* more.

895 *of grace:* for grace or mercy.

897 *yaf:* gave; *al . . . wille:* entirely at her disposal.
898 *chese:* choose; *wolde:* wished; *save or spille:* to save or destroy (him).

901 *saugh:* saw; *tyme:* opportunity.
902 *quod:* said; *array:* condition, plight.
903 *hastow:* have you; *suretee:* guarantee.

905 *moost:* most.
906 *be war:* beware; *iren:* i.e., the sword.
907 *anon:* at once.
908 *yeve:* give; *leve:* leave; *gon:* go.
909 *seche:* seek; *lere:* learn.

910 *suffisant:* satisfactory.
911 *han:* have; *er:* before; *pace:* depart.
912 *yelden:* yield, i.e., that you will surrender yourself here.
913 *wo:* woe; *siketh:* sighs.
914 *al:* entirely; *hym liketh:* it pleases him.

And at the laste he chees hym for to wende, 915
And come agayn right at the yeres ende,
With swich answere as God wolde hym purveye;
And taketh his leve and wendeth forth his weye.

He seketh every hous and every place
Where as he hopeth for to fynde grace, 920
To lerne what thyng wommen loven moost;
But he ne koude arryven in no coost
Wher as he myghte fynde in this mateere
Two creatures accordynge in-feere.

Somme seyde wommen loven best richesse, 925
Somme seyde honour, somme seyde jolynesse,
Somme riche array, somme seyden lust abedde,
And oftetyme to be wydwe and wedde.
Somme seyde that oure hertes been moost esed
Whan that we been yflatered and yplesed— 930
He gooth ful ny the sothe, I wol nat lye.
A man shal wynne us best with flaterye;
And with attendance and with bisynesse
Been we ylymed, bothe moore and lesse.

And somme seyen that we loven best 935
For to be free, and do right as us lest,
And that no man repreve us of oure vice,
But seye that we be wise and no thyng nyce.
For trewely ther is noon of us alle,
If any wight wol clawe us on the galle, 940
That we nyl kike for he seith us sooth.
Assay, and he shal fynde it that so dooth;
For, be we never so vicious withinne,
We wol been holden wise and clene of synne.

915 *chees:* chose; *for to wende:* to go.
916 *yeres:* year's.
917 *purveye:* provide.
918 *leve:* leave.
919 *seketh:* visits.

922 *ne koude:* could not; *arryven:* i.e., find his way to; *coost:* region.
923 *wher as:* where.
924 *accordynge:* agreeing; *in-feere:* together.

927 *array:* clothes; *lust:* pleasure; *abedde:* in bed.
928 *wydwe:* a widow; *wedde:* wedded.
929 *esed:* comforted.

930 *been:* are; *yflatered:* flattered.
931 *gooth:* goes; *ny:* near; *sothe:* truth; *lye:* lie.
932 *wynne:* win.
933 *attendance:* attentiveness; *bisynesse:* diligence.
934 *ylymed:* limed, snared; *moore and lesse:* high and low.

936 *us lest:* it pleases us.
937 *repreve:* should reprove; *of:* for.
938 *seye:* i.e., he should say; *no thyng:* in no way; *nyce:* foolish.
939 *noon:* none.

940 *wight:* person; *wol clawe:* should scratch; *galle:* sore spot.
941 *nyl:* will not; *kike:* kick; *for:* because; *seith:* tells; *sooth:* truth.
942 *assay:* try (it); *fynde it:* find it so; *so dooth:* does this.
943 *withinne:* inside, i.e., in our hearts.
944 *wol been holden:* want to be considered; *clene:* pure.

And somme seyn that greet delit han we *945*
For to been holden stable, and eek secree,
And in o purpos stedefastly to dwelle,
And nat biwreye thyng that men us telle—
But that tale is nat worth a rake-stele.
Pardee, we wommen konne no thyng hele; *950*
Witnesse on Myda,—wol ye heere the tale?

Ovyde, amonges othere thynges smale,
Seyde Myda hadde, under his longe heres,
Growynge upon his heed two asses eres,
The whiche vice he hidde, as he best myghte, *955*
Ful subtilly from every mannes sighte,
That, save his wyf, ther wiste of it namo.
He loved hire moost, and trusted hire also;
He preyed hire that to no creature
She sholde tellen of his disfigure. *960*

She swoor him, "Nay," for al this world to wynne,
She nolde do that vileynye or synne,
To make hir housbonde han so foul a name.
She nolde nat telle it for hir owene shame.
But nathelees, hir thoughte that she dyde, *965*
That she so longe sholde a conseil hyde;
Hir thoughte it swal so soore aboute hir herte
That nedely som word hire moste asterte;
And sith she dorste telle it to no man,
Doun to a marys faste by she ran— *970*
Til she cam there, hir herte was afyre—
And as a bitore bombleth in the myre,
She leyde hir mouth unto the water doun:
"Biwrey me nat, thou water, with thy soun,"

946 *stable:* reliable; *eek:* also; *secree:* discreet.
947 *o:* one, the same; *dwelle:* remain.
948 *biwreye:* reveal.
949 *rake-stele:* rake handle.

950 *pardee:* indeed; *konne:* can; *hele:* conceal.
951 *witnesse on:* take witness of; *Myda:* Midas.
952 *Ovyde:* Ovid, in *Metamorphoses,* XI: 174ff.; *smale:* little.
953 *heres:* hair.
954 *eres:* ears.

955 *vice:* deformity.
956 *subtilly:* craftily.
957 *save:* except; *wiste:* knew; *namo:* no more, no other.
958 *hire:* her; in Ovid it is Midas's barber who shares the secret.

960 *disfigure:* disfigurement.
961 *for al . . .:* i.e., (she wouldn't tell it) for the world.
962 *nolde:* would not; *vileynye:* low or shameful deed.
963 *han:* have.

965 *hir thoughte:* it seemed to her; *dyde:* would die.
966 *that:* i.e., because; *sholde:* had to; *conseil:* secret.
967 *swal:* swelled; *soore aboute:* sorely in.
968 *nedely:* necessarily; *hire moste asterte:* must escape her.
969 *sith:* since; *dorste:* durst.

970 *marys:* marsh; *faste:* near.
971 *afyre:* on fire.
972 *bitore:* bittern, heron; *bombleth:* booms; *myre:* mire.

974 *biwrey:* betray; *soun:* sound, i.e., voice.

Quod she. "To thee I telle it and namo; *975*
Myn housbonde hath longe asses erys two!
Now is myn herte al hool, now is it oute.
I myghte no lenger kepe it, out of doute."
Heere may ye se, thogh we a tyme abyde,
Yet out it moot; we kan no conseil hyde. *980*
The remenant of the tale if ye wol heere,
Redeth Ovyde, and ther ye may it leere.
  This knyght of which my tale is specially,
Whan that he saugh he myghte nat come therby,
This is to seye, what wommen loven moost, *985*
Withinne his brest ful sorweful was the goost.
But hoom he gooth, he myghte nat sojourne;
The day was come that homward moste he tourne.
And in his wey it happed hym to ryde
In al this care under a forest syde, *990*
Wher as he saugh upon a daunce go
Of ladyes foure and twenty and yet mo;
Toward the whiche daunce he drow ful yerne,
In hope that som wysdom sholde he lerne.
But certeinly, er he cam fully there, *995*
Vanysshed was this daunce, he nyste where.
No creature saugh he that bar lyf,
Save on the grene he saugh sittynge a wyf—
A fouler wight ther may no man devyse.
Agayn the knyght this olde wyf gan ryse, *1000*
And seyde, "Sire knyght, heer forth ne lith no wey.
Tel me what ye seken, by youre fey!
Paraventure it may the bettre be;
Thise olde folk kan muchel thyng," quod she.

977 *hool:* whole, i.e., no longer bursting with the secret.
978 *myghte:* could; *out of doute:* doubtless.
979 *se:* see; *abyde:* wait, i.e., keep it (for a time).

980 *moot:* must; *conseil:* secret.
982 *leere:* learn; some reeds grew from the spot and when they were stirred by the breeze they whispered the words and betrayed the secret.

984 *saugh:* saw; *come therby:* find it out.

986 *goost:* spirit.
987 *hoom:* home; *sojourne:* stay, delay.
988 *moste:* must; *tourne:* turn.
989 *in:* on; *happed:* chanced.

990 *care:* anxiety; *syde:* edge.
991 *upon:* in; *go:* i.e., dancing.
992 *mo:* more.
993 *drow:* drew; *yerne:* quickly.

995 *er:* ere, before.
996 *nyste: (ne wiste)* knew not.
997 *that bar lyf:* who bore life, i.e., living.
998 *save:* except; *grene:* green; *wyf:* woman.
999 *fouler:* uglier; *wight:* person; *devyse:* imagine.

1000 *agayn:* toward, i.e., to meet; *gan ryse:* arose.
1001 *heer forth:* on from here; *lith:* lies; *wey:* road.
1002 *seken:* seek; *fey:* faith.
1003 *paraventure:* perhaps; *it may . . .:* it may be best.
1004 *kan:* know.

"My leeve moder," quod this knyght, "certeyn, *1005*
I nam but deed, but if that I kan seyn
What thyng it is that wommen moost desire.
Koude ye me wisse, I wolde wel quite youre hire."
"Plight me thy trouthe here in myn hand," quod she,
"The nexte thyng that I requere thee, *1010*
Thou shalt it do, if it lye in thy myght,
And I wol telle it yow er it be nyght."
"Have here my trouthe," quod the knyght, "I grante."
"Thanne," quod she, "I dar me wel avante
Thy lyf is sauf; for I wol stonde therby, *1015*
Upon my lyf, the queene wol seye as I.
Lat see which is the proudeste of hem alle
That wereth on a coverchief or a calle
That dar seye nay of that I shal thee teche.
Lat us go forth withouten lenger speche." *1020*
Tho rowned she a pistel in his ere,
And bad hym to be glad and have no fere.
Whan they be comen to the court, this knyght
Seyde he had holde his day, as he had hight,
And redy was his answere, as he sayde. *1025*
Ful many a noble wyf, and many a mayde,
And many a wydwe, for that they been wise,
The queene hirself sittyng as justise,
Assembled been, his answere for to heere;
And afterward this knyght was bode appeere. *1030*
To every wight comanded was silence,
And that the knyght sholde telle in audience
What thyng that worldly wommen loven best.
This knyght ne stood nat stille as doth a best,

1005 *leeve:* dear; *moder:* mother.
1006 *nam:* am not, i.e., I am as good as; *but if:* unless.

1008 *koude ye:* if you could; *wisse:* tell; *quite:* reward; *hire:* payment.
1009 *plight:* pledge; *trouthe:* promise; *hand:* i.e., by handshake.
1010 *requere:* require.
1011 *lye:* lies; *myght:* power.
1012 *it:* i.e., what you want to know; *er:* before.
1013 *grante:* agree.
1014 *dar:* dare; *avante:* boast.

1015 *sauf:* safe; *stonde therby:* stand by it, guarantee it.
1016 *seye as I:* agree with me.
1017-19 *lat see which . . . that:* show me (even the proudest) . . . who.
1018 *that wereth on:* who wears; *calle:* headdress.
1019 *dar:* will dare; *of:* to, concerning; *teche:* teach.

1021 *tho:* then; *rowned:* whispered; *pistel:* epistle, message.
1022 *fere:* fear.
1023 *be comen:* were come.
1024 *holde:* kept; *hight:* promised.

1027 *wydwe:* widow; *for that:* because.
1028 *justise:* judge.
1029 *been:* are.

1030 *bode:* ordered to.

1032 *audience:* open assembly.

1034 *best:* beast.

But to his questioun anon answerde *1035*
With manly voys, that al the court it herde:
"My lige lady, generally," quod he,
"Wommen desiren to have sovereyntee
As wel over hir housbond as hir love,
And for to been in maistrie hym above. *1040*
This is youre mooste desir, thogh ye me kille.
Dooth as yow list; I am here at youre wille."
In al the court ne was ther wyf, ne mayde,
Ne wydwe, that contraried that he sayde,
But seyden he was worthy han his lyf. *1045*
And with that word up stirte the olde wyf,
Which that the knyght saugh sittyng on the grene;
"Mercy," quod she, "my sovereyn lady queene!
Er that youre court departe, do me right.
I taughte this answere unto the knyght; *1050*
For which he plighte me his trouthe there,
The firste thyng that I wolde hym requere
He wolde it do, if it lay in his myght.
Bifore the court thanne preye I thee, sir knyght,"
Quod she, "that thou me take unto thy wyf; *1055*
For wel thou woost that I have kept thy lyf.
If I seye fals, sey nay, upon thy fey!"
This knyght answerde, "Allas and weylawey!
I woot right wel that swich was my biheste.
For Goddes love, as chees a newe requeste! *1060*
Taak al my good and lat my body go."
"Nay thanne," quod she, "I shrewe us bothe two!
For thogh that I be foul and oold and poore,
I nolde for al the metal ne for oore

1035 *anon:* at once.
1036 *that:* so that.
1037 *lige:* liege.
1038 *sovereyntee:* dominion.
1039 *as wel:* as much; *love:* lover.

1040 *maistrie:* control; *above:* over.
1041 *mooste:* greatest.
1042 *yow list:* it pleases you.

1044 *contraried:* contradicted; *that:* what.
1045 *han:* to have.
1046 *stirte:* started, jumped.
1047 *which that:* who.

1049 *er:* before.

1051 *plighte:* pledged; *trouthe:* promise.
1052 *requere:* require of.

1055 *unto:* to be.
1056 *woost:* know; *kept:* saved.
1057 *seye fals:* speak falsely; *fey:* faith.
1058 *weylawey:* woe!
1059 *woot:* know; *swich:* such; *biheste:* promise.

1060 *as* is an intensive with imperatives; *chees:* choose.
1061 *good:* property.
1062 *thanne:* then; *shrewe:* curse.
1063 *foul:* ugly.
1064 *nolde:* would not (desire anything); *oore:* ore.

That under erthe is grave or lith above, 1065
But if thy wyf I were and eek thy love."
"My love?" quod he, "nay, my dampnacion!
Allas, that any of my nacion
Sholde evere so foule disparaged be!"
But al for noght; the ende is this, that he 1070
Constreyned was, he nedes moste hire wedde,
And taketh his olde wyf, and goth to bedde.
Now wolden som men seye, paraventure,
That for my necligence I do no cure
To tellen yow the joye and al th'array 1075
That at the feste was that ilke day.
To which thyng shortly answeren I shal:
I seye ther nas no joye ne feste at al;
Ther nas but hevynesse and muche sorwe.
For prively he wedded hire on morwe, 1080
And al day after hidde hym as an owle,
So wo was hym, his wyf looked so foule.
Greet was the wo the knyght hadde in his thoght,
Whan he was with his wyf abedde ybroght;
He walweth and he turneth to and fro. 1085
His olde wyf lay smylyng everemo,
And seyde, "O deere housbonde, *benedicitee!*
Fareth every knyght thus with his wyf as ye?
Is this the lawe of kyng Arthures hous?
Is every knyght of his so dangerous? 1090
I am youre owene love and eek youre wyf;
I am she which that saved hath youre lyf;
And, certes, yet dide I yow nevere unright;
Why fare ye thus with me this firste nyght?

1065 *grave:* buried; *lith:* lies.
1066 *but if:* except; *eek:* also.

1068 *nacion:* (high) birth.
1069 *foule:* foully; *disparaged:* dishonored.

1071 *constreyned:* forced; *nedes moste:* needs must.

1074 *for:* on account of; *do no cure:* do not take the trouble.

1075 *array:* (festive) arrangements.
1076 *feste:* celebration; *ilke:* same.

1078 *nas: (ne was)* was not.
1079 *hevynesse:* grief.

1080 *prively:* secretly; *on morwe:* in the morning.
1081 *al day after:* i.e., all the rest of the day; *hym:* himself.
1082 *wo:* woeful; *was hym:* it was to him.
1083 *thoght:* mind.
1084 *abedde:* to bed; *ybroght:* brought.

1085 *walweth:* tosses.
1086 *everemo:* all the while.
1087 *benedicitee:* bless you; in three syllables, *bén-cĭ-tée.*
1088 *fareth:* behaves; *as ye:* as you (do).

1090 *dangerous:* standoffish.

1092 *which that:* who.
1093 *certes:* certainly; *unright:* wrong.
1094 *fare:* behave.

Ye faren lyk a man had lost his wit. *1095*
What is my gilt? For Goddes love, tel it,
And it shal been amended if I may."
"Amended?" quod this knyght, "allas! nay, nay!
It wol nat been amended nevere mo.
Thou art so loothly, and so old also, *1100*
And therto comen of so lowe a kynde,
That litel wonder is thogh I walwe and wynde.
So wolde God myn herte wolde breste!"
"Is this," quod she, "the cause of youre unreste?"
"Ye, certeinly," quod he, "no wonder is." *1105*
"Now, sire," quod she, "I koude amende al this,
If that me liste, er it were dayes thre,
So wel ye myghte bere yow unto me.
But, for ye speken of swich gentillesse
As is descended out of old richesse, *1110*
That therfore sholden ye be gentil men,
Swich arrogance is nat worth an hen.
Looke who that is moost vertuous alway,
Pryvee and apert, and moost entendeth ay
To do the gentil dedes that he kan; *1115*
Taak hym for the grettest gentil man.
Crist wole we clayme of hym oure gentillesse,
Nat of oure eldres for hir old richesse.
For thogh they yeve us al hir heritage,
For which we clayme to been of heigh parage, *1120*
Yet may they nat biquethe, for no thyng,
To noon of us hir vertuous lyvyng
That made hem gentil men ycalled be,
And bad us folwen hem in swich degree.

1095 *had:* who had.
1096 *gilt:* offense.
1097 *amended:* remedied.

1100 *loothly:* hideous.
1101 *therto:* in addition; *of:* from; *kynde:* lineage.
1102 *is:* it is; *walwe:* wallow; *wynde:* twist.
1103 *so wolde God:* would to God; *herte:* heart; *breste:* burst.

1107 *me liste:* it pleased me; *er:* before.
1108 *so:* provided that; *bere yow:* bear yourself, behave.
1109 *for:* since; *swich:* such, the kind of; *gentillesse:* gentility.

1110 *old richesse:* inherited wealth and position.
1111 *therfore:* i.e., because you are born to wealth and position.

1113 *looke . . . is:* behold whosoever is.
1114 *pryvee:* in private; *apert:* in public; *entendeth:* strives; *ay:* ever.
1115 *the:* all the; *dedes:* deeds; the doctrine throughout here is a familiar argument of medieval Christian literature.
1117 *wole:* desires (that); *of:* from.
1118 *eldres:* ancestors; *for:* on account of; *hir:* their.
1119 *yeve:* give.

1120 *heigh:* high; *parage:* lineage.
1121 *for no thyng:* by any means.
1122 *lyvyng:* manner of living.
1123 *hem:* them; *ycalled be:* be called.
1124 *bad:* i.e., their virtue encouraged us; *folwen:* to follow; *in swich degree:* in like manner.

Wel kan the wise poete of Florence, 1125
That highte Dant, speken in this sentence.
Lo, in swich maner rym is Dantes tale:
'Ful selde up riseth by his branches smale
Prowesse of man, for God, of his goodnesse,
Wol that of hym we clayme oure gentilesse'; 1130
For of oure eldres may we no thyng clayme
But temporel thyng that man may hurte and mayme.
Eek every wight woot this as wel as I,
If gentillesse were planted naturelly
Unto a certeyn lynage doun the lyne, 1135
Pryvee and apert, thanne wolde they nevere fyne
To doon of gentillesse the faire office;
They myghte do no vileynye or vice.
Taak fyr, and bere it in the derkeste hous
Bitwix this and the mount of Kaukasous, 1140
And lat men shette the dores and go thenne;
Yet wol the fyr as faire lye and brenne
As twenty thousand men myghte it biholde;
His office naturel ay wol it holde,
Up peril of my lyf, til that it dye. 1145
Here may ye se wel how that genterye
Is nat annexed to possession,
Sith folk ne doon hir operacion
Alwey, as dooth the fyr, lo, in his kynde.
For, God it woot, men may wel often fynde 1150
A lordes sone do shame and vileynye.
And he that wol han pris of his gentrye,
For he was boren of a gentil hous,
And hadde his eldres noble and vertuous,

1126 *highte:* is named; *Dant:* Dante; *sentence:* theme.
1127 *swich maner:* this kind of; *rym:* rhyme; *tale:* discourse.
1128 *ful selde:* very seldom; *branches:* i.e., efforts.
1129 *prowesse:* excellence, i.e., man seldom achieves excellence by his own efforts.
1130 *wol:* desires; *of:* from.

1132 *but:* except; *temporel:* worldly; *may ... mayme:* may injure (a man).
1133 *eek:* also; *woot:* knows.
1134 *naturelly:* by nature.
1135 *unto:* in; *lynage:* family; *doun ... lyne:* in every generation.
1136 *pryvee, apert:* see l. 1114; *fyne:* cease.
1137 *doon:* do; *office:* function.

1139 *fyr:* fire; *bere:* carry.
1140 *this:* here; *Kaukasous:* Caucasus.
1141 *lat men shette:* let (the doors) be shut; *thenne:* thence.
1142 *lye:* blaze; *brenne:* burn.
1143 *as:* i.e., as it would if; *myghte:* were to.
1144 *his:* its; *office:* function; *ay:* ever; *holde:* keep to.

1145 *up:* upon, i.e., upon my life.
1146 *genterye:* gentility.
1147 *annexed:* necessarily related.
1148 *sith:* since; *doon hir operacion:* perform their function, i.e., behave.
1149 *alwey:* i.e., consistently; *in ... kynde:* according to its nature.
1150 *woot:* knows.
1152 *wol han pris of:* wishes to have a reputation for.
1153 *for:* because; *boren:* born.
1154 *eldres:* ancestors.

And nyl hymselven do no gentil dedis, *1155*
Ne folwen his gentil auncestre that deed is,
He nys nat gentil, be he duc or erl;
For vileyns synful dedes make a cherl.
For gentillesse nys but renomee
Of thyne auncestres, for hir heigh bountee, *1160*
Which is a strange thyng to thy persone.
Thy gentillesse cometh fro God allone.
Thanne comth oure verray gentillesse of grace;
It was no thyng biquethe us with oure place.
Thenketh how noble, as seith Valerius, *1165*
Was thilke Tullius Hostillius,
That out of poverte roos to heigh noblesse.
Redeth Senek, and redeth eek Boece;
Ther shul ye seen expres that it no drede is
That he is gentil that dooth gentil dedis. *1170*
And therfore, leeve housbonde, I thus conclude:
Al were it that myne auncestres were rude,
Yet may the hye God, and so hope I,
Grante me grace to lyven vertuously.
Thanne am I gentil, whan that I bigynne *1175*
To lyven vertuously and weyve synne.
And ther as ye of poverte me repreeve,
The hye God on whom that we bileeve,
In wilful poverte chees to lyve his lyf.
And certes every man, mayden, or wyf, *1180*
May understonde that Jhesus, hevene kyng,
Ne wolde nat chese a vicious lyvyng.
Glad poverte is an honest thyng, certeyn;
This wol Senec and othere clerkes seyn.

1155 *nyl: (ne wol)* will not; *dedis:* deeds.
1156 *folwen:* follow (the example of); *deed:* dead.
1157 *nys: (ne is)* is not; *be:* whether (he) be.
1158 *vileyns:* of a villein, i.e., base; *cherl:* churl.
1159 *nys but:* is nothing but; *renomee:* the renown.

1160 *for:* i.e., which they won by; *bountee:* goodness.
1161 *strange:* foreign, i.e., not something native or inherited.

1163 *verray:* true; *of grace:* from (God's) grace.
1164 *no thyng:* by no means; *biquethe:* bequeathed; *place:* rank.
1165 Valerius Maximus, a Roman historian.
1166 Tullus Hostilius, supposed to have risen from a herdsman to become king of Rome.
1168 Seneca and Boethius, Roman philosophers.
1169 *seen:* see; *expres:* expressly; *drede:* doubt.

1170 *that:* who.
1171 *leeve:* dear.
1172 *al were it that:* although; *rude:* lowborn.

1174 *lyven:* live.

1176 *weyve:* avoid.
1177 *ther as:* whereas; *poverte:* poverty; *repreeve:* reproach.

1179 *wilful:* willing; *chees:* chose.

1181 *hevene:* heaven's.
1182 *vicious:* full of vice; *lyvyng:* way of living.
1183 *glad:* cheerful; *honest:* honorable.
1184 *clerkes:* learned men.

Whoso that halt hym payd of his poverte, 1185
I holde hym riche, al hadde he nat a sherte.
He that coveiteth is a povre wight,
For he wolde han that is nat in his myght;
But he that noght hath, ne coveiteth have,
Is riche, although ye holde hym but a knave. 1190
  Verray poverte, it syngeth proprely;
Juvenal seith of poverte myrily:
'The povre man, whan he goth by the weye,
Bifore the theves he may synge and pleye.'
Poverte is hateful good and, as I gesse, 1195
A ful greet bryngere out of bisynesse;
A greet amendere eek of sapience
To hym that taketh it in pacience.
Poverte is this, although it seme alenge,
Possession that no wight wol chalenge. 1200
Poverte ful ofte, whan a man is lowe,
Maketh his God and eek hymself to knowe.
Poverte a spectacle is, as thynketh me,
Thurgh which he may his verray freendes see.
And therfore, sire, syn that I noght yow greve, 1205
Of my poverte namoore ye me repreve.
  Now, sire, of elde ye repreve me;
And certes, sire, thogh noon auctoritee
Were in no book, ye gentils of honour
Seyn that men sholde an old wight doon favour, 1210
And clepe hym fader, for youre gentillesse;
And auctours shal I fynden, as I gesse.
  Now ther ye seye that I am foul and old,
Than drede you noght to been a cokewold;

1185 *whoso:* whoever; *halt hym:* considers himself; *payd of:* satisfied with.
1186 *holde:* consider; *al:* although; *sherte:* shirt.
1187 *coveiteth:* covets; *povre wight:* poor person.
1188 *wolde han:* wishes to have; *that:* what; *myght:* power.
1189 *noght:* nothing; *have:* to have.

1190 *knave:* low born fellow.
1191 *verray:* true; *proprely:* naturally.
1192 *myrily:* merrily.
1193 *goth by the weye:* walks on his way.
1194 *theves:* thieves.

1195 *hateful good:* unpleasant, yet good for us.
1196 *bryngere out:* remover; *bisynesse:* care.
1197 *amendere:* improver; *eek:* also; *sapience:* wisdom.

1199 *seme:* may seem; *alenge:* miserable.
1200 *no wight:* nobody; *chalenge:* claim.
1201 *lowe:* humble.
1202 *maketh:* makes (him know).
1203 *spectacle:* eyeglass; *thynketh me:* it seems to me.
1204 *verray:* true.

1205 *syn:* since; *greve:* harm.
1206 *repreve:* reproach.
1207 *elde:* old age.
1208 *auctoritee:* authoritative text (i.e., to quote as in l. 1192).
1209 *gentils of honour:* honorable gentlefolk.

1210 *doon favour:* treat kindly.
1211 *clepe:* call; *fader:* father.
1212 *auctours:* i.e., authorities.
1213 *ther:* whereas.
1214 *than:* then; *cokewold:* cuckold.

For filthe and eelde, also moot I thee, *1215*
Been grete wardeyns upon chastitee.
But nathelees, syn I knowe youre delit,
I shal fulfille youre worldly appetit.
  Chese now," quod she, "oon of thise thynges tweye:
To han me foul and old til that I deye, *1220*
And be to yow a trewe, humble wyf,
And nevere yow displese in al my lyf;
Or elles ye wol han me yong and fair,
And take youre aventure of the repair
That shal be to youre hous by cause of me, *1225*
Or in som oother place, may wel be.
Now chese yourselven wheither that yow liketh."
  This knyght avyseth hym and sore siketh,
But atte laste he seyde in this manere:
"My lady and my love, and wyf so deere, *1230*
I put me in youre wise governance;
Cheseth youreself which may be moost plesance
And moost honour to yow and me also.
I do no fors the wheither of the two;
For as yow liketh, it suffiseth me." *1235*
  "Thanne have I gete of yow maistrie," quod she,
"Syn I may chese and governe as me lest?"
  "Ye, certes, wyf," quod he, "I holde it best."
  "Kys me," quod she, "we be no lenger wrothe;
For, by my trouthe, I wol be to yow bothe, *1240*
This is to seyn, ye, bothe fair and good.
I prey to God that I moote sterven wood,
But I to yow be also good and trewe
As evere was wyf syn that the world was newe.

1215 *eelde:* age; *also . . . thee:* as I may prosper.
1216 *wardeyns:* guardians; *upon:* over.
1217 *syn:* since; *delit:* pleasure.

1219 *chese:* choose; *tweye:* two.

1220 *foul:* ugly; *deye:* die.

1223 *elles:* else.
1224 *aventure:* chance; *repair:* visits, i.e., of lovers.

1227 *wheither:* whichever; *yow liketh:* pleases you.
1228 *avyseth hym:* considers; *sore:* sorely; *siketh:* sighs.
1229 *atte:* at the; *seyde:* spoke.

1231 *put me in:* put myself under.
1232 *cheseth:* choose; *plesance:* pleasure.

1234 *do no fors:* do not care; *the wheither:* whichever.
1235 *yow liketh:* it pleases you.
1236 *gete:* gotten.
1237 *syn:* since; *me lest:* it pleases me.
1238 *holde:* think.
1239 *wrothe:* angry.

1240 *trouthe:* faith.
1241 *ye:* yea.
1242 *moote:* may; *sterven wood:* die mad.
1243 *but:* unless; *also:* as.
1244 *syn:* since.

And but I be to-morn as fair to seene *1245*
As any lady, emperice, or queene,
That is bitwixe the est and eek the west,
Do with my lyf and deth right as yow lest.
Cast up the curtyn, looke how that it is."
And whan the knyght saugh verraily al this, *1250*
That she so fair was, and so yong therto,
For joye he hente hire in his armes two,
His herte bathed in a bath of blisse.
A thousand tyme a-rewe he gan hir kisse,
And she obeyed hym in every thyng *1255*
That myghte do hym plesance or likyng.
And thus they lyve unto hir lyves ende
In parfit joye; and Jhesu Crist us sende
Housbondes meeke, yonge, and fressh abedde,
And grace t'overbyde hem that we wedde; *1260*
And eek I praye Jhesu shorte hir lyves
That wol nat be governed by hir wyves;
And olde and angry nygardes of dispence,
God sende hem soone verray pestilence!

Heere endeth the Wyves Tale of Bathe.

Following this tale in Fragment III are the tales of the Friar and the Summoner, two more *fabliaux*, each of which, like the stories of the Miller and the Reeve, is directed at discomfiting the teller of the other. Fragment IV follows with the tales of the Clerk and the Merchant, the former an account of the trials of an incredibly patient wife, Griselda, and the latter a ribald and brilliantly witty satire on old husbands and young wives. Fragment V contains the tales of the Squire and the Franklin. The first is an oriental tale of wonder and magic which breaks off unfinished, the

1245 *but:* unless; *seene:* look at.
1246 *emperice:* empress.

1248 *yow lest:* it pleases you, i.e., kill me if you wish.
1249 *cast up:* raise; *curtyn:* i.e., the bed hangings.

1251 *therto:* also.
1252 *hente:* seized.

1254 *tyme:* times; *a-rewe:* in a row; *gan kisse:* did kiss.

1256 *plesance:* pleasure; *likyng:* delight.
1257 *hir:* their.
1258 *parfit:* perfect.
1259 *abedde:* in bed.

1260 *t'overbyde:* to outlive; *hem:* them.
1261 *shorte:* shorten.
1262 *that:* who.
1263 *nygardes:* niggards, misers; *dispence:* expenditure.
1264 *verray:* true, veritable.

latter a Breton story of a knight and his wife whose love for and faith in each other enable them to withstand successfully an elaborately plotted attempt on the wife's virtue. Fragment VI consists of the *Physician's Tale* and the *Pardoner's Tale*. The former is a story of a conspiracy between an unscrupulous judge and a churl to secure by means of a false lawsuit the person of a beautiful Roman maiden. The maiden's father kills her to save her honor. To this sad conclusion the Host reacts with characteristic unrestraint and naïveté.

FRAGMENT VI

The wordes of the hoost to the phisicien and the pardoner.

Oure Hooste gan to swere as he were wood; *287*
"Harrow!" quod he, "by nayles and by blood!
This was a fals cherl and a fals justise.
As shameful deeth as herte kan devyse *290*
Come to thise juges and hir advocatz!
Algate this sely mayde is slayn, allas!
Allas, to deere boughte she beautee!
Wherfore I seye alday that men may see
That yiftes of Fortune and of Nature *295*
Been cause of deeth to many a creature.
Hire beautee was hir deth, I dar wel sayn.
Allas, so pitously as she was slayn!
Of bothe yiftes that I speke of now,
Men han ful ofte moore for harm than prow. *300*
But trewely, myn owene maister deere,
This is a pitous tale for to heere.
But nathelees, passe over, is no fors.
I pray to God to save thy gentil cors,

287 *gan:* began; *as:* as if; *wood:* mad.
288 *harrow . . .:* oaths, i.e., "by the nails of the cross and the blood of Christ."
289 *cherl:* churl, a man of the lowest rank of freemen.

291 *advocatz:* pleaders, lawyers.
292 *algate:* nevertheless; *sely:* innocent.
293 *deere:* dearly; i.e., paid too dearly for.
294 *alday:* every day.

295 *yiftes:* gifts.
296 *been:* are.

299 *of bothe yiftes:* i.e., from the gifts of Fortune and of Nature.

300 *han:* get; *for harm than prow:* of harm than good.
301 *maister:* master, i.e., the Physician.
302 *heere:* hear.
303 *passe over:* let's pass over it, forget it; *no fors:* no matter.
304 *cors:* body.

And eek thyne urinals and thy jurdones, 305
Thyn ypocras, and eek thy galiones,
And every boyste ful of thy letuarie;
God blesse hem, and oure lady Seinte Marie!
So mote I theen, thou art a propre man,
And lyk a prelat, by Seint Ronyan! 310
Seyde I nat wel? I kan nat speke in terme.
But wel I woot, thou doost myn herte to erme
That I almoost have caught a cardynacle.
By corpus bones, but I have triacle,
Or elles a draughte of moyste and corny ale, 315
Or but I heere anon a myrie tale,
Myn herte is lost for pitee of this mayde.
Thou beel amy, thou Pardoner," he sayde,
"Tel us som myrthe or japes right anon."
"It shal be doon," quod he, "by Seint Ronyon! 320
But first," quod he, "heere at this ale-stake
I wol bothe drynke and eten of a cake."
But right anon thise gentils gonne to crye,
"Nay, lat him telle us of no ribaudye!
Tel us som moral thyng that we may leere 325
Som wit, and thanne wol we gladly heere."
"I graunte, ywis," quod he, "but I moot thynke
Upon som honeste thyng whil that I drynke."

305 *jurdones:* chamber pots.
306 *ypocras:* a medicinal drink; *galiones:* a medicine (?) named after Galen, perhaps an invention of the host.
307 *boyste:* box; *letuarie:* medicine.

309 *so . . . theen:* as I may thrive; *propre:* real, fine.
310 *lyk:* like; *prelat:* prelate, a high church official.
311 *wel:* i.e., in medical language; *terme:* technical language.
312 *doost . . . to erme:* cause to grieve.
313 *cardynacle,* the Host's mistake for the technical term "cardiacle."
314 *corpus bones,* a confusion of a Latin and an English oath; *but:* unless; *triacle:* remedy.
315 *draughte:* drink; *moyste:* fresh; *corny:* malty.
316 *but:* unless.

318 *beel amy:* fair friend.
319 *myrthe:* something amusing; *japes:* jokes.

321 *ale-stake:* sign of an alehouse.
322 *cake:* loaf.
323 *right anon:* then at once; *gentils:* gentlefolk; *gonne:* began.
324 *ribaudye:* ribaldry.

325 *leere:* learn.
326 *wit:* wisdom.
327 *graunte:* agree; *ywis:* indeed; *moot:* must.
328 *honeste:* respectable.

THE PARDONER'S PROLOGUE

One of the most frequently recurring themes in fourteenth-century literature is the corruption of the Church and her ministers. Not only vigorous reformers like John Wyclif and his supporters, but poets like Langland and the conservative Gower unite in charging the clergy with greed, idleness, unchastity, and irreverence. And the charges do not appear to vary much throughout the age. From Dante and St. Bonaventura in the thirteenth century to St. Catherine of Siena in the fourteenth and the distinguished chancellor of Oxford University, Thomas Gascoigne, in the fifteenth the theme is a consistent one. Parish priests, monks, friars, abbots, bishops, and the Pope's highest officers: among the lowest and the highest, worldliness and corruption are commonplace.

In this literature one of the most consistent objects of scorn was the seller of indulgences, the pardoner. The official view of the Church is stated to have been that writs of indulgence conferred upon the recipient remission of temporal punishment for sin, including both penance and purgatorial punishment, but it is clear that they were widely held by seller and buyer to be purely and simply remissions of sin. Gascoigne writes in 1456,

> Sinners say nowadays, "I care not what or how many evils I do before God, for I can get at once, without the least difficulty, plenary remission of any guilt or sin whatsoever through an Indulgence granted me by the Pope, whose written grant I have bought for fourpence . . ." for, indeed, these granters of letters of Indulgence run about from place to place and sometimes give a letter for twopence, sometimes for a good drink of wine or beer . . . sometimes for the hire of a prostitute.

What was conceived, then, as an evidence of God's mercy to the truly repentant sinner had become a means of enrichment to the Church and her unscrupulous agents and a license for sinning to the purchaser.

The practices of Chaucer's Pardoner are apparently typical of these rascally confidence men. But in the Pardoner himself Chaucer has fashioned an individual. The satire of the portrait depends, like all satire, upon the representation of typical vices. Even in the Pardoner's somewhat unrealistically frank exposure of himself as an unscrupulous scoundrel he quite clearly derives from conventional vice figures of medieval satire who traditionally reveal themselves in such a monologue as this. But though he is compounded of conventions and though he represents a well-known type of vice, his cheerful cynicism, his undeniable excellence as a preacher, his vigorous use of language and imagery, and his sardonic humor mark him as a true Chaucerian individual. The self-portrait which his prologue offers us shows him to be, like the Friar and the Summoner, a wicked perverter of sacred things. But in spite of our moral judgment of him, he is such an extraordinary figure that he has for us a kind of repellent fascination.

Heere folweth the Prologe of the Pardoners Tale.

"Lordynges," quod he, "in chirches whan I preche,
I peyne me to han an hauteyn speche, 330
And rynge it out as round as gooth a belle,
For I kan al by rote that I telle.
My theme is alwey oon, and evere was:
Radix malorum est cupiditas.
First I pronounce whennes that I come, 335
And thanne my bulles shewe I, alle and some:
Oure lige lordes seel on my patente,
That shewe I first, my body to warente,
That no man be so boold, ne preest ne clerk,
Me to destourbe of Cristes holy werk; 340
And after that thanne telle I forth my tales;
Bulles of popes and of cardynales,
Of patriarkes and bisshopes I shewe,
And in Latyn I speke a wordes fewe,
To saffron with my predicacion, 345
And for to stire hem to devocion.
Thanne shewe I forth my longe cristal stones,
Ycrammed ful of cloutes and of bones—
Relikes been they, as wenen they echoon.
Thanne have I in latoun a sholder-boon 350
Which that was of an holy Jewes sheep.
'Goode men,' I seye, 'taak of my wordes keep:
If that this boon be wasshe in any welle,
If cow, or calf, or sheep, or oxe swelle,

330 *peyne me:* take pains; *han:* have, use; *hauteyn:* loud.
331 *round:* sonorously; *gooth:* goes, i.e., rings.
332 *kan al by rote:* know all by heart.
333 *oon:* one, the same.
334 "The root of evil is avarice" (I Timothy 6:10).

335 *pronounce:* declare; *whennes:* from whence.
336 *bulles:* mandates from church authorities, credentials.
337 *lige lord:* liege lord, i.e., the bishop; *seel:* seal; *patente:* licence.
338 *warente:* protect.
339 *be:* may be; *ne . . . ne:* neither . . . nor.
340 *destourbe of:* hinder from.
341 *telle . . . tales:* go on with my discourse.

345 *saffron:* flavor; *predicacion:* preaching.

347 *cristal stones:* glass jars or cases.
348 *ycrammed:* packed; *cloutes:* rags.
349 *relikes:* relics, sacred articles once a part of or associated with a holy person; *wenen:* suppose; *echoon:* each one.
350 *latoun:* a brassy metal, i.e., a cheap metal box.
351 *holy Jewes:* i.e., of a Biblical character or prophet.
352 *taak keep:* take notice.
353 *wasshe:* washed.
354 *swelle:* swells, i.e., from the poisonous effect (of the worm).

That any worm hath ete, or worm ystonge, 355
Taak water of that welle and wassh his tonge,
And it is hool anon. And forthermoor,
Of pokkes and of scabbe and every soor
Shal every sheep be hool that of this welle
Drynketh a draughte. Taak kepe eek what I telle: 360
If that the goode man that the beestes oweth
Wol every wyke, er that the cok hym croweth,
Fastynge, drynken of this welle a draughte,
As thilke holy Jew oure eldres taughte,
His beestes and his stoor shal multiplie. 365
'And sires, also it heeleth jalousie;
For though a man be falle in jalous rage,
Lat maken with this water his potage,
And nevere shal he moore his wyf mystriste,
Though he the soothe of hir defaute wiste, 370
Al hadde she taken preestes two or thre.
'Heere is a miteyn eek that ye may se;
He that his hand wol putte in this mitayn,
He shal have multipliyng of his grayn,
Whan he hath sowen, be it whete or otes— 375
So that he offre pens or elles grotes.
'Goode men and wommen, o thyng warne I yow:
If any wight be in this chirche now
That hath doon synne horrible, that he
Dar nat for shame of it yshryven be, 380
Or any womman, be she yong or old,
That hath ymaad hir housbonde cokewold,
Swich folk shal have no power ne no grace
To offren to my relikes in this place.

355 *that . . . ete:* that has eaten any worm; *or . . . ystonge:* or has been stung by any snake.

357 *it:* i.e., the animal; *hool:* healthy.
358 *pokkes:* pox; *soor:* sore.
359 *hool:* healed.
360 *taak kepe:* l. 352.
361 *goode man:* farmer; *beestes:* animals; *oweth:* owns.
362 *wyke:* week; *er:* before; *hym croweth:* crows.
363 *fastynge:* i.e., before breakfast.
364 *thilke:* this (same); *eldres:* ancestors.

365 *his:* i.e., the farmer's; *stoor:* stock.
366 *heeleth:* heals.
367 *falle:* fallen.
368 *lat maken:* have (his potage) made; *potage:* soup.
369 *mystriste:* mistrust.

370 *soothe . . . defaute:* the truth about her infidelity; *wiste:* should know.
371 *al:* although; *taken:* i.e., taken as lovers.
372 *miteyn:* mitten; *se:* see.

376 *so that:* provided that; *offre:* puts in the offering; *pens, grotes:* coins.
377 *o thyng:* of one thing.
378 *wight:* person.
379 *that he:* so that he.
380 *dar nat:* dares not; *yshryven be:* be shriven.
381 *or . . .:* or (if there be) any woman, whether young or old.
382 *ymaad:* made; *cokewold:* cuckold, a man whose wife has been unfaithful.

384 *to offren:* to give gifts to me out of reverence for my relics.

And whoso fyndeth hym out of swich blame, 385
He wol come up and offre in Goddes name,
And I assoile hym by the auctoritee
Which that by bulle ygraunted was to me.'
 By this gaude have I wonne, yeer by yeer,
An hundred mark sith I was pardoner. 390
I stonde lyk a clerk in my pulpet,
And whan the lewed peple is doun yset,
I preche so as ye han herd bifore,
And telle an hundred false japes more.
Thanne peyne I me to strecche forth the nekke, 395
And est and west upon the peple I bekke
As dooth a dowve, sittyng on a berne;
Myne handes and my tonge goon so yerne
That it is joye to se my bisynesse!
Of avarice and of swich cursednesse 400
Is al my prechyng, for to make hem free
To yeven hir pens, and namely unto me.
For myn entente is nat but for to wynne,
And no thyng for correccion of synne.
I rekke nevere, whan that they been beryed, 405
Though that hir soules goon a-blakeberyed!
For certes, many a predicacion
Comth ofte tyme of yvel entencion;
Som for plesance of folk and flaterye,
To been avaunced by ypocrisye, 410
And som for veyne glorie, and som for hate;
For whan I dar noon oother weyes debate,
Thanne wol I stynge hym with my tonge smerte
In prechyng, so that he shal nat asterte

385 *fyndeth . . .:* is innocent of such sin.

387 *and I assoile:* and I (will) absolve.

389 *gaude:* trick; *wonne:* gotten; *yeer by yeer:* year after year.

390 *hundred mark:* in purchasing power equal to considerably more than $10,000; *sith:* since.

391 *clerk:* cleric.

392 *lewed:* ignorant; *doun yset:* seated.

393 *so as . . .:* i.e., as I have described.

394 *japes:* tricks, falsehoods.

395 *peyne I me:* I take pains.

396 *bekke:* nod.

397 *dowve:* dove; *berne:* barn.

398 *tonge:* tongue; *goon:* go; *yerne:* eagerly.

400 *of:* concerning.

401 *make hem free:* make them (the people) liberal.

402 *yeven:* give; *namely:* especially.

403 *entente:* intention, aim; *nat but:* only; *wynne:* profit.

405 *rekke nevere:* care nothing; *beryed:* buried.

406 *goon a-blakeberyed:* go blackberrying, i.e., to hell.

407 *certes:* certainly; *predicacion:* sermon.

408 *comth:* comes, is motivated by; *yvel:* evil.

409 *som:* some (sermons); *plesance:* pleasing.

410 *avaunced:* advanced, promoted; *ypocrisye:* hypocrisy.

411 *veyne glorie:* pride.

412 *dar:* dare; *debate:* speak against an enemy.

413 *stynge . . . :* i.e., attack him in a sermon; *smerte:* smartly.

414 *asterte:* escape.

To been defamed falsly, if that he *415*
Hath trespased to my bretheren or to me.
For though I telle noght his propre name,
Men shal wel knowe that it is the same,
By signes and by othere circumstances.
Thus quyte I folk that doon us displesances; *420*
Thus spitte I out my venym under hewe
Of holynesse, to semen holy and trewe.
But shortly myn entente I wol devyse:
I preche of no thyng but for coveityse;
Therfore my theme is yet, and evere was, *425*
Radix malorum est cupiditas.
Thus kan I preche agayn that same vice
Which that I use, and that is avarice.
But though myself be gilty in that synne,
Yet kan I maken oother folk to twynne *430*
From avarice, and soore to repente.
But that is nat my principal entente;
I preche no thyng but for coveitise.
Of this matere it oghte ynogh suffise.
Thanne telle I hem ensamples many oon *435*
Of olde stories longe tyme agoon;
For lewed peple loven tales olde;
Swiche thynges kan they wel reporte and holde.
What, trowe ye that whiles I may preche,
And wynne gold and silver for I teche, *440*
That I wol lyve in poverte wilfully?
Nay, nay, I thoghte it nevere, trewely!
For I wol preche and begge in sondry landes;
I wol nat do no labour with myne handes,

415 *to been:* being.

418 *that . . . same:* i.e., who it is.
419 *signes:* hints, clues.

420 *quyte:* pay back; *displesances:* discourtesies, offenses.
421 *venym:* venom; *hewe:* disguise.
422 *semen:* seem.
423 *shortly:* briefly; *devyse:* describe.
424 *of:* for; *coveityse:* covetousness.

427 *agayn:* against.
428 *use:* practice.
429 *in:* of.

430 *twynne:* cease.
431 *soore:* sorely.

434 i.e., enough has been said of this matter.

435 *hem:* them, i.e., the people; *ensamples:* exempla, moral stories illustrating a sermon; *many oon:* many a one.
436 *of:* from.
437 *lewed:* ignorant.
438 *reporte and holde:* repeat and remember.
439 *trowe:* think; *may:* am able to.

440 *for I teche:* by teaching.

442 *thoghte:* intended.
443 *sondry:* various.

Ne make baskettes and lyve therby, 445
By cause I wol nat beggen ydelly.
I wol none of the Apostles countrefete;
I wol have moneye, wolle, chese, and whete,
Al were it yeven of the povereste page,
Or of the povereste widwe in a village, 450
Al sholde hir children sterve for famyne.
Nay, I wol drynke licour of the vyne
And have a joly wenche in every toun.
But herkneth, lordynges, in conclusioun,
Youre likyng is that I shal telle a tale. 455
Now have I dronke a draughte of corny ale,
By God, I hope I shal yow telle a thyng
That shal by reson been at youre likyng;
For though myself be a ful vicious man,
A moral tale yet I yow telle kan, 460
Which I am wont to preche for to wynne.
Now holde youre pees, my tale I wol bigynne."

THE PARDONER'S TALE

The tale which the Pardoner tells is an exemplum, an illustrative story set in a sermon on his favorite text, *radix malorum est cupiditas*. And both the story and the sermon mark him as a superb practitioner of his art. The vigorous, high-sounding rhetoric of the sermon—"O wombe! O bely! O stinking cod!" "O cursed sinne of alle cursednesse!"—and the colorfully detailed descriptions—the snoring of the drunkard and the oaths and cries of the dicers—testify to his excellence as a preacher as well as, perhaps, to his intimate personal familiarity with these favorite vices.

The story itself is an old tale found in many literatures and here elaborately dressed by the Pardoner in details which suit it

445 *ne:* nor; *lyve therby:* i.e., live by making baskets (rather than by begging).
446 *ydelly:* idly, without working.
447 *wol countrefete:* will imitate.
448 *wolle:* wool.
449 *al were it:* although it were; *yeven:* given; *of:* by.

451 *al sholde:* although (her children) should; *sterve:* die.

458 *by reson:* for good reason; *at . . . likyng:* to your liking.

461 *wont:* accustomed; *for to wynne:* as a means of profiting.

to his didactic purpose. The contrast between the utter bestiality of the rioters and the moving dignity of the old man is one of the finest things in any of the *Tales.* The manner of narration is particularly interesting. Almost the entire story consists of the actual dialogue of the actors; the details of the action, including the swift denouement, are regularly understated in brief summary form. The effect of this, of course, is to throw the emphasis entirely upon the character and vices of the rioters and to present their fate as inevitably deriving from these.

Heere bigynneth the Pardoners Tale.

In Flaundres whilom was a compaignye
Of yonge folk that haunteden folye,
As riot, hasard, stewes, and tavernes, *465*
Where as with harpes, lutes, and gyternes,
They daunce and pleye at dees bothe day and nyght,
And ete also and drynken over hir myght,
Thurgh which they doon the devel sacrifise
Withinne that develes temple in cursed wise *470*
By superfluytee abhomynable.
Hir othes been so grete and so dampnable
That it is grisly for to heere hem swere.
Oure blessed Lordes body they totere—
Hem thoughte that Jewes rente hym noght ynough; *475*
And ech of hem at otheres synne lough.
And right anon thanne comen tombesteres
Fetys and smale, and yonge frutesteres,
Syngeres with harpes, baudes, wafereres,

463 *Flaundres:* Flanders; *whilom:* once.
464 *haunteden:* practiced; *folye:* folly.

465 *riot:* riotous living; *hasard:* gambling; *stewes:* brothels.
466 *where as:* where; *gytornes:* guitars.
467 *dees:* dice.
468 *over hir myght:* over their capacity.
469 *doon sacrifise:* make sacrifice to.

470 *develes temple:* i.e., a tavern; *wise:* manner.
471 *superfluytee:* excess; *abhomynable:* unnatural.
472 *hir:* their; *othes:* oaths.

474 *totere:* tear apart, i.e., by swearing by the parts of the body; see l. 651ff.
475 *hem thoughte:* it seemed to them; *rente:* tore; *noght:* not.
476 *lough:* laughed.
477 *anon:* forthwith; *tombesteres:* dancing girls.
478 *fetys:* graceful; *frutesteres:* female fruit sellers.
479 *baudes:* prostitutes; *wafereres:* sellers of cakes.

Which been the verray develes officeres 480
To kyndle and blowe the fyr of lecherye
That is annexed unto glotonye.
The holy writ take I to my witnesse
That luxurie is in wyn and dronkenesse.
Lo, how that dronken Loth, unkyndely, 485
Lay by his doghtres two unwityngly;
So dronke he was he nyste what he wroghte.
Herodes, who so wel the stories soghte,
Whan he of wyn was repleet at his feste,
Right at his owene table he yaf his heste 490
To sleen the Baptist John, ful giltelees.
Senek seith a good word doutelees:
He seith he kan no difference fynde
Bitwix a man that is out of his mynde
And a man which that is dronkelewe, 495
But that woodnesse, yfallen in a shrewe,
Persevereth lenger than dooth dronkenesse.
O glotonye, ful of cursednesse!
O cause first of oure confusion!
O original of oure dampnacion, 500
Til Crist hadde boght us with his blood agayn!
Lo, how deere, shortly for to sayn,
Aboght was thilke cursed vileynye!
Corrupt was al this world for glotonye:
Adam oure fader and his wyf also 505
Fro Paradys to labour and to wo
Were dryven for that vice, it is no drede.
For whil that Adam fasted, as I rede,
He was in Paradys; and whan that he

480 *verray:* true.

482 *annexed:* allied; *glotonye:* gluttony.

484 *luxurie:* lechery, lust.

485 *Lo, how:* Lo, see how; *Loth:* Lot; *unkyndely:* unnaturally.
486 *unwityngly:* unknowingly.
487 *nyste:* knew not; *wroghte:* did; see Genesis 19:32ff.
488 *Herodes:* King Herod, see Matthew 14, Mark 6; *who . . .:* (as anyone would see) who would consult the stories carefully.
489 *repleet:* full; *feste:* feast.
490 *owene:* own; *yaf:* gave; *heste:* command.
491 *sleen:* slay, *ful . . .:* (though he was) entirely guiltless.
492 Seneca, the Roman Stoic philosopher.

494 *bitwix:* between.
495 *dronkelewe:* drunk.
496 *but:* except; *woodnesse:* madness; *yfallen in:* come upon; *shrewe:* scoundrel.

499 *cause first:* original cause; *confusion:* downfall.
500 *dampnacion:* damnation.
501 *boght:* redeemed.
502 *deere:* dearly, expensively.
503 *aboght:* paid for; *thilke:* that.
504 *corrupt:* corrupted.

507 *drede:* fear, doubt.
508 *rede:* read, interpret.

Eet of the fruyt defended on a tree, *510*
Anon he was out cast to wo and peyne.
O glotonye, on thee wel oghte us pleyne!
O, wiste a man how manye maladies
Folwen of excesse and of glotonyes,
He wolde been the moore mesurable *515*
Of his diete, sittyng at his table.
Allas, the shorte throte, the tendre mouth,
Maketh that est and west and north and south,
In erthe, in eyr, in water, men to swynke
To gete a gloton deyntee mete and drynke! *520*
Of this matere, O Paul, wel kanstow trete:
"Mete unto wombe, and wombe eek unto mete,
Shal God destroyen bothe," as Paulus seith.
Allas, a foul thyng is it, by my feith,
To seye this word, and fouler is the dede, *525*
Whan man so drynketh of the white and rede
That of his throte he maketh his pryvee
Thurgh thilke cursed superfluitee.
The Apostle wepyng seith ful pitously,
"Ther walken manye of whiche yow toold have I— *530*
I seye it now wepyng with pitous voys—
That they been enemys of Cristes croys,
Of whiche the ende is deeth; wombe is hir god!"
O wombe! O bely! O stynkyng cod,
Fulfilled of dong and of corrupcioun! *535*
At either ende of thee foul is the soun.
How greet labour and cost is thee to fynde!
Thise cookes, how they stampe and streyne and grynde,
And turnen substaunce into accident,

510 *eet:* ate; *defended:* forbidden.

512 *on:* of; *pleyne:* to complain.
513 *wiste:* if (a man) knew.
514 *folwen of:* follow from.
515 *mesurable:* moderate.

517 *shorte throte:* brief pleasure of swallowing; *tendre:* sensitive.
518 *est and west:* i.e., everywhere.
519 *swynke:* labor.

520 *gloton:* i.e., to get (dainty foods) for a glutton; *mete:* food.
521 *kanstow:* can you; *trete:* treat, discuss.
522-23 "Meats for the belly, and the belly for meats: but God shall destroy both it and them." I Corinthians 6:13; *wombe:* belly.

526 *white and rede:* i.e., white and red wine.
527 *pryvee:* privy.
528 *thilke:* this; *superfluitee:* excess.

530 Philippians 30:18-19; *of whiche . . .:* of whom I have told you.
532 *croys:* cross.
533 *of whiche:* whose; *wombe:* belly; *hir:* their.
534 *cod:* bag.

535 *fulfilled:* filled full; *dong:* dung.
536 *soun:* sound.
537 *how:* what a; *is:* it is; *thee to fynde:* to provide for you.
538 *stampe:* pound.
539 *substaunce:* the real inner nature of a thing; *accident:* external appearance of a thing; thus the glutton perverts the substance of food, which is a means of nourishment, to a mere means of pleasing the palate.

To fulfille al thy likerous talent! *540*
Out of the harde bones knokke they
The mary, for they caste noght awey
That may go thurgh the golet softe and soote.
Of spicerie of leef and bark and roote
Shal been his sauce ymaked by delit, *545*
To make hym yet a newer appetit.
But certes, he that haunteth swiche delices
Is deed whil that he lyveth in tho vices.
A lecherous thyng is wyn, and dronkenesse
Is ful of stryvyng and of wrecchednesse. *550*
O dronke man, disfigured is thy face!
Sour is thy breeth! foul artow to embrace!
And thurgh thy dronke nose semeth the soun
As though thou seydest ay "Sampsoun Sampsoun."
And yet, God woot, Sampsoun drank nevere no wyn. *555*
Thou fallest as it were a stiked swyn;
Thy tonge is lost, and al thyn honeste cure;
For dronkenesse is verray sepulture
Of mannes wit and his discrecion.
In whom that drynke hath dominacion *560*
He kan no conseil kepe, it is no drede.
Now kepe yow fro the white and fro the red,
And namely fro the white wyn of Lepe,
That is to selle in Fisshstrete or in Chepe:
This wyn of Spaigne crepeth subtilly *565*
In othere wynes growyng faste by,
Of which ther riseth swich fumositee
That whan a man hath dronken draughtes thre
And weneth that he be at hoom in Chepe,

540 *fulfille:* gratify; *likerous talent:* dainty appetite.

542 *mary:* marrow.
543 *golet:* gullet; *soote:* sweetly.
544 *spicerie:* spices.
545 *by delit:* delightfully.
546 *newer:* sharper.
547 *haunteth:* practices; *delices:* pleasures.
548 *deed:* dead, i.e., spiritually dead; *tho:* those.

550 *stryvyng:* strife.

552 *artow:* are you.
553 *semeth the soun:* the sound, i.e., of thy heavy breathing, seems.
554 *ay:* always.

555 *woot:* knows.
556 *fallest:* i.e., fall down; *as . . . swyn:* like a stuck pig.
557 *honeste cure:* regard for decency.
558 *verray sepulture:* true tomb.
559 *wit:* wisdom.

560 *in whom:* the man in whom.
561 *conseil:* secrets; *drede:* fear, doubt.

563 *Lepe:* a town near Cadiz, Spain.
564 *to selle:* for sale; Fishstreet and Cheapside are in London.

566 *in:* into; *growyng faste by:* that grow nearby; this is an allusion to the adulteration of good wines with the stronger and cheaper Spanish wines.
567 *of:* from; *riseth:* i.e., in the drinker's brain; *fumositee:* heady fumes.

569 *weneth:* thinks; *be:* is.

He is in Spaigne, right at the toune of Lepe, *570*
Nat at The Rochele ne at Burdeux toun;
And thanne wol he seyn "Sampsoun, Sampsoun."
But herkneth, lordynges, o word I yow preye,
That alle the sovereyn actes, dar I seye,
Of victories in the Olde Testament, *575*
Thurgh verray God that is omnipotent,
Were doon in abstinence and in prayere.
Looketh the Bible and ther ye may it leere.
Looke, Attilla, the grete conquerour,
Deyde in his sleep with shame and dishonour, *580*
Bledyng at his nose in dronkenesse.
A capitayn sholde lyve in sobrenesse.
And over al this, avyseth yow right wel
What was comaunded unto Lamuel—
Nat Samuel, but Lamuel, seye I— *585*
Redeth the Bible and fynde it expresly
Of wyn-yevyng to hem that han justise.
Namoore of this, for it may wel suffise.
And now that I have spoken of glotonye,
Now wol I yow defenden hasardrye. *590*
Hasard is verray moder of lesynges,
And of deceite, and cursed forswerynges,
Blaspheme of Crist, manslaughtre, and wast also
Of catel and of tyme; and forthermo,
It is repreeve and contrarie of honour *595*
For to ben holde a commune hasardour.
And ever the hyer he is of estaat
The moore is he yholden desolaat.
If that a prynce useth hasardrye,

570 *is:* i.e., is transported by the wine.
571 i.e., not at La Rochelle or Bordeaux where the wines are weaker.

573 *herknetho word:* listen to one word.
574 *sovereyn actes:* most famous records; *dar:* dare.

576 *thurgh . . .:* through the agency of God (they were performed).
578 *looketh:* consult; *leere:* learn.
579 *Attilla,* king of the Huns, who is said to have died of a burst blood vessel on the night of his marriage to a beautiful maiden whom he had added to his many other wives.

582 *capitayn:* a military leader.
583 *over:* above; *avyseth yow:* consider.
584 *Lamuel:* King Lemuel; see Proverbs 31:4-5.

587 *of:* about; *wyn-yevyng:* serving of wine; *hem:* them; *han:* i.e., administer.

590 *yow defenden:* forbid to you; *hasardrye:* gambling.
591 *verray:* true; *moder:* mother; *lesynges:* lying.
592 *cursed forswerynges:* accursed perjury.
593 *blaspheme:* blasphemy; *wast:* waste.
594 *catel:* property.

595 *repreeve:* disgrace; *contrarie:* opposite.
596 *ben holde:* be held, regarded as; *hasardour:* gambler.
597 *ever* is redundant; *hyer:* higher; *estaat:* condition, rank.
598 *desolaat:* dissolute.
599 *useth:* practices.

In alle governance and policye *600*
He is, as by commune opinion,
Yholde the lasse in reputacion.
Stilbon, that was a wys embassadour,
Was sent to Corynthe in ful greet honour
Fro Lacedomye to make hir alliaunce; *605*
And whan he cam, hym happede parchaunce
That alle the gretteste that were of that lond,
Pleiyng atte hasard he hem fond.
For which, as soone as it mighte be,
He stal hym hoom agayn to his contree, *610*
And seyde, "Ther wol I nat lese my name,
N'I wol nat take on me so greet defame
Yow for to allie unto none hasardours.
Sendeth othere wise embassadours,
For, by my trouthe, me were levere dye *615*
Than I yow sholde to hasardours allye.
For ye, that been so glorious in honours,
Shal nat allyen yow with hasardours
As by my wyl, ne as by my tretee."
This wise philosophre, thus seyde he. *620*
Looke eek that to the kyng Demetrius,
The kyng of Parthes, as the book seith us,
Sente him a paire of dees of gold in scorn,
For he hadde used hasard ther-biforn;
For which he heeld his glorie or his renoun *625*
At no value or reputacioun.
Lordes may fynden oother maner pley
Honeste ynough to dryve the day awey.
Now wol I speke of othes false and grete

600 *governance and policye:* governmental and political affairs.

602 *yholde:* held, regarded as; *lasse:* less.

604 Corinth, in Greece.

605 *fro:* from; *Lacedomye:* Sparta; *hir alliaunce:* alliance of them.
606 *hym happede parchaunce:* it befell him by chance.
607 *gretteste:* greatest men.
608 *he hem fond:* he found them.
609 *for which:* for which reason; *as . . . be:* as possible.
610 *stal hym:* stole, or went, away.
611 *lese:* lose; *name:* honor.
612 *n'I:* nor I; *defame:* dishonor.
613 *yow:* i.e., the Spartans; *allie:* ally.

615 *me were levere:* it were preferable to me.
616 *I yow sholde:* I should (ally) you.

619 *as* is redundant here; *wyl:* will; *tretee:* treaty.

621 *looke eek:* behold also.
622 *Parthes:* the Parthians.
623 *dees:* dice; *in scorn:* i.e., as a gesture of scorn.
624 *for:* because; *he:* i.e., Demetrius; *used:* practiced; *therbiforn:* in the past.
625 *he:* the Parthian king; *his:* Demetrius's.

627 *fynden:* find; *maner pley:* kinds of amusement.
628 *honeste:* fitting; *dryve . . . awey:* i.e., pass the time.
629 *othes:* oaths are distinguished into false oaths (or false swearing), by which is meant perjury, and great oaths (or great swearing), by which is meant profanity.

A word or two, as olde bookes trete. *630*
Greet sweryng is a thyng abhominable,
And fals sweryng is yet moore reprevable.
The heighe God forbad sweryng at al—
Witnesse on Mathew; but in special
Of sweryng seith the holy Jeremye, *635*
"Thou shalt swere sooth thyne othes and nat lye,
And swere in doom, and eek in rightwisnesse";
But ydel sweryng is a cursednesse.
Bihoold and se that in the firste table
Of heighe Goddes hestes honurable *640*
How that the seconde heste of hym is this:
"Take nat my name in ydel or amys."
Lo, rather he forbedeth swich sweryng
Than homycide, or many a cursed thyng;
I seye that as by ordre thus it standeth; *645*
This knoweth that his hestes understandeth,
How that the seconde heste of God is that.
And forther over, I wol thee telle al plat,
That vengeance shal nat parten from his hous
That of his othes is to outrageous. *650*
"By Goddes precious herte!" and "By his nayles!"
And "By the blood of Crist that is in Hayles,
Sevene is my chaunce, and thyn is cynk and treye!"
"By Goddes armes, if thou falsly pleye
This daggere shal thurghout thyn herte go!"— *655*
This fruyt cometh of the bicched bones two,
Forsweryng, ire, falsnesse, homycide.
Now, for the love of Crist, that for us dyde,
Lete youre othes bothe grete and smale.

630 *trete:* treat, discuss.

632 *reprevable:* reprehensible.

634 see Matthew 5:34ff.; *in special:* especially.
635 *of:* concerning; see Jeremiah 4:2.
636 *sooth:* truly.
637 *doom:* judgment; *rightwisnesse:* righteousness.
638 *ydel sweryng:* swearing in vain or uselessly; *cursednesse:* wickedness.
639 *se:* see; *firste table:* the ten commandments are variously divided into two tables by various authorities.
640 *hestes:* commandments.
641 *how:* i.e., (see) how; *seconde:* equal to the Protestant third.
642 *ydel:* vain.
643 *rather:* earlier, i.e., in the order of the commandments.

645 *as by ordre:* in the order.
646 *that:* he who; i.e., he who understands them knows this.

648 *forther over:* furthermore; *al plat:* flatly, plainly.
649 *parten:* depart, be absent from.

651 *nayles:* either fingernails or the nails of the cross.
652 *Hayles:* in the abbey at Hayles was preserved a phial supposedly containing some of Christ's blood.
653 *chaunce:* point; *cynk:* five; *treye:* three; a reference to hazard, a dice game resembling modern craps. The Pardoner is imitating the cries of a dice player.

656 *fruyt:* i.e., result; *bicched bones:* cursed bones, dice.
657 *ire:* anger.
658 *dyde:* died.
659 *lete:* leave, cease.

But sires, now wol I telle forth my tale. *660*
  Thise riotoures thre of whiche I telle,
Longe erst er prime rong of any belle,
Were set hem in a taverne for to drynke,
And as they sat, they herde a belle clynke
Biforn a cors was caried to his grave. *665*
That oon of hem gan callen to his knave:
"Go bet," quod he, "and axe redily
What cors is this that passeth heer forby;
And looke that thou reporte his name weel."
  "Sire," quod this boy, "it nedeth neveradeel; *670*
It was me told er ye cam heer two houres.
He was, pardee, an old felawe of youres,
And sodeynly he was yslayn to-nyght,
Fordronke, as he sat on his bench upright.
Ther cam a privee theef men clepeth Deeth, *675*
That in this contree al the peple sleeth,
And with his spere he smoot his herte atwo,
And wente his wey withouten wordes mo.
He hath a thousand slayn this pestilence.
And, maister, er ye come in his presence, *680*
Me thynketh that it were necessarie
For to be war of swich an adversarie;
Beth redy for to meete hym everemoore;
Thus taughte me my dame; I sey namoore."
  "By Seinte Marie," seyde this taverner, *685*
"The child seith sooth, for he hath slayn this yeer,
Henne over a mile, withinne a greet village,
Bothe man and womman, child, and hyne, and page;
I trowe his habitacion be there.

661 *riotoures:* revelers.
662 *erst er:* before; *prime:* the first canonical hour of the day, beginning at 6 A.M. and extending until 9; *er prime* = before 9, half prime = 7:30, past prime = after 9.
663 *set hem:* seated.

665 *cors:* corpse; a hand bell was carried before the corpse in a funeral procession; *was:* i.e., that was.
666 *that oon:* a certain one; *gan:* did; *knave:* boy, servant.
667 *bet:* better, i.e., quickly; *axe:* ask; *redily:* without delay.
668 *heer forby:* past here.
669 *reporte weel:* report accurately.
670 *nedeth:* is (not) necessary; *neveradeel:* not a bit.
671 *er . . . two houres:* two hours before.
672 *pardee:* indeed, literally "by God"; *felawe:* companion.
673 *to-nyght:* last night.
674 *fordronke:* very drunk.

675 *privee:* secret; *clepeth:* call.
676 *contree:* country; *sleeth:* slayeth.
677 *spere:* spear; *atwo:* in two.
678 *withouten . . . mo:* without another word.
679 *this:* during this; *pestilence:* plague.

681 *me thynketh:* it seems to me.
682 *for . . . war:* for you to be wary; *adversarie:* opponent.
683 *beth redy everemoore:* be always ready.
684 *dame:* mother.

686 *seith sooth:* speaks truly.
687 *henne:* hence, from here.
688 *hyne:* farm laborer.
689 *trowe:* believe; *habitacion:* home.

To been avysed greet wisdom it were, *690*
Er that he dide a man a dishonour."
"Ye, Goddes armes!" quod this riotour,
"Is it swich peril with hym for to meete?
I shal hym seke by wey and eek by strete,
I make avow to Goddes digne bones! *695*
Herkneth, felawes, we thre been al ones;
Lat ech of us holde up his hand til oother,
And ech of us bicomen otheres brother,
And we wol sleen this false traytour Deeth.
He shal be slayn, he that so manye sleeth, *700*
By Goddes dignitee, er it be nyght!"
Togidres han thise thre hir trouthes plight
To lyve and dyen ech of hem for oother,
As though he were his owene ybore brother.
And up they stirte, al dronken in this rage, *705*
And forth they goon towardes that village
Of which the taverner hadde spoke biforn.
And many a grisly ooth thanne han they sworn,
And Cristes blessed body they torente:
Deeth shal be deed if that they may hym hente! *710*
Whan they han goon nat fully half a mile,
Right as they wolde han troden over a stile,
An old man and a povre with hem mette.
This olde man ful mekely hem grette,
And seyde thus, "Now lordes, God you see!" *715*
The proudeste of thise riotoures three
Answerde agayn, "What, carl, with sory grace!
Why artow al forwrapped save thy face?
Why lyvestow so longe in so greet age?"

690 *been avysed:* be forewarned.
691 *er . . . man:* lest that he should do one.

693 *swich:* such, so great.
694 *by wey:* on the byways; *by strete:* on the highways.

695 *avow:* vow; *digne:* worthy.
696 *herkneth:* listen; *al ones:* of one mind.
697 *holde . . . hand:* swear loyalty; *til:* to.

701 *er:* before.
702 *togidres:* together; *han:* have; *trouthes plight:* words of honor pledged.

704 *ybore:* born.
705 *stirte:* started, jumped.

709 *torente:* tore to bits.
710 *deed:* dead; *hente:* catch.

712 *right:* just; *troden:* stepped.
713 *an old . . . povre:* an old, poor man.
714 *mekely:* meekly; *grette:* greeted.

715 *you see:* watch, or protect, you.
716 *proudeste:* proudest.
717 *agayn:* back; *carl:* fellow; *with . . . grace:* ill luck or favor to you, an imprecation.
718 *artow:* are you; *forwrapped:* wrapped up; *save:* except.
719 *lyvestow:* do you live.

This olde man gan looke in his visage, *720*
And seyde thus: "For I ne kan nat fynde
A man, though that I walked into Inde,
Neither in citee ne in no village,
That wolde chaunge his youthe for myn age;
And therfore moot I han myn age stille, *725*
As longe tyme as it is Goddes wille.
Ne Deeth, allas, ne wol nat han my lyf.
Thus walke I lyk a restelees caytyf,
And on the ground, which is my modres gate,
I knokke with my staf bothe erly and late, *730*
And seye, 'Leeve moder, leet me in!
Lo, how I vanysshe, flessh and blood and skyn!
Allas, whan shal my bones been at reste?
Moder, with yow wolde I chaunge my cheste
That in my chambre longe tyme hath be, *735*
Ye, for an heyre clowt to wrappe in me.'
But yet to me she wol nat do that grace,
For which ful pale and welked is my face.
But sires, to yow it is no curteisye
To speken to an old man vileynye, *740*
But he trespasse in word or elles in dede.
In Holy Writ ye may yourself wel rede:
'Agayns an old man, hoor upon his heed,
Ye sholde arise.' Wherfore I yeve yow reed,
Ne dooth unto an old man noon harm now, *745*
Namoore than that ye wolde men did to yow
In age, if that ye so longe abyde.
And God be with yow, wher ye go or ryde;
I moot go thider as I have to go."

720 *gan:* did, literally "began."
721 *for:* because.
722 *Inde:* India.

724 *chaunge:* exchange.

725 *moot:* must; *han:* have, keep.

727 *ne:* nor.
728 *caytyf:* wretch.
729 *modres:* mother's, i.e., with every step he taps with his staff on the ground, which is Mother Earth's gate, asking for admission (to the grave).

731 *leeve:* dear; *leet:* let.
732 *how:* see how.

734 *chaunge:* exchange; *cheste:* i.e., the chest containing my worldly possessions.

735 *be:* been.
736 *ye:* yea; *heyre clowt:* a haircloth shroud.
737 *grace:* favor.
738 *welked:* withered.
739 *to yow:* in you.

740 *vileynye:* rude language.
741 *but:* unless; *he:* i.e., the old man.

743 *agayns:* in the presence of; *hoor:* white-haired; see Leviticus 19:32.
744 *arise:* stand up; *yeve:* give; *reed:* advice.

745 *ne dooth:* do not.
746 *namoore:* no more; *that:* that which; *wolde:* would wish.
747 *in age:* in your old age; *abyde:* stay (on earth).
748 *wher:* whether; *go:* walk.
749 *moot:* must; *thider:* thither; *as:* where.

"Nay, olde cherl, by God thou shalt nat so," *750*
Seyde this oother hasardour anon.
"Thou partest nat so lightly, by Seint John!
Thou spak right now of thilke traytour Deeth,
That in this contree alle oure freendes sleeth;
Have here my trouthe, as thou art his espye, *755*
Telle wher he is, or thou shalt it abye,
By God and by the holy sacrament!
For soothly thou art oon of his assent
To sleen us yonge folk, thou false theef!"
"Now sires," quod he, "if that ye be so leef *760*
To fynde Deeth, turne up this croked wey,
For in that grove I lafte hym, by my fey,
Under a tree, and ther he wol abyde;
Nat for youre boost he wol hym no thyng hyde.
Se ye that ook? Right ther ye shal hym fynde. *765*
God save yow, that boghte agayn mankynde,
And yow amende." Thus seyde this olde man.
And everich of thise riotoures ran
Til he cam to that tree, and ther they founde
Of floryns fyne of gold ycoyned rounde *770*
Wel ny an eighte busshels, as hem thoughte.
Ne lenger thanne after Deeth they soughte,
But ech of hem so glad was of the sighte,
For that the floryns been so faire and brighte,
That doun they sette hem by this precious hoord. *775*
The worste of hem he spak the firste word:
"Bretheren," quod he, "taak kepe what that I seye;
My wit is greet, though that I bourde and pleye.
This tresor hath Fortune unto us yiven,

752 *partest:* i.e, you part from us; *lightly:* easily.
753 *spak:* spoke; *thilke:* this.

755 *trouthe:* promise; *espye:* spy.
756 *abye:* pay for.

758 *oon:* one; *of his assent:* in agreement or conspiracy with him.

760 *leef:* anxious.

762 *lafte:* left; *by my fey:* by my faith.
763 *abyde:* stay, wait.
764 *for . . . boost:* on account of your boasting; *no thyng:* not at all.
765 *ook:* oak.
766 *boghte agayn:* redeemed.
767 *yow amende:* (may God) improve you.
768 *everich:* each.

770 *floryn:* a coin; *fyne of gold:* of fine, or pure, gold.
771 *ny:* nigh; *an eighte:* eight; *as hem thoughte:* as it seemed to them.
772 *ne lenger:* no longer.

774 *been:* were.
775 *hoord:* hoard.
776 *spak:* spoke.
777 *taak kepe:* take notice of.
778 *greet:* great; *bourde:* jest.

In myrthe and jolitee oure lyf to lyven, *780*
And lightly as it comth, so wol we spende.
Ey! Goddes precious dignitee! who wende
Today that we sholde han so fair a grace?
But myghte this gold be caried fro this place
Hoom to myn hous—or elles unto youres— *785*
For wel ye woot that al this gold is oures—
Thanne were we in heigh felicitee.
But trewely, by daye it may nat be;
Men wolde seyn that we were theves stronge,
And for oure owene tresor doon us honge. *790*
This tresor moste ycaried be by nyghte,
As wisely and as slyly as it myghte.
Wherfore I rede that cut among us alle
Be drawe, and lat se wher the cut wol falle;
And he that hath the cut with herte blithe *795*
Shal renne to the town, and that ful swithe,
And brynge us breed and wyn ful pryvely.
And two of us shal kepen subtilly
This tresor wel; and if he wol nat tarie,
Whan it is nyght we wol this tresor carie *800*
By oon assent wher as us thynketh best."
That oon of hem the cut broghte in his fest
And bad hem drawe and looke wher it wol falle;
And it fil on the yongeste of hem alle,
And forth toward the toun he wente anon. *805*
And also soone as that he was agon,
That oon of hem spak thus unto that oother:
"Thow knowest wel thow art my sworen brother;
Thy profit wol I telle thee anon:

780 *to lyven:* i.e., so that we may live.
781 *lightly:* easily, i.e., easy come, easy go.
782 *wende:* would have thought.
783 *grace:* favor, fortune.
784 *but myghte:* if (the gold) only could; *fro:* from.

786 *woot:* know.
787 *were we:* would we be; *heigh felicitee:* high felicity.

789 *seyn:* say; *theves stronge:* great thieves.
790 *doon us honge:* have us hanged.
791 *moste ycaried be:* must be carried.
792 *as it myghte:* as possible.
793 *rede:* suggest; *cut:* a cut, i.e., a drawing of lots.
794 *drawe:* drawn; *lat se:* let's see; *the cut . . . falle:* i.e., who will draw the short straw.
795 *blithe:* happy.
796 *renne:* run; *swithe:* quickly.
797 *pryvely:* secretly.
798 *kepen:* guard; *subtilly:* carefully.
799 *tarie:* tarry.

801 *by oon assent:* by common consent; *us thynketh:* it seems to us.
802 *that oon:* one; *fest:* fist.
803 *bad:* bade; *looke:* see.

806 *also:* just as; *agon:* gone.

809 *profit:* advantage.

Thou woost wel that oure felawe is agon, *810*
And heere is gold, and that ſul greet plentee,
That shal departed been among us thre.
But nathelees, if I kan shape it so
That it departed were among us two,
Hadde I nat doon a freendes torn to thee?" *815*
  That oother answerde, "I noot how that mey be.
He woot wel that the gold is with us tweye.
What shal we doon? What shal we to hym seye?"
  "Shal it be conseil?" seyde the firste shrewe,
"And I shal tellen in a wordes fewe *820*
What we shal doon, and brynge it wel aboute."
  "I graunte," quod that oother, "out of doute,
That, by my trouthe, I wol thee nat biwreye."
  "Now," quod the firste, "thou woost wel we be tweye,
And two of us shul strenger be than oon. *825*
Looke whan that he is set, that right anoon
Arys as though thou woldest with hym pleye,
And I shal ryve hym thurgh the sydes tweye
Whil that thou strogelest with hym as in game,
And with thy daggere looke thou do the same; *830*
And thanne shal al this gold departed be,
My deere freend, bitwixen me and thee.
Thanne may we bothe oure lustes al fulfille,
And pleye at dees right at oure owene wille."
And thus acorded been thise shrewes tweye *835*
To sleen the thridde, as ye han herd me seye.
  This yongeste, which that wente to the toun,
Ful ofte in herte he rolleth up and doun
The beautee of thise floryns newe and brighte.

810 *woost:* know.

812 *departed been:* be divided.
813 *nathelees:* nevertheless; *shape:* arrange.

815 *doon . . . torn:* done a friendly deed.
816 *noot:* know not.
817 *woot:* knows; *tweye:* two.

819 *conseil:* a secret; *shrewe:* scoundrel.

821 *wel:* successfully.
822 *graunte:* agree; *out of doute:* certainly.
823 *biwreye:* betray.
824 *woost:* know.

825 *shul:* must; *strenger:* stronger.
826 *looke:* see to it that; *set:* seated; *right anoon:* suddenly.
827 *arys:* (you) get up; *pleye:* wrestle in sport.
828 *ryve:* stab; *tweye:* two.

831 *departed:* divided.

833 *lustes:* desires.
834 *dees:* dice; *right . . . wille:* just as we please.

835 *acorded:* agreed.
836 *thridde:* third; *herd:* heard.

838 *herte:* mind.

"O Lord!" quod he, "if so were that I myghte *840*
Have al this tresor to myself allone,
Ther is no man that lyveth under the trone
Of God that sholde lyve so murye as I!"
And atte laste the feend, oure enemy,
Putte in his thought that he sholde poyson beye, *845*
With which he myghte sleen his felawes tweye;
Forwhy the feend foond hym in swich lyvynge
That he hadde leve hym to sorwe brynge;
For this was outrely his ful entente,
To sleen hem bothe, and nevere to repente. *850*
And forth he gooth—no lenger wolde he tarie—
Into the toun unto a pothecarie,
And preyed hym that he hym wolde selle
Som poyson that he myghte his rattes quelle;
And eek ther was a polcat in his hawe *855*
That, as he seyde, his capons hadde yslawe,
And fayn he wolde wreke hym if he myghte
On vermyn that destroyed hym by nyghte.
The pothecarie answerde, "And thou shalt have
A thyng that, also God my soule save, *860*
In al this world ther is no creature,
That ete or dronke hath of this confiture
Nat but the montance of a corn of whete,
That he ne shal his lif anon forlete;
Ye, sterve he shal, and that in lasse while *865*
That thou wolt goon a paas nat but a mile,
The poysoun is so strong and violent."
This cursed man hath in his hond yhent
This poyson in a box, and sith he ran

840 *so were:* it were so.

842 *trone:* throne.
843 *murye:* merry.
844 *feend:* fiend, the Devil.

845 *beye:* buy.
847 *forwhy:* because; *foond:* found; *in . . . lyvynge:* living in such (a sinful) manner, i.e., because he had the sin of avarice in his heart the Devil was free to tempt him to murder.
848 *he:* the Devil; *leve:* permission (from God); *hym:* the youngest; *sorwe:* sorrow.
849 *outrely:* plainly.

851 *tarie:* tarry.
852 *pothecarie:* apothecary, pharmacist.
853 *preyed:* asked.
854 *quelle:* kill.
855 *hawe:* yard.
856 *yslawe:* slain.
857 *fayn:* gladly; *wreke hym:* avenge himself.
858 *destroyed:* harassed.

860 *also . . . save:* as God may save my soul.

862 *dronke:* drunk; *confiture:* mixture.
863 *montance of:* amount equal to; *corn:* grain.
864 *ne shal:* shall not; *forlete:* lose.

865 *sterve:* die; *lasse:* less.
866 *goon a paas:* walk; *nat but:* not more than.

868 *yhent:* taken.
869 *sith:* afterward.

Into the nexte strete unto a man, *870*
And borwed of hym large botels thre,
And in the two his poyson poured he;
The thridde he kepte clene for his drynke,
For al the nyght he shoop hym for to swynke
In cariyng of the gold out of that place. *875*
And whan this riotour, with sory grace,
Hadde filled with wyn his grete botels thre,
To hise felawes agayn repaireth he.

What nedeth it to sermone of it moore?
For right as they hadde cast his deeth bifore, *880*
Right so they han hym slayn, and that anon.
And whan that this was doon, thus spak that oon:
"Now lat us sitte and drynke and make us merye,
And afterward we wol his body berye."
And with that word it happed hym, par cas, *885*
To take the botel ther the poyson was,
And drank, and yaf his felawe drynke also,
For which anon they storven bothe two.

But certes I suppose that Avycen
Wroot nevere in no canon ne in no fen *890*
Mo wonder signes of empoisonyng
Than hadde thise wrecches two er hir endyng.
Thus ended been thise homicides two,
And eek the false empoysonere also.

O cursed synne of alle cursednesse! *895*
O traytours homicide! O wikkednesse!
O glotonye, luxurie, and hasardrye!
Thou blasphemour of Crist with vileynye
And othes grete of usage and of pride!

871 *borwed:* borrowed; *botels:* bottles.

873 *clene:* i.e., free of the poison.
874 *shoop hym:* planned; *swynke:* work.

876 *with sory grace:* bad luck to him.

878 *repaireth:* returns.
879 *what . . . sermone:* what is the need of preaching.

880 *cast:* planned.
881 *han:* have.
882 *that oon:* one of them.

884 *berye:* bury.

885 *happed:* befell; *par cas:* by chance.
886 *ther:* wherc, in which.
887 *yaf:* gave.
888 *storven:* died.
889-90 The famous Arab physician, Avicenna, divided his treatise, *The Canon in Medicine,* into chapters called "fens."

891 *wonder:* wonderful; *signes:* symptoms.
892 *er hir ondyng:* before their death.

895 Most cursed of all sins.
896 *traytours:* treacherous.
897 *luxurie:* lechery; *hasardrye:* gambling.
898 *with vileynye:* with low language.
899 *of usage:* from habit.

Allas, mankynde, how may it bitide *900*
That to thy Creatour, which that thee wroghte,
And with his precious herte blood thee boghte,
Thou art so fals and so unkynde, allas?
Now goode men, God foryeve yow youre trespas,
And ware yow fro the synne of avarice. *905*
Myn holy pardon may yow alle warice.
So that ye offre nobles or sterlynges,
Or elles silver broches, spoones, rynges.
Boweth youre heed under this holy bulle!
Cometh up, ye wyves, offreth of youre wolle! *910*
Youre names I entre here in my rolle anon;
Into the blisse of hevene shul ye gon.
I yow assoille, by myn heigh power—
Yow that wol offre—as clene and eek as cleer
As ye were born.—And lo, sires, thus I preche. *915*
And Jesu Crist that is oure soules leche
So graunte yow his pardon to receyve,
For that is best; I wol yow nat deceyve.
"But sires, o word forgat I in my tale:
I have relikes and pardon in my male *920*
As faire as any man in Engelond,
Whiche were me yeven by the Popes hond.
If any of yow wol, of devocion,
Offren and han myn absolucion,
Com forth anon, and kneleth here adoun, *925*
And mekely receyveth my pardoun;
Or elles taketh pardon as ye wende,
Al newe and fressh at every miles ende—
So that ye offren alwey newe and newe

900 *bitide:* happen.
901 *which:* who; *wroghte:* made.
902 *boghte:* redeemed.
903 *unkynde:* unnatural.
904 *foryeve:* forgive; *trespas:* faults.

905 *ware:* guard.
906 *pardon:* indulgence; *may:* can; *warice:* save.
907 *so that:* provided that; *nobles, sterlynges:* valuable coins.

910 *wolle:* wool.
911 *rolle:* list of names.
912 *shul ye gon:* shall you go.
913 *assoille:* absolve.
914 Those of you who will give money; *cleer:* clear (of sin).

915 Here the Pardoner, ending his sermon, addresses the pilgrims directly.
916 *leche:* physician.
917 *so . . . yow:* grant it that you may.

919 *o word:* one word.
920 *male:* bag.
921 *faire:* good.
922 *yeven:* given; *hond:* hand.
923 *of:* out of.
924 *offren:* i.e., will offer; *han:* i.e. will have.

927 *wende:* go, i.e., on horseback.

929 *newe and newe:* again and again, i.e., for each pardon.

Nobles or pens whiche that be goode and trewe. *930*
It is an honour to everich that is heer
That ye mowe have a suffisant pardoner
T'assoille yow in contree as ye ryde,
For aventures whiche that may bityde.
Paraventure ther may falle oon or two *935*
Doun of his hors and breke his nekke atwo.
Looke which a seuretee is it to yow alle
That I am in youre felaweship yfalle,
That may assoille yow, bothe moore and lasse,
Whan that the soule shal fro the body passe. *940*
I rede that oure Hoost heere shal bigynne,
For he is moost envoluped in synne.
Com forth, sire Hoost, and offre first anon,
And thou shalt kisse the relikes everychon,
Ye, for a grote! unbokele anon thy purs." *945*
"Nay, Nay," quod he, "thanne have I Cristes curs!
Lat be," quod he, "it shal nat be, so theech!
Thow woldest make me kisse thyn olde breech
And swere it were a relyk of a seint,
Though it were with thy fundement depeint! *950*
But, by the croys which that seint Eleyne fond,
I wolde I hadde thy coillons in myn hond
In stede of relikes or of seintuarie.
Lat kutte hem of, I wol thee helpe hem carie;
They shul be shryned in an hogges toord!" *955*
This Pardoner answerde nat a word;
So wrooth he was, no word ne wolde he seye.
"Now," quod oure Hoost, "I wol no lenger pleye
With thee, ne with noon oother angry man."

930 *goode and trewe:* i.e., not counterfeit.
931 *everich:* each one; *heer:* here.
932 *mowe:* may; *suffisant:* competent.
933 *assoille:* l. 913.
934 *for:* in case of; *aventures:* accidents; *bityde:* happen.

935 *paraventure:* by chance.

937 *which:* what; *seuretee:* safeguard.
938 *yfalle:* fallen.
939 *moore and lasse:* high and low.

941 *rede:* suggest.
942 *envoluped:* enveloped.

944 *everychon:* everyone.

945 *ye:* yea; *grote:* groat, a coin worth fourpence; *unbokele:* unbuckle.
946 *thanne have I:* then may I have.
947 *lat be:* stop; *so theech:* as I may thrive.
948 *woldest:* would; *breech:* breeches.

950 *fundement:* excrement; *depeint:* smeared.
951 *croys:* cross; *Eleyne:* St. Helen, mother of the emperor Constantine, believed to have been the finder of the true cross.
952 *wolde:* wish; *coillons:* testicles.
953 *seintuarie:* holy objects.
954 *lat kutte hem of:* let them be cut off; *helpe hem carie:* help carry them.
955 *shryned:* enshrined; *toord:* piece of dung.

957 *wrooth:* angry.

But right anon the worthy Knyght bigan, 960
Whan that he saugh that al the peple lough,
"Namoore of this, for it is right ynough!
Sire Pardoner, be glad and murye of cheere;
And ye, sir Hoost, that been to me so deere,
I pray yow that ye kisse the Pardoner. 965
And Pardoner, I pray thee, draw thee neer,
And as we diden lat us laughe and pleye."
Anon they kiste and ryden forth hir weye.

Heere is ended the Pardoners Tale.

961 *saugh:* saw; *lough:* laughed.
962 *ynough:* enough.
963 *cheere:* face.

967 *diden:* did (before).

FRAGMENT VII

Fragment VII opens with the *Shipman's Tale,* another rather ribald fabliau, followed by the *Prioress's Tale.* The link at the end of the *Shipman's Tale* shows the Host in an interesting and characteristic performance.

Bihoold the murie wordes of the Host to the Shipman and to the lady Prioresse.

"Wel seyd, by corpus dominus," quod oure Host, *435*
"Now longe moote thou saille by the cost,
Sire gentil maister, gentil maryneer!
God yeve the monk a thousand last quade yeer.
A ha, felawes! Beth ware of swich a jape!
The monk putte in the mannes hood an ape, *440*
And in his wyves eek, by Seint Austyn!
Draweth no monkes moore unto youre in.
But now passe over, and lat us seke aboute,
Who shal now telle first of al this route
Another tale." And with that word he sayde *445*
As curteisly as it had been a mayde,
"My lady Prioresse, by youre leve,
So that I wiste I sholde yow nat greve,
I wolde demen that ye tellen sholde
A tale next, if so were that ye wolde. *450*
Now wol ye vouche sauf, my lady deere?"
"Gladly," quod she, and seyde as ye shal heere.

A four-stanza invocation to the Virgin spoken by the Prioress before the opening of her tale is omitted.

435 *corpus dominus:* an error for "Corpus Domini," the body of God.

436 *moote:* may; *cost:* coast.

438 *yeve:* give; *last:* cartloads; *quade yeer:* of bad years.

439 *beth ware:* beware; *jape:* trick, i.e., the trick played on the man and his wife by the monk in the *Shipman's Tale.*

440 *putte . . . ape:* to put an ape in one's hood is to make a fool of him.

442 *draweth:* bring; *in:* dwelling.

443 *passe over:* i.e., let it pass; *seke:* seek, look.

444 *route:* company.

446 *as it:* as if he.

447 *leve:* leave, permission.

448 *so that I wiste:* if I knew; *greve:* offend.

449 *demen:* decree, make it my ruling.

450 *if so were:* if it were so; *wolde:* wished (it).

451 *vouche sauf:* vouchsafe, grant it.

THE PRIORESS'S TALE

This tale, a legend of the type known as the "miracle of the Virgin," is again an example of the perfection of form and tone which Chaucer could give to popular materials. In style and language it is uniformly suited to the character of the teller. The gentle piety, the "conscience and tendre herte," of the Prioress are consistently reflected in such touches as the allusion to the infant St. Nicholas, the generous use of pious figures such as "gemme of chastitee," the sentimental insistence upon the "*litel* clergeoun" with his "*litel* body sweete."

The ironic contrast between this gentle tone and the savage execution of the Jews by torture and by drawing with wild horses is more apparent to modern than to medieval eyes. Though Jews had been virtually unknown in England since their expulsion in 1290, the traditional notions of their evil genius were still very much alive and received continual reinforcement from the continent, where persecution was at a high point.

Persecution of the Jews in Europe, while far from unknown earlier, had begun to rise in frequency and intensity in the twelfth century. It was given impetus by the decrees of the Third Lateran Council renewing the Church's prohibitions upon usury and association, the result of which was to encourage the official establishment of ghettos and increase the tendency to limit banking to Jewish hands (usually to the profit of the local ruler, who levied very heavy assessments upon the moneylenders, cf. ll. 490-91). Christian hatred of infidels, stimulated by the Crusades, was also an important factor in the increasing persecution, as the first act of the Crusaders before setting out for the Holy Land was usually to exterminate the unbelievers in their midst. Thus in England on the occasion of the coronation of Richard I in 1189 at the opening of the Third Crusade, the London Jewry was sacked and many of the residents killed.

Together with and stimulated by these events there appeared also a great increase in the number of tales of Jewish atrocities.

Circumstantial accounts of the poisoning of wells and of various secret murders of Christians by Jews were common, and in 1348 it was widely believed throughout Europe that the Jews were responsible for the plague. The "ritual murder," the legend of the sacrifice of Christian children in celebration of Passover, was one of the commoner of these recurring reports. The story of Hugh of Lincoln, alluded to in ll. 684ff., is typcial. It is recorded in a contemporary thirteenth-century chronicle that the Jews of Lincoln had seized an eight-year-old Christian boy, Hugh, crucified him, and used parts of his body in magical rites. Finding the body in a pit, the authorities extracted a confession from a local Jew, whereupon he, together with eighteen of the richest Jews of the city, was drawn and hanged and their property seized.

Not all men in this period, however, viewed this savage violence with sympathy. From the time of Pope Gregory the Great, the Papacy, concurrently with its severe restrictions on Jewish activities, had consistently reiterated its official disapproval of violence and its tolerance of the Jewish communities. Most specifically relevant to the problem of the *Prioress's Tale* is a series of bulls beginning with that of Innocent IV in 1247 on the subject of the increasingly numerous charges of ritual murder. In a bull of 1272, Pope Gregory X, after discussing the ritual murder charges at length, writes, "We decree, therefore, . . . that Jews seized under such a silly pretext be freed from imprisonment, and that they shall not be arrested henceforth on such a miserable pretext, unless — which we do not believe — they be caught in the commission of the crime."

It is in the light of this conflict between a very widespread climate of persecution and a more humane, though very imperfectly observed, official policy that the *Prioress's Tale* should be read. When her choice of a tale containing these elements of savagery is contrasted with her tender solicitude for dogs and for little mice, it would appear that we are presented with another of the ironies in which her portrait is so rich. And like these other ironies, it is produced by the dramatic inconsistency between the perfection of her expression of gentle piety and tenderness of heart and her failure to grasp the profounder principles appropriate to a Christian religious.

Heere bigynneth the Prioresses Tale.

Ther was in Asye, in a greet citee,
Amonges Cristen folk a Jewerye,
Sustened by a lord of that contree 490
For foule usure and lucre of vileynye,
Hateful to Crist and to his compaignye;
And thurgh the strete men myghte ride or wende,
For it was free and open at eyther ende.

A litel scole of Cristen folk ther stood 495
Doun at the ferther ende, in which ther were
Children an heepe, ycomen of Cristen blood,
That lerned in that scole yeer by yeer
Swich manere doctrine as men used there,
This is to seyn, to syngen and to rede, 500
As smale children doon in hir childhede.

Among thise children was a wydwes sone,
A litel clergeon, seven yeer of age,
That day by day to scole was his wone,
And eek also, where as he saugh th'ymage 505
Of Cristes moder, hadde he in usage,
As hym was taught, to knele adoun and seye
His *Ave Marie* as he goth by the weye.

Thus hath this wydwe hir litel sone ytaught
Oure blisful Lady, Cristes moder deere, 510
To worshipe ay, and he forgat it naught,
For sely child wol alday soone lere.
But ay, whan I remembre on this matere,
Seint Nicholas stant evere in my presence,
For he so yong to Crist dide reverence. 515

488 *Asye:* Asia.
489 *Jewerye:* ghetto.

490 *sustened:* maintained.
491 *lucre of vileynye:* filthy lucre, wicked profit. Jews were permitted to charge interest on loans (usury), forbidden to Christians by church law; hence, banking was chiefly in the hands of Jews.
492 *compaignye:* followers.
493 *strete:* i.e., the main street of the ghetto; *wende:* walk.

495 *scole:* school.

497 *an heepe:* a great many; *ycomen of:* being of.
498 *yeer by yeer:* year after year.
499 *swich manere:* that kind of; *doctrine:* instruction; *used:* practiced, taught.
500 *rede:* read.
501 *hir:* their; singing of anthems was a regular part of such instruction.
502 *wydwes:* widow's.
503 *clergeon:* diminutive of "clerk," scholar.
504 *to scole:* i.e., to go to school; *wone:* custom.

505 *eek:* also; *also:* in addition; *whereas:* where; *saugh:* saw; *ymage:* figure or representation, e.g., of the Virgin.
506 *moder:* mother; *hadde in usage:* was accustomed.
507 *hym:* to him; *knele:* kneel.
508 *Ave Marie:* "Hail Mary," a Latin prayer to the Virgin; *by the weye:* on his way.

511 *ay:* always; the modern order of words here would be "the widow taught her son to worship Our Lady."
512 *sely:* good; *alday:* always; *soone:* quickly; *lere:* learn.
513 *remembre on:* think about.
514 *stant:* stands, i.e., comes to my mind.
515 It is said that, as an infant, St. Nicholas refrained from suckling on days of abstinence (Fridays and certain Wednesdays) except for one meal in the evening.

This litel child, his litel book lernynge,
As he sat in the scole at his prymer,
He *Alma redemptoris* herde synge,
As children lerned hir antiphoner;
And as he dorste, he drow hym ner and ner, 520
And herkned ay the wordes and the note,
Til he the firste vers koude al by rote.

Noght wiste he what this Latyn was to seye,
For he so yong and tendre was of age,
But on a day his felawe gan he preye 525
T'expounden hym this song in his langage,
Or telle hym why this song was in usage;
This preyde he hym to construe and declare
Ful often tyme upon his knowes bare.

His felawe, which that elder was than he, 530
Answerde hym thus: "This song, I have herd seye,
Was maked of our blisful Lady free,
Hire to salue and eek hire for to preye
To been oure help and socour whan we deye.
I kan namoore expounde in this matere; 535
I lerne song, I kan but smal gramere."

"And is this song maked in reverence
Of Cristes moder?" seyde this innocent.
"Now, certes, I wol do my diligence
To konne it al er Cristemasse be went. 540
Though that I for my prymer shal be shent,
And shal be beten thries in an houre,
I wol it konne, Oure Lady for to honoure!"

His felawe taughte hym homward privély,
Fro day to day, til he koude it by rote, 545

516 *lernynge:* learning, i.e., while studying.
517 *prymer:* a prayer book used as a first reader in school.
518 *Alma redemptoris (mater):* "gracious mother of the Redeemer," the first words of an antiphon in the breviary.
519 *antiphoner:* book of anthems, also sometimes studied in school.
520 *dorste:* dared; *drow hym ner:* drew nearer.
521 *herkned:* listened; *ay:* ever, i.e., closely; *note:* notes.
522 *koude:* knew; *by rote:* by heart.
523 *noghte . . . he:* he knew not; *was to seye:* i.e., meant.

525 *on a day:* one day; *felawe:* friend; *gan preye:* did beg.
526 *expounden:* explain; *in his langage:* i.e., in English.
527 *in usage:* being practiced at this time; the antiphon was sung from Advent Eve to Candlemas Day.
528 *construe:* explain.
529 *knowes:* knees.

530 *which:* who.

532 *of:* i.e., in honor of; *free:* bountiful.
533 *salue:* greet.
534 *socour:* succor; *deye:* die.

536 *kan:* know; *smal:* little; *gramere:* grammar (of Latin).
537 *maked:* made.

539 *certes:* certainly; *do my diligence:* work diligently.

540 *konne:* learn; *er:* before; *be went:* is passed.
541 *for my prymer:* i.e., for not knowing my primer; *shent:* punished.
542 *beten:* beaten; *thries:* thrice.

544 *homward:* on the way home; *prively:* secretly.
545 *koude:* knew; *by rote:* by heart.

And thanne he song it wel and boldely,
Fro word to word, acordyng with the note.
Twies a day it passed thurgh his throte,
To scoleward and homward whan he wente;
On Cristes moder set was his entente. 550

As I have seyd, thurghout the Juerie
This litel child, as he cam to and fro,
Ful murily than wolde he synge and crye
O Alma redemptoris everemo.
The swetnesse hath his herte perced so 555
Of Cristes moder that, to hire to preye,
He kan nat stynte of syngyng by the weye.

Oure firste foo, the serpent Sathanas,
That hath in Jewes herte his waspes nest,
Up swal and seide, "O Hebrayk peple, allas! 560
Is this to yow a thyng that is honest,
That swich a boy shal walken as hym lest
In youre despit, and synge of swich sentence
Which is agayn youre lawes reverence?"

Fro thennes forth the Jewes han conspired 565
This innocent out of this world to chace.
An homycide therto han they hyred,
That in an aleye hadde a privee place;
And as the child gan forby for to pace,
This cursed Jew hym hente, and heeld hym faste, 570
And kitte his throte, and in a pit hym caste.

I seye that in a wardrobe they hym threwe,
Where as thise Jewes purgen hir entraille.
O cursed folk of Herodes al newe,
What may youre yvel entente yow availle? 575

547 *acordyng . . . note:* with the right notes.

549 *scoleward:* toward school.

550 *entente:* mind.

553 *murily:* pleasantly.
554 *everemo:* continually.

555 *perced:* pierced.

557 *stynte:* cease.
558 *foo:* foe, enemy.

560 *up swal:* swelled up, i.e., rose up.
561 *honest:* honorable.
562 *swich:* such; *hym lest:* it pleases him.
563 *youre despit:* scorn of you; *sentence:* subject, theme.
564 *agayn:* against; *youre . . . reverence:* respect for your laws.

565 *fro:* from; *thennes forth:* thenceforth; *han:* have.
566 *chace:* drive.
567 *homycide:* murderer; *therto:* also.
568 *aleye:* alley; *privee:* secret, hidden.
569 *gan . . . pace:* did pass by.

570 *hente:* seized.
571 *kitte:* cut.
572 *seye:* say; *wardrobe:* privy.
573 *purgen:* purge; *hir:* their; *entraille:* bowels.
574 *Herodes al newe:* modern Herods (cursed now as they were cursed before for the crimes of Herod and his descendants, see Matthew 2:16, 14:10, Luke 23:11, Acts 12:2).
575 *yvel:* evil; *entente:* purpose; *availle:* avail.

Mordre wol out, certeyn, it wol nat faille,
And namely ther th'onour of God shal sprede;
The blood out crieth on youre cursed dede.

O martir, sowded to virginitee,
Now maystow syngen, folwyng evere in oon 580
The white Lamb celestial—quod she—
Of which the grete evangelist, Seint John,
In Pathmos wroot, which seith that they that gon
Biforn this Lamb and synge a song al newe,
That nevere, fleshly, wommen they ne knewe. 585

This povre wydwe awaiteth al that nyght
After hir litel child, but he cam noght;
For which, as soone as it was dayes lyght,
With face pale of drede and bisy thoght,
She hath at scole and elleswhere hym soght, 590
Til finally she gan so fer espie
That he last seyn was in the Jewerie.

With modres pitee in hir brest enclosed,
She goth, as she were half out of hir mynde,
To every place where she hath supposed 595
By liklihede hir litel child to fynde;
And evere on Cristes moder meeke and kynde
She cryde, and at the laste thus she wroghte,
Among the cursed Jewes she hym soghte.

She frayneth and she preyeth pitously 600
To every Jew that dwelte in thilke place,
To telle hire if hir child wente oght forby.
They seyde "nay," but Jhesu of his grace
Yaf in hir thoght, inwith a litel space,

576 *mordre:* murder; *faille:* fail.
577 *namely:* especially; *ther:* where; *onour:* honor; *sprede:* be magnified.

579 *sowded:* confirmed, dedicated.
580 *maystow:* may you; *evere in oon:* always.
581 see Revelation 14:3-4, "And they sung . . . a new song before the throne, . . . and no man could learn that song but [those] which were redeemed from the earth. These are they which were not defiled with women; for they are virgins. These are they which follow the Lamb whithersoever he goeth."
583 *Pathmos:* Patmos, where John wrote Revelation; *which:* i.e., John; *gon:* walk.
585 *fleshly:* carnally.
586 *povre:* poor; *awaiteth:* watches, waits.

589 *of drede:* from fear; *bisy:* anxious.

591 *gan espie:* did learn; *so fer:* thus much.
592 *seyn:* seen.

594 *goth:* goes; *as:* as if.

596 *liklihede:* likelihood.

598 *cryde:* called, prayed; *wroghte:* did.

600 *frayneth:* asks, begs.
601 *thilke:* that.
602 *wente forby:* had passed by; *oght:* at all.

604 *yaf:* gave, put; *thoght:* i.e., mind; *inwith:* within; *space:* time.

That in that place after hir sone she cryde 605
Where he was casten in a pit bisyde.

O grete God, that parfournest thy laude
By mouth of innocentz, lo, heere thy myght!
This gemme of chastitee, this emeraude,
And eek of martirdom the ruby bright, 610
Ther he with throte ykorven lay upright,
He *Alma redemptoris* gan to synge
So loude that al the place gan to rynge.

The Cristen folk that thurgh the strete wente
In coomen for to wondre upon this thyng, 615
And hastily they for the provost sente;
He cam anon withouten tariyng,
And herieth Crist that is of hevene kyng,
And eek his moder, honour of mankynde,
And after that the Jewes leet he bynde. 620

This child with pitous lamentacion
Up taken was, syngynge his song alway,
And with honour of greet procession
They carien hym unto the nexte abbay.
His moder swownyng by the beere lay; 625
Unnethe myghte the peple that was there
This newe Rachel bryngen fro his beere.

With torment and with shameful deeth echon
This provost dooth thise Jewes for to sterve
That of this mordre wiste, and that anon. 630
He nolde no swich cursednesse observe.
"Yvel shal have that yvel wol deserve";
Therfore with wilde hors he dide hem drawe,
And after that he heng hem by the lawe.

605 *that:* so that; *after hir sone:* for her son; *cryde:* called.
606 *where:* i.e., that place where; *bisyde:* nearby.
607 *parfournest:* dost celebrate; *laude:* praise.
608 *by:* through; *heere:* here (is an instance of).
609 *emeraude:* emerald.

610 *eek:* also.
611 *ther:* where; *ykorven:* cut; *upright:* supine.
612 *gan:* began.

615 *coomen:* came.
616 *provost:* chief magistrate.
617 *anon:* at once; *tariyng:* delaying.
618 *herieth:* praises.

620 *leet he bynde:* he caused to be bound, i.e., he had them tied up or put in chains.
622 *alway:* all the while.

624 *carien:* carry; *nexte:* nearest.

625 *swownyng:* swooning; *beere:* bier.
626 *unnethe:* hardly.
627 see Jeremiah 31:15 for Rachel, wife of Jacob, weeping for her children. Matthew 2:18 alludes to this as prophetic of the lamentation of the mothers whose children were slain by Herod; *bryngen fro:* lead away from.
628 *torment:* torture; *echon:* to each one.
629 *dooth:* causes; *sterve:* die.
630 *wiste:* knew.
631 *nolde:* would not; *swich:* such; *observe:* tolerate.
632 *yvel . . . have:* he shall have evil; *that:* who.
633 *hors:* horses; *dide . . . drawe:* caused them to be drawn (probably, to be dragged to death).
634 *heng:* hanged.

Upon this beere ay lith this innocent *635*
Biforn the chief auter, whil masse laste;
And after that the abbot with his covent
Han sped hem for to burien hym ful faste;
And whan they holy water on hym caste,
Yet spak this child, whan spreynd was holy water, *640*
And song *O Alma redemptoris mater!*

This abbot, which that was an holy man,
As monkes been, or elles oghten be,
This yonge child to conjure he bigan,
And seyde, "O deere child, I halse thee, *645*
In vertu of the holy Trinitee,
Tel me what is thy cause for to synge,
Sith that thy throte is kut to my semynge?"

"My throte is kut unto my nekke boon,"
Seyde this child, "and, as by wey of kynde, *650*
I sholde have dyed, ye, longe tyme agon.
But Jhesu Crist, as ye in bookes fynde,
Wil that his glorie laste and be in mynde,
And for the worship of his Moder deere
Yet may I synge *O Alma* loude and cleere. *655*

"This welle of mercy, Cristes moder sweete,
I loved alwey, as after my konnynge;
And whan that I my lyf sholde forlete,
To me she cam, and bad me for to synge
This antheme, verraily, in my deiynge, *660*
As ye han herd, and whan that I had songe,
Me thoughte she leyde a greyn upon my tonge.

"Wherfore I synge, and synge moot, certeyn,
In honour of that blisful Mayden free,

635 *ay:* all the while; *lith:* lies.
636 *auter:* altar (a place of honor); *laste:* lasted.
637 *covent:* convent, i.e., the other monks.
638 *han sped hem:* hastened.

640 *yet:* still; *spreynd:* sprinkled.

643 *oghten be:* ought to be, probably in allusion to the distinctly unholy monk of the immediately preceding *Shipman's Tale.*
644 *conjure:* to call upon in the name of a divinity.

645 *halse:* beseech.
646 *in vertu of:* by the power of.

648 *sith that:* since; *to my semynge:* as it appears to me.

650 *kynde:* nature.
651 *ye:* yea; *agon:* ago.

653 *wil:* desires; *laste:* should last; *mynde:* memory.

655 *may:* can.

657 *after:* according to; *konnynge:* ability.
658 *sholde forlete:* was to give up.
659 *bad:* commanded.

660 *verraily:* truly; *in my deiynge:* as I was dying.
661 *songe:* sung.
662 *me thoughte:* it seemed to me; *greyn:* grain, seed, or perhaps a prayer bead or a pearl (regarded as a symbol of the Virgin); both of the latter are early senses of the word.
663 *synge moot:* must sing; *certeyn:* certainly.
664 *free:* bountiful.

Til fro my tonge of taken is the greyn; *665*
And after that thus seyde she to me:
'My litel child, now wol I fecche thee
Whan that the greyn is fro thy tonge ytake.
Be nat agast, I wol thee nat forsake.' "

This holy monk, this abbot, hym meene I, *670*
His tonge out caughte and took awey the greyn,
And he yaf up the goost ful softely.
And whan this abbot hadde this wonder seyn,
His salte teeris trikled doun as reyn,
And gruf he fil al plat upon the grounde, *675*
And stille he lay as he had ben ybounde.

The covent eek lay on the pavement,
Wepynge, and herying Cristes moder deere,
And after that they ryse, and forth been went,
And toke awey this martir from his beere; *680*
And in a tombe of marbul stones cleere
Enclosen they his litel body sweete.
Ther he is now, God leve us for to meete!

O yonge Hugh of Lyncoln, slayn also
With cursed Jewes, as it is notable, *685*
For it is but a litel while ago,
Preye eek for us, we synful folk unstable,
That of his mercy God so merciable
On us his grete mercy multiplie,
For reverence of his moder Marie. *690*

Amen

Heere is ended the Prioresses Tale.

665 *of:* off.

667 *wol:* will; *fecche:* fetch, i.e., to Heaven.
668 *ytake:* taken.
669 *agast:* afraid.

670 *meene:* mean.
671 *out caughte:* pulled out.
672 *yaf:* gave; *goost:* spirit, soul.
673 *seyn:* seen.
674 *teeris:* tears.

675 *gruf:* on his face, groveling; *plat:* flat.
676 *as:* as if; *ybounde:* bound.
677 *covent:* convent; *eek:* also.
678 *herying:* praising.
679 *ryse:* rise; *been went:* have gone.

680 *toke:* took.
681 *cleere:* bright.

683 *ther:* where; *leve:* grant.
684 *Hugh:* see the preface to this tale, p. 257.

685 *with:* by; *notable:* well-known.

687 *unstable:* fickle, weak.
688 *merciable:* merciful.

Following the Prioress in Fragment VII are the two tales told by the pilgrim Chaucer. The first, *Sir Thopas,* is in reality a skillful parody of the popular type of the metrical romance, but its general foolishness as well as its dreadful jingle becomes so painful to the Host that he cuts the narrator off. The docile Chaucer then substitutes the *Tale of Melibee,* a moral tale in prose of a wise wife whose husband profits well by her excellent advice. The Monk is called upon for the next tale and responds with a seemingly endless series of depressing accounts of the fall of men from high place. This series of "tragedies" becomes too much for the Knight, who interrupts. The Host then calls upon one of the three priests accompanying the Prioress.

The Prologe of the Nonnes Preestes Tale

Thanne spak oure Hoost with rude speche and boold,
And seyde unto the Nonnes Preest anon,
"Com neer, thou Preest, com hider, thou sir John! *2810*
Telle us swich thyng as may oure hertes glade.
Be blithe, though thou ryde upon a jade!
What though thyn hors be bothe foul and lene?
If he wol serve thee, rekke nat a bene.
Looke that thyn herte be murye everemo." *2815*
"Yis, sire," quod he, "Yis, Hoost, so mote I go,
But I be murye, ywis, I wol be blamed."
And right anon his tale he hath attamed;
And thus he seyde unto us everichon,
This sweete Preest, this goodly man sire John. *2820*

THE NUN'S PRIEST'S TALE

In the *Nun's Priest's Tale,* Chaucer is using a story drawn from another large body of medieval popular fiction. This is the beast epic, stories of animals who behave like men and whose adventures commonly were used as the basis of satire on human

2808 *spak:* spoke; *rude:* rough.
2809 One of the three (?) priests accompanying the Prioress, see I: 164.
2810 *hider:* hither; *Sir John* is a stock name for a priest.
2811 *swich:* such; *glade:* gladden.
2812 *jade:* nag.
2813 *foul:* wretched; *lene:* lean.
2814 *rekke:* care; *bene:* bean.

2815 *looke:* see to it; *murye:* merry; *everemo:* always.
2816 *yis:* the emphatic form of "yes"; *so . . . go:* as sure as I walk.
2817 *but:* unless; *ywis:* indeed.
2818 *attamed:* broached, begun.
2819 *everichon:* cach one.

weaknesses. Upon this borrowed core of narrative, Chaucer has created what is surely the wittiest of all his tales. It is a mock-epic: it employs the epic manner, all the language and devices appropriate to the highest of persons and subjects — the splendor and the elegant manners of courtly life, the rhetoric and allusion of the world of learning — in the treatment of the lowest of material, the adventures of a barnyard fowl.

The principal source of wit is in the skillful balance that is maintained between this ridiculously inappropriate manner and matter. In the description of the hero and heroine, language and imagery suitable to the most elegant of chivalric lovers are with the greatest adroitness juxtaposed to features unmistakably of the chicken. Unpredictably, from moment to moment, we are now in the world of court or university, now in the barnyard; now Chantecleer, royal as a prince in his hall, calls his wives about him with a "chuk," to share the bounty of some corns of wheat. Colored like fine coral and crenelated like the battlements of a castle is Chantecleer's indubitably galline comb. His paramour, the fair damosel Pertelote, is the finest of courtly ladies, "discreet and debonaire and compaignable"; the beauty of her face is such that her lover's courage is restored by the mere sight of her — she is so scarlet red about her eyes.

This witty balance of incongruities is maintained in every detail throughout the poem. The arguments of the hen are learned and allusive enough to persuade any but the even more learned and allusive cock. The barnyard catastrophe, when it comes, is on the grand scale, to be compared by the poet with the fall of Carthage and the burning of Rome. It is by these additions to his source materials that the poet has transformed them and by which they become Chaucerian.

Heere bigynneth the Nonnes Preestes Tale.

A povre widwe somdeel stape in age *2821*
Was whilom dwellyng in a narwe cotage,
Biside a grove, stonding in a dale.
This widwe of which I telle yow my tale,

2821 *povre:* poor; *widwe:* widow; *somdeel:* somewhat; *stape:* advanced.

2822 *whilom:* once; *narwe:* small.

Syn thilke day that she was last a wyf, 2825
In pacience ladde a ful symple lyf,
For litel was hir catel and hir rente.
By housbondrye of swich as God hire sente
She foond hirself and eek hir doghtren two.
Thre large sowes hadde she, and namo, 2830
Thre kyn, and eek a sheep that highte Malle.
Ful sooty was hire bour and eek hire halle,
In which she eet ful many a sclendre meel.
Of poynaunt sauce hire neded neveradeel;
No deyntee morsel passed thurgh hir throte; 2835
Hir diete was acordant to hir cote.
Repleccion ne made hire nevere sik;
Attempree diete was al hir phisik,
And exercise, and hertes suffisaunce.
The goute lette hire nothyng for to daunce, 2840
N'apoplexie shente nat hir heed.
No wyn ne drank she, neither whit ne reed;
Hir bord was served moost with whit and blak—
Milk and broun breed, in which she foond no lak,
Seynd bacon, and somtyme an ey or tweye, 2845
For she was, as it were, a maner deye.
A yeerd she hadde, enclosed al aboute
With stikkes, and a drye dych withoute,
In which she hadde a cok hight Chauntecleer.
In al the land, of crowyng nas his peer. 2850
His voys was murier than the murie orgon
On massedayes that in the chirche gon.
Wel sikerer was his crowyng in his logge
Than is a clokke or an abbey orlogge;

2825 *syn:* since; *thilke:* that; *last . . .:* i.e., when her husband died.
2826 *pacience:* patience; *ladde:* led.
2827 *litel:* small; *catel:* property; *rente:* income.
2828 *housbondrye:* economy; *swich as:* that which; *hire sente:* sent to her.
2829 *foond:* provided for; *eek:* also; *doghtren:* daughters.

2830 *sowes:* sows; *namo:* no more.
2831 *kyn:* cows; *highte:* was named.
2832 *hire:* her; *bour:* bower, private chamber; *halle:* hall; these are terms appropriate to the living quarters and great hall of a great town or country house. This use of "heroic" language with "low" subjects is characteristic of mock-heroic style.
2833 *sclendre:* slender, scanty; *meel:* meal.
2834 *poynaunt:* pungent, i.e., to sharpen her appetite; *hire neded:* was needful to her; *neveradeel:* not a bit.
2836 *acordant:* in keeping with; *cote:* coat, or (?) cottage, i.e., her diet was simple and poor.
2837 *repleccion:* overeating; *sik:* sick.
2838 *attempree:* moderate; *al . . . phisik:* the only medicine she needed.
2839 *hertes suffisaunce:* contentment of heart.
2840 *goute:* gout, a painful inflammation, especially of the big toe, traditionally associated with rich diet and port wine; *lette:* prevented; *nothyng:* not at all.
2841 *n'apoplexie:* nor apoplexy; *shente:* injured.
2843 *bord:* table.
2844 *foond:* had; *lak:* lack.
2845 *seynd:* broiled; *ey:* egg.
2846 *maner:* sort of; *deye:* dairywoman.
2847 *yeerd:* yard.
2848 *stikkes:* i.e., palings; *dych:* ditch.
2849 *cok:* cock; *hight:* named.
2850 *of:* for; *nas:* there was not; *peer:* equal.
2851 *murier:* pleasanter.
2852 *massedayes:* feast days; *gon:* plays.
2853 *wel sikerer:* much more reliable; *logge:* lodge, dwelling.
2854 *orlogge:* timepiece.

By nature he knew ech ascensioun 2855
Of th'equinoxial in thilke toun;
For whan degrees fiftene were ascended,
Thanne crew he that it myghte nat been amended.
His comb was redder than the fyn coral,
And batailled as it were a castel wal; 2860
His byle was blak, and as the jeet it shoon;
Lyk asure were his legges and his toon;
Hise nayles whiter than the lylye flour,
And lyk the burned gold was his colour.
This gentil cok hadde in his governaunce 2865
Sevene hennes for to doon al his plesaunce,
Whiche were his sustres and his paramours,
And wonder lyk to hym as of colours;
Of whiche the faireste hewed on hir throte
Was cleped faire damoysele Pertelote. 2870
Curteys she was, discreet, and debonaire,
And compaignable, and bar hirself so faire,
Sin thilke day that she was seven nyght oold,
That trewely she hath the herte in hoold
Of Chauntecleer, loken in every lith; 2875
He loved hire so that wel was hym therwith.
But swich a joye was it to here hem synge,
Whan that the brighte sonne gan to sprynge,
In sweete accord, "My lief is faren in londe."
For thilke tyme, as I have understonde, 2880
Beestes and briddes koude speke and synge.
And so bifel that in a dawenynge,
As Chauntecleer among his wyves alle
Sat on his perche that was in the halle,

2855-56 *by nature:* i.e., by instinct; the *equinoxial* is a circle bisecting the (ninth) sphere of the heavens in the plane of the earth's equator. This sphere rotates 360 degrees about the earth every twenty-four hours, thus moving through an "ascensioun" of fifteen degrees each hour.

2858 *amended:* improved.

2859 *fyn coral:* fine coral.

2860 *batailled:* crenelated.

2861 *byle:* bill; *jeet:* jet.

2862 *asure:* azure; *toon:* toes.

2864 *burned:* burnished.

2865 *gentil:* having a courtly or noble character; *governaunce:* dominion, control.

2866 *doon . . . plesaunce:* give him all pleasures.

2867 *sustres:* sisters; *paramours:* mistresses.

2868 *wonder lyk:* wonderfully similar; *as of:* in.

2869 *faireste . . .:* the one with the fairest colors on the throat.

2870 *cleped:* called; *damoysele:* lady, mistress.

2871 *curteys:* of courtly manner; *debonaire:* gracious.

2872 *compaignable:* friendly; *bar:* bore.

2873 *sin thilke:* since that; *seven nyght:* a week.

2874 *in hoold:* in (her) possession.

2875 *loken . . . lith:* locked in every limb.

2876 *wel was hym:* it was a joy to him.

2877 *here:* hear; *hem:* them.

2878 *gan:* began; *spryngе:* rise.

2879 *accord:* harmony; *my lief . . .:* my love is gone away.

2880 *thilke tyme:* i.e., at that time.

2881 *briddes:* birds.

2882 *bifel:* it happened; *dawenynge:* dawn.

2884 see l. 2832.

And next hym sat this faire Pertelote, 2885
This Chauntecleer gan gronen in his throte,
As man that in his dreem is drecched soore.
And whan that Pertelote thus herde hym rore,
She was agast, and seyde, "Herte deere,
What eyleth yow to grone in this manere? 2890
Ye been a verray sleper, fy, for shame!"
  And he answerde and seyde thus, "Madame,
I pray yow that ye take it nat agrief.
By God, me mette I was in swich meschief
Right now, that yet myn herte is soore afright. 2895
Now God," quod he, "my swevene recche aright,
And kepe my body out of foul prisoun!
Me mette how that I romed up and down
Withinne oure yeerd, where as I saugh a beest
Was lyk an hound, and wolde han maad areest 2900
Upon my body, and han had me deed.
His colour was bitwixe yelow and reed,
And tipped was his tayl and bothe his erys
With blak, unlik the remenant of his herys;
His snowte smal, with glowyng eyen tweye. 2905
Yet of his look for fere almoost I deye;
This caused me my gronyng, doutelees."
  "Avoy!" quod she, "fy on yow, hertelees!
Allas," quod she, "for, by that God above,
Now han ye lost myn herte and al my love! 2910
I kan nat love a coward, by my feith!
For certes, what so any womman seith,
We alle desiren, if it myghte be,
To han housbondes hardy, wise, and free,

2886 *gan gronen:* began to groan.
2887 *man:* one; *dreem:* dream; *drecched:* troubled.
2888 *rore:* roar.
2889 *agast:* frightened.

2890 *eyleth:* ails.
2891 *verray:* fine; *sleper:* sleeper.

2893 *agrief:* amiss.
2894 *me mette:* I dreamed; *meschief:* trouble.

2895 *right:* just; *afright:* afraid.
2896 *swevene:* dream; *recche:* interpret; *aright:* favorably.

2898 *romed:* roamed.
2899 *where as:* where; *saugh:* saw.

2900 *was:* i.e., that was; *maad areest upon:* seized.
2901 *had:* made.

2904 *unlik . . . remenant:* in contrast to the rest; *herys:* hairs.

2905 *snowte:* snout.
2906 *of his look:* from his appearance; *fere:* fear; *deye:* die.

2908 *avoy:* away! an exclamation of reproach used, e.g., in *Roman de la Rose,* 7284; *fy:* fie; *hertelees:* coward.

2910 *han:* have.

2912 *certes:* certainly; *what so:* whatever.
2913 *desiren:* desire; *if . . . be:* if possible.
2914 *hardy:* bold; *free:* liberal.

And secree, and no nygard, ne no fool, *2915*
Ne hym that is agast of every tool,
Ne noon avauntour. By that God above,
How dorste ye seyn, for shame, unto youre love
That any thyng myghte make yow aferd?
Have ye no mannes herte, and han a berd? *2920*
Allas, and konne ye been agast of swevenys?
No thyng, God woot, but vanitee in sweven is!
Swevenes engendren of replecciones,
And ofte of fume and of complecciones,
Whan humours been to habundant in a wight. *2925*
Certes, this dreem which ye han met tonyght
Comth of the grete superfluytee
Of youre rede colera, pardee,
Which causeth folk to dreden in hir dremes
Of arwes, and of fyr with rede lemes, *2930*
Of rede beestes, that they wol hem byte,
Of contek, and of whelpes grete and lyte;
Right as the humour of malencolie
Causeth ful many a man in sleep to crie
For fere of blake beres, or boles blake, *2935*
Or elles blake develes wol hem take.
Of othere humours koude I telle also
That werken many a man in sleep ful wo,
But I wol passe as lightly as I kan.
Lo, Caton, which that was so wys a man, *2940*
Seyde he nat thus, 'Ne do no fors of dremes'?
Now, sire," quod she, "whan we flee fro the bemes,
For Goddes love, as taak som laxatif.
Up peril of my soule and of my lif,

2915 *secree:* discreet; *nygard:* miser; this catalogue of virtues lists those typically required of the chivalric lover.
2916 *agast:* afraid; *tool:* weapon.
2917 *avauntour:* boaster.
2918 *dorste:* dare; *seyn:* say.
2919 *aferd:* afraid.
2920 *mannes herte:* man's heart; *and han:* though (you) have; *berd:* beard.
2921 *konne:* can; *swevenys:* dreams.
2922 *vanitee:* futility, folly.
2923 *engendren:* are produced by; *repleccions:* overeating.
2924 *fume:* vapors (from the stomach); *compleccions:* i.e., an improper balance of the humors, see 1:420.
2925 *habundant:* abundant; *wight:* person.
2926 *met:* dreamed.
2927 *comth:* comes; *superfluytee:* excess.
2928 *rede colera:* an excess of choler and blood; Pertelote's is an accurate description of the symptoms of choler and melancholy.
2929 *dreden:* be afraid; *hir:* their.
2930 *arwes:* arrows; *lemes:* flames.
2931 *hem:* i.e., the dreamers.
2932 *contek:* strife; *whelpes:* dogs; *lyte:* little.
2933 *right:* just.

2935 *blake:* black; *beres:* bears; *boles:* bulls.
2936 *elles:* else that.

2938 *werken:* cause; *ful wo:* much woe.
2939 *passe:* pass over; *lightly:* quickly.

2940 *Caton:* Dionysius Cato, the supposed author of a book of maxims used in the grammar schools.
2941 *ne . . . of:* pay no attention to.
2942 *flee:* fly; *bemes:* rafters.
2943 *as* is an intensive in imperative sentences, equal to "please."
2944 *up:* upon.

I conseille yow the beste, I wol nat lye, *2945*
That bothe of colere and of malencolye
Ye purge yow; and for ye shal nat tarye,
Though in this toun is noon apothecarye,
I shal myself to herbes techen yow
That shul been for youre hele and for youre prow; *2950*
And in oure yeerd tho herbes shal I fynde,
The whiche han of hire propretee by kynde
To purge yow bynethe and eek above.
Foryet nat this, for Goddes owene love.
Ye been ful colerik of complexion; *2955*
Ware the sonne in his ascension
Ne fynde yow nat repleet of humours hote;
And if it do, I dar wel leye a grote
That ye shul have a fevere terciane,
Or an agu that may be youre bane. *2960*
A day or two ye shul have digestyves
Of wormes, er ye take youre laxatyves
Of lauriol, centaure, and fumetere,
Or elles of ellebor that groweth there,
Of katapuce, or of gaitrys beryis, *2965*
Of herbe yve growyng in oure yerd ther merye is.
Pekke hem up right as they growe and ete hem in.
Be myrie, housbonde, for youre fader kyn!
Dredeth no dreem; I kan sey yow namoore."
"Madame," quod he, "graunt mercy of youre loore. *2970*
But nathelees, as touchyng daun Catoun,
That hath of wisdom swich a greet renoun,
Though that he bad no dremes for to drede,
By God, men may in olde bookes rede

2947 *ye purge yow:* (I counsel that) you purge yourself; *for:* so that; *tarye:* be delayed.
2948 *is noon:* there is no.
2949 *to . . . yow:* teach or show you some herbs.
2950 *for:* i.e., good for; *hele:* health; *prow:* benefit.
2951 *tho:* those.
2952 *the whiche:* which; *of hire propretee:* the special property; *by kynde:* by their nature.
2953 *bynethe:* below.
2954 *foryet:* forget.

2956 *ware:* beware (that the sun does not find you); *ascencion:* l. 2855.
2957 *repleet:* full; *hote:* hot.
2958 *leye:* bet; *grote:* a coin.
2959 *fevere terciane:* a kind of fever that recurs every other day.
2960 *agu:* ague; *bane:* death.
2961 *a day:* i.e., for a day; *digestyves:* medicines for absorbing choler or a melancholy.
2962 *wormes:* worms were recommended in the treatment of fevers, but of course they are appropriate here for other reasons as well.
2963 laurel, centaury, fumitory, hellebore, catapuce, buckthorn *(gaitrys)* berries, herb ivy are all mentioned in early medical authorities.
2966 *yerd:* yard; *ther merye is:* where it is pleasant.
2968 *for . . . kyn:* in the name of your father's family.

2970 *graunt mercy of:* much thanks for; *loore:* instruction.
2971 *as touchyng:* concerning.

2973 *bad:* bade (us not to fear . . . .).
2974 *rede:* read.

Of many a man moore of auctoritee *2975*
Than evere Caton was, so mote I thee,
That al the revers seyn of this sentence,
And han wel founden by experience
That dremes been significacions
As wel of joye as of tribulacions *2980*
That folk enduren in this lif present.
Ther nedeth make of this noon argument;
The verray preeve sheweth it in dede.

Oon of the gretteste auctour that men rede
Seith thus: that whilom two felawes wente *2985*
On pilgrimage in a ful good entente,
And happed so they coomen in a toun
Where as ther was swich congregacioun
Of peple, and eek so streit of herbergage,
That they ne founde as muche as o cotage *2990*
In which they bothe myghte ylogged be.
Wherfore they mosten of necessitee,
As for that nyght, departen compaignye;
And ech of hem gooth to his hostelrye,
And took his loggyng as it wolde falle. *2995*
That oon of hem was logged in a stalle,
Fer in a yeerd, with oxen of the plough;
That oother man was logged wel ynough,
As was his aventure or his fortune,
That us governeth alle as in commune. *3000*

And so bifel that longe er it were day,
This man mette in his bed, ther as he lay,
How that his felawe gan upon hym calle,
And seyde, 'Allas, for in an oxes stalle

2975 *moore of auctoritee:* having greater authority.

2976 *so . . . thee:* as I may thrive.

2977 *that:* who; *al the revers:* entirely the opposite; *this sentence:* this (Cato's) opinion.

2978 *and han:* and (they) have; *founden:* found, learned.

2979 *significacions:* signs.

2980 *tribulacions:* troubles.

2982 *ther nedeth make:* there is (no) need to make.

2983 *verray preeve:* actual experience; *dede:* fact.

2984 *auctour:* author, possibly Cicero.

2985 *felawes:* companions.

2986 *ful . . . entente:* devout intentions.

2987 *happed:* it chanced; *coomen:* came.

2988 *congregacioun:* crowd.

2989 *streit:* shortagc; *herbergage:* lodging.

2990 *o:* one.

2991 *ylogged be:* bc lodged.

2992 *wherfore:* for which reason; *mosten:* had to.

2993 *as* is redundant; *departen:* part.

2994 *hostelrye:* i.e., sleeping accommodations.

2995 *loggyng:* lodging; *as . . . falle:* as chance befell (him).

2996 *that oon:* one.

2997 *fer:* far away; *yeerd:* barnyard.

2999 *aventure:* chance, luck.

3000 *us governeth:* governs us; *as* is redundant.

3001 *er:* before.

3002 *this man:* the latter; *mette:* dreamed; *ther as:* where.

3003 *gan:* began, did.

This nyght I shal be mordred ther I lye. *3005*
Now help me, deere brother, or I dye!
In alle haste com to me!' he sayde.
This man out of his sleep for feere abrayde;
But whan that he was wakened of his sleep,
He turned hym and took of this no keep; *3010*
Hym thoughte his dreem nas but a vanitee.
Thus twies in his slepyng dremed he;
And atte thridde tyme yet his felawe
Cam, as hym thoughte, and seyde, 'I am now slawe.
Bihoold my bloody woundes depe and wyde! *3015*
Arys up erly in the morwe tyde,
And at the west gate of the toun,' quod he,
'A carte ful of dong ther shaltow se,
In which my body is hid ful prively;
Do thilke carte arresten boldely. *3020*
My gold caused my mordre, sooth to sayn.'
And tolde hym every point how he was slayn,
With a ful pitous face, pale of hewe.
And truste wel, his dreem he foond ful trewe,
For on the morwe as soone as it was day, *3025*
To his felawes in he took the way;
And whan that he cam to this oxes stalle,
After his felawe he bigan to calle.
The hostiler answerde hym anon,
And seyde, 'Sire, youre felawe is agon; *3030*
As soone as day he wente out of the toun.'
This man gan fallen in suspecioun,
Remembrynge on his dremes that he mette,
And forth he gooth, no lenger wolde he lette,

3005 *mordred:* murdered; *ther:* where.

3008 *feere:* fear; *abrayde:* started.

3010 *took no keep:* paid no attention.
3011 *hym thoughte:* it seemed to him; *nas:* was not; *vanitee:* idle fancy.

3013 *atte thridde:* at the third.
3014 *slawe:* slain.

3016 *arys:* arise; *morwe tyde:* morning time.

3018 *dong:* dung; *shaltow:* shall you.
3019 *prively:* secretly.

3020 *do . . . arresten:* have (it) stopped.
3021 *sooth:* truth.
3022 *point:* detail.
3023 *hewe:* hue, color.
3024 *foond:* found.

3025 *morwe:* morrow.
3026 *in:* inn, i.e., sleeping place; *took . . . way:* went.

3029 *hostiler:* innkeeper.

3031 *day:* i.e., daybreak.
3032 *gan fallen in suspecioun:* began to be suspicious.
3033 *mette:* dreamed.
3034 *lenger:* longer; *lette:* stay.

Unto the west gate of the toun, and fond *3035*
A dong carte, wente as it were to donge lond,
That was arrayed in that same wise
As ye han herd the dede man devyse,
And with an hardy herte he gan to crye
Vengeance and justice of this felonye: *3040*
'My felawe mordred is this same nyght,
And in this carte he lith gapyng upright!
I crye out on the ministres,' quod he,
'That sholden kepe and reulen this citee.
Harrow! allas! heere lith my felawe slayn!' *3045*
What sholde I moore unto this tale sayn?
The peple out sterte and caste the cart to grounde,
And in the myddel of the dong they founde
The dede man that mordred was al newe.
O blisful God, that art so just and trewe, *3050*
Lo, how that thou biwreyest mordre alway!
Mordre wol out, that se we day by day.
Mordre is so wlatsom and abhomynable
To God, that is so just and resonable,
That he ne wol nat suffre it heled be, *3055*
Though it abyde a yeer, or two, or thre.
Mordre wol out, this my conclusioun.
And right anon, ministres of that toun
Han hent the carter and so soore hym pyned,
And eek the hostiler so soore engyned, *3060*
That they biknewe hir wikkednesse anon,
And were anhanged by the nekke bon.
Heere may men seen that dremes been to drede.
And certes, in the same book I rede,

3036 *wente:* (that) was going; *as:* as if; *donge:* spread dung on.
3037 *was arrayed:* had the appearance; *wise:* manner.
3038 *dede:* dead; *devyse:* describe.
3039 *hardy:* bold; *he:* the other companion; *crye:* call for.

3040 *of:* for.

3042 *lith:* lies; *gapyng:* with gaping mouth; *upright:* supine.
3043 *ministres:* magistrates.
3044 *kepe:* guard; *reulen:* rule.

3046 *sayn:* say.
3047 *sterte:* started, rushed.

3049 *al newe:* newly.

3051 *biwreyest:* reveal; *alway:* always.
3052 *out:* i.e., be revealed; *day by day:* every day.
3053 *wlatsom:* loathsome.
3054 *that:* who.

3055 *suffre it:* allow it (murder); *heled:* concealed.
3056 *it abyde:* it (the murder) wait.

3059 *han hent:* have seized; *soore:* sorely; *pyned:* tortured.

3060 *engyned:* placed on an engine of torture, racked.
3061 *biknewe:* confessed.
3062 *anhanged:* hanged.
3063 *to drede:* worthy to be feared.

Right in the nexte chapitre after this— *3065*
I gabbe nat, so have I joye or blis—
Two men that wolde han passed over see,
For certeyn cause, into a fer contree,
If that the wynd ne hadde been contrarie,
That made hem in a citee for to tarie *3070*
That stood ful myrie upon an haven syde;
But on a day agayn the even-tyde
The wynd gan chaunge, and blew right as hem leste.
Jolif and glad they wente unto hir reste,
And casten hem ful erly for to saille. *3075*
  But to that o man fil a greet mervaille:
That oon of hem, in slepyng as he lay,
Hym mette a wonder dreem agayn the day.
Hym thoughte a man stood by his beddes syde,
And hym comanded that he sholde abyde, *3080*
And seyde hym thus: 'If thou tomorwe wende,
Thou shalt be dreynt; my tale is at an ende.'
  He wook and tolde his felawe what he mette,
And preyed hym his viage to lette;
As for that day, he preyde hym to abyde. *3085*
His felawe, that lay by his beddes syde,
Gan for to laughe, and scorned hym ful faste.
'No dreem,' quod he, 'may so myn herte agaste
That I wol lette for to do my thynges.
I sette nat a straw by thy dremynges, *3090*
For swevenes been but vanytees and japes;
Men dreme alday of owles or of apes,
And eek of many a maze therwithal;
Men dreme of thyng that nevere was ne shal.

3066 *gabbe:* lie; *so have I:* as I may have.
3067 *wolde han:* would have; *see:* sea.
3068 *certeyn cause:* a certain reason; *fer:* far.
3069 *ne . . . contrarie:* had not been in the wrong direction.

3070 *tarie:* wait.
3071 *myrie:* pleasant; *upon . . . syde:* on the shore of a harbor.
3072 *agayn:* toward; *even-tyde:* evening.
3073 *gan chaunge:* changed; *hem leste:* they wished.
3074 *jolif:* merry; *reste:* bed.

3075 *casten hem:* planned.
3076 *that o man:* one of the men; *fil:* befell; *mervaille:* marvel.

3078 *hym mette:* he dreamed; *agayn:* toward; *day:* dawn.
3079 *hym thoughte:* it seemed to him.

3080 *abyde:* wait, stay.
3081 *wende:* go.
3082 *dreynt:* drowned.
3083 *wook:* woke.
3084 *preyed:* asked; *viage:* voyage; *lette:* delay.

3085 *as:* just; *abyde:* wait.

3087 *gan:* began; *scorned . . .:* spoke very scornfully to him.
3088 *agaste:* terrify.
3089 *thynges:* business.

3090 *sette . . . by:* care not a straw for.
3091 *swevenes:* dreams; *vanytees:* follies; *japes:* tricks.
3092 *alday:* all the time; *owles, apes:* i.e., ridiculous things.
3093 *maze:* delusion; *therwithal:* in addition.
3094 *was ne shal:* was nor shall be.

But sith I see that thou wolt here abyde, *3095*
And thus forslewthen wilfully thy tyde,
God woot, it reweth me; and have good day!'
And thus he took his leve and wente his way.
But er that he hadde half his cours yseyled,
Noot I nat why, ne what meshaunce it eyled, *3100*
But casuelly the shippes botme rente,
And ship and man under the water wente
In sighte of othere shippes it bisyde,
That with hem seyled at the same tyde.
And therfore, faire Pertelote so deere, *3105*
By swiche ensamples olde maistow leere
That no man sholde been too recchelees
Of dremes, for I seye thee, doutelees,
That many a dreem ful soore is for to drede.
  Lo, in the lyf of Seint Kenelm I rede, *3110*
That was Kenulphus sone, the noble kyng
Of Mercenrike, how Kenelm mette a thyng:
A lite er he was mordred on a day,
His mordre in his avysion he say.
His norice hym expowned everydeel *3115*
His swevene, and bad hym for to kepe hym weel
For traison; but he nas but seven yeer old,
And therfore litel tale hath he told
Of any dreem, so holy was his herte.
By God, I hadde levere than my sherte *3120*
That ye hadde rad his legende as have I.
  Dame Pertelote, I sey yow trewely,
Macrobeus, that writ the Avision
In Affrike of the worthy Cipion,

3096 *forslewthen:* waste; *tyde:* time.
3097 *woot:* knows; *it . . . me:* I am sorry; *have . . . day:* good-by.

3099 *er:* before; *yseyled:* sailed.

3100 *noot:* know not; *what . . . eyled:* what was the trouble with it.
3101 *casuelly:* accidentally; *botme:* bottom; *rente:* ripped.

3103 *in sighte of:* within sight of; *it bisyde:* right beside it.
3104 *tyde:* time.

3106 *swiche:* such; *ensamples olde:* old stories; *maistow:* may you; *leere:* learn.
3107 *recchelees:* careless.
3108 *seye:* tell.
3109 *ful soore:* most sorely; *for to drede:* to be feared.
3110 Kenelm succeeded his father Kenulphus on the throne of Mercia in 821 at the age of seven; his aunt procured his murder.

3113 *lite:* little (while).
3114 *avysion:* dream; *say:* saw.
3115 *norice:* nurse; *hym expowned:* explained to him; *everydeel:* every bit.
3116 *bad:* urged; *kepe hym weel:* guard himself well.
3117 *for:* from; *nas:* was not.
3118 *litel . . . told:* he paid little attention.

3120 *levere:* rather, i.e., I'd give my shirt.
3121 *rad:* read.

3123 *Macrobeus* (ca. A.D. 400) wrote a well-known commentary on Cicero's *Somnium Scipionis* (Dream of Scipio).
3124 *Affrike:* Africa.

Affermeth dremes, and seith that they been *3125*
Warnynge of thynges that men after seen.
  And forthermoore, I pray yow, looketh wel
In the Olde Testament of Daniel,
If he heeld dremes any vanitee.
  Rede eek of Joseph and there shul ye see *3130*
Wher dremes be somtyme—I sey nat alle—
Warnynge of thynges that shul after falle.
  Looke of Egipte the kyng, daun Pharao,
His baker and his butiller also,
Wher they ne felte noon effect in dremes. *3135*
Whoso wol seken actes of sondry remes
May rede of dremes many a wonder thyng.
  Lo Cresus, which that was of Lyde kyng,
Mette he nat that he sat upon a tree,
Which signified he sholde anhanged be? *3140*
  Lo heere Andromacha, Ectores wyf,
That day that Ector sholde lese his lyf,
She dremed on the same nyght biforn
How that the lyf of Ector sholde be lorn,
If thilke day he wente into bataille. *3145*
She warned hym, but it myghte nat availle;
He wente for to fighte nathelees,
But he was slayn anon of Achilles.
But thilke tale is al to long to telle,
And eek it is ny day, I may nat dwelle. *3150*
Shortly I seye, as for conclusion,
That I shal han of this avision
Adversitee; and I seye forthermoor
That I ne telle of laxatyves no stoor,

3125 *affermeth:* confirms.
3126 *after seen:* see afterward.

3128 see Daniel 7:1ff.
3129 *heeld:* considered.

3130-35 see Genesis 37, 40, and 41.
3131 *wher:* whether; *alle:* i.e., all the time.
3132 *falle:* happen.
3133 *daun Pharao:* lord Pharaoh.
3134 *butiller:* butler.

3135 *ne . . . in:* felt no consequences of.
3136 *seken:* look at; *actes:* histories; *sondry remes:* various realms.

3138 *Cresus:* Croesus, king of Lydia, the story of whose dream and its interpretation is told in the *Monk's Tale.*
3139 *mette he nat:* did he not dream.

3141 Andromache, the wife of Hector; this dream is not found in Homer, but appears in a popular medieval account of the Trojan War.
3142 *sholde lese:* was to lose.
3144 *lorn:* lost.
3145 *thilke:* that; *bataille:* battle.
3146 *availle:* do any good.

3148 *of:* by.

3150 *ny:* near; *dwelle:* linger.

3152 *han of:* have from or in accordance with.
3153 *adversitee:* adversity.
3154 *ne telle no stoor:* set no store by, have no faith in.

For they been venymous, I woot it weel; 3155
I hem diffye, I love hem never a deel!
Now lat us speke of myrthe and stynte al this.
Madame Pertelote, so have I blis,
Of o thyng God hath sent me large grace;
For whan I se the beautee of youre face, 3160
Ye been so scarlet reed aboute youre yën,
It maketh al my drede for to dyen;
For also siker as *In principio,*
Mulier est hominis confusio—
Madame, the sentence of this Latyn is, 3165
'Womman is mannes joye and al his blis.'
For whan I feele anyght youre softe syde,
Al be it that I may nat on yow ryde,
For that oure perche is maad so narwe, allas,
I am so ful of joye and of solas 3170
That I deffye bothe swevene and dreem."
And with that word he fley doun fro the beem,
For it was day, and eek his hennes alle,
And with a "chuk" he gan hem for to calle,
For he hadde founde a corn, lay in the yerd. 3175
Real he was; he was namoore aferd.
He fethered Pertelote twenty tyme,
And trad hire eek as ofte er it was pryme.
He looketh as it were a grym leoun,
And on his toos he rometh up and doun; 3180
Hym deigned nat to sette his foot to grounde.
He chukketh whan he hath a corn yfounde,
And to hym rennen thanne his wyves alle.
Thus roial, as a prince is in his halle,

3155 *venymous:* poisonous; *woot:* know.
3156 *hem diffye:* defy or spurn them; *never a deel:* never a bit.
3157 *stynte:* stop.
3158 *so . . . blis:* as I may have bliss.
3159 *o:* one; *large grace:* great good fortune.

3161 *yën:* eyes.
3162 *drede:* fear; *dyen:* die.
3163 *also siker as:* just as sure as; *in principio:* "in the beginning," the first words of the Gospel of St. John, thus, "as sure as gospel truth."
3164 *mulier . . .:* "woman is man's ruin," a common medieval sentiment.
3165 *sentence:* meaning.
3167 *anyght:* at night.
3168 *al be it:* although.
3169 *maad:* made; *narwe:* narrow.

3170 *solas:* delight.
3171 *swevene and dreem:* vision and dream.
3172 *fley:* flew.

3174 *gan . . . calle:* began to call them.

3175 *corn:* grain; *lay:* i.e., that lay.
3176 *real:* royal.
3177 *fethered:* copulated with.
3178 *trad:* trod, copulated with; *er:* before; *pryme:* 9 A.M., see VI:662.
3179 *as it were:* like; *leoun:* lion.
3180 *rometh:* stalks.
3181 *hym deigned:* he deigned.

3183 *rennen:* run.

Leve I this Chauntecleer in his pasture, *3185*
And after wol I telle his aventure.
Whan that the monthe in which the world bigan,
That highte March, whan God first maked man,
Was compleet, and passed were also,
Syn March bigan, thritty dayes and two, *3190*
Bifel that Chauntecleer in al his pryde,
His sevene wyves walkyng by his syde,
Caste up his eyen to the brighte sonne,
That in the signe of Taurus hadde yronne
Twenty degrees and oon and somwhat moore, *3195*
And knew by kynde, and by noon oother loore,
That it was pryme, and crew with blisful stevene.
"The sonne," he seyde, "is clomben up on hevene
Fourty degrees and oon and moore, ywis.
Madame Pertelote, my worldes blis, *3200*
Herkneth thise blisful briddes how they synge,
And se the fresshe floures how they sprynge;
Ful is myn herte of revel and solas!"
But sodeynly hym fil a sorweful cas,
For evere the latter ende of joye is wo. *3205*
God woot that worldly joye is soone ago,
And if a rethor koude faire endite,
He in a cronycle saufly myghte it write
As for a sovereyn notabilitee.
Now every wys man, lat hym herkne me; *3210*
This storie is also trewe, I undertake,
As is the book of Launcelot de Lake,
That wommen holde in ful greet reverence.
Now wol I torne agayn to my sentence.

3187 The world was thought to have been created at the vernal equinox.
3188 *highte:* is called.

3190 *syn March bigan* seems to mean "since March ended," since the resulting date, May 3, would correspond to that indicated by the astrological calculation at 3195 below.
3191 *bifel:* it happened.
3194ff On May 3 the sun would have passed twenty-one degrees of the zodiacal sign of Taurus, and its altitude above the horizon at 9:00 would have been forty-one degrees.
3196 *kynde:* nature, instinct; *loore:* learning.
3197 *pryme:* 9 A.M.; *stevene:* voice.
3198 *clomben:* climbed; *on:* in.

3201 *herkneth:* listen to; *briddes:* birds.

3203 *revel:* joy; *solas:* pleasure.
3204 *hym fil:* there befell him; *cas:* mischance.

3205 *evere:* always; *latter ende:* conclusion; *wo:* woe.
3206 *woot:* knows; *ago:* gone, passed.
3207 *rethor:* rhetorician; *koude:* knew how to; *endite:* write.
3208 *cronycle:* chronicle history; *saufly:* confidently; *it:* i.e., Chauntecleer's mischance.
3209 *as for:* for; *sovereyn:* great; *notabilitee:* notable event.
3210 *herkne:* listen to.
3211 *also:* just as.
3212 *Launcelot:* the knight of Arthur's court.

3214 *sentence:* subject.

A colfox, ful of sly iniquitee, *3215*
That in the grove hadde woned yeres three,
By heigh ymaginacion forncast,
The same nyght thurghout the hegges brast
Into the yerd ther Chauntecleer the faire
Was wont, and eek his wyves, to repaire; *3220*
And in a bed of wortes stille he lay
Til it was passed undren of the day,
Waitynge his tyme on Chauntecleer to falle,
As gladly doon thise homycides alle
That in await liggen to mordre men. *3225*
O false mordrour, lurkynge in thy den!
O newe Scariot! Newe Genylon!
False dissimilour! O Greek Synon,
That broghtest Troye al outrely to sorwe!
O Chauntecleer, acursed be that morwe *3230*
That thou into the yerd flaugh fro the bemes!
Thou were ful wel ywarned by thy dremes
That thilke day was perilous to thee;
But what that God forwoot moot nedes be,
After the opinion of certein clerkis. *3235*
Witnesse on hym that any parfit clerk is,
That in scole is greet altercacion
In this matere, and greet disputison,
And hath been of an hundred thousand men.
But I ne kan nat bulte it to the bren *3240*
As kan the holy doctour Augustyn,
Or Boece, or the bisshop Bradwardyn,
Wheither that Goddes worthy forwityng
Streyneth me nedely for to doon a thyng

3215 *colfox:* a fox with black markings.
3216 *woned:* lived; *yeres:* years.
3217 "by divine foreknowledge predestined."
3218 *thurghout:* through; *hegges:* hedges; *brast:* burst.
3219 *ther:* where.

3220 *wont:* accustomed; *repaire:* retire to.
3221 *wortes:* herbs.
3222 *undren:* a varying time, perhaps noon here.
3223 *tyme:* opportunity.
3224 *gladly:* usually.

3225 *in await liggen:* lie in wait; *mordre:* murder.
3227 *newe:* i.e., modern; *Scariot:* Judas Iscariot; *Genylon:* Ganelon, the betrayer of Roland.
3228 *dissimilour:* dissembler; *Synon:* in the *Aeneid,* the Greek who tricked the Trojans into admitting the Trojan horse into the city.
3229 *outrely:* utterly.
3230 *morwe:* morning.
3231 *flaugh:* flew.

3234 *forwoot:* foreknows; *moot nedes:* must needs.

3235 *after:* according to; *clerkis:* scholars.
3236 *witnesse on:* take witness from.
3237 *scole:* the universities; *altercacion:* argument.
3238 *disputison:* disputation.
3239 *of:* by.

3240 "bolt it to the bran" = sift the flour from the bran = sift truth from falsehood.
3241 The writings of St. Augustine and Boethius and Thomas Bradwardyne, archbishop of Canterbury, discuss the problem of predestination and free will.

3243 *forwityng:* foreknowledge.
3244 *streyneth:* constrains; *nedely:* necessarily.

("Nedely" clepe I symple necessitee), 3245
Or elles if free choys be graunted me
To do that same thyng, or do it noght,
Though God forwoot it er that I was wroght;
Or if his wityng streyneth never a deel
But by necessitee condicioneel. 3250
I wol nat han to do of swich matere;
My tale is of a cok, as ye may heere,
That took his conseil of his wyf with sorwe,
To walken in the yerd upon that morwe
That he hadde met that dreem that I yow tolde. 3255
Wommennes conseils been ful ofte colde;
Wommannes conseil broghte us first to wo,
And made Adam fro Paradys to go,
Ther as he was ful myrie and wel at ese.
But for I noot to whom it myght displese 3260
If I conseil of wommen wolde blame,
Passe over, for I seyde it in my game.
Rede auctours where they trete of swich matere,
And what they seyn of wommen ye may heere.
Thise been the cokkes wordes and nat myne; 3265
I kan noon harm of no womman divyne.

Faire in the sond to bathe hire myrily
Lith Pertelote, and alle hir sustres by,
Agayn the sonne, and Chauntecleer so free
Soong murier than the mermayde in the see— 3270
For Phisiologus seith sikerly
How that they syngen wel and myrily.
And so bifel that as he caste his yë
Among the wortes on a boterflye,

3245 *clepe:* call; simple necessity is distinguished from conditional necessity by Boethius, see l. 3250.

3248 *forwoot:* foreknew; *er:* before; *wroght:* made.
3249 *wityng:* knowing; *streyneth:* constrains; *never a deel:* not a bit.

3250 *but:* except; Boethius defines conditional necessity as permitting some free will.
3251 *han . . . of:* have anything to do with.

3253 *his conseil:* the advice; *with sorwe:* to his sorrow.

3255 *met:* dreamed.
3256 *colde:* fatal; the line is proverbial.
3257 *wo:* woe.

3259 *ther as:* there where.

3260 *for:* because; *noot:* know not.
3261 *wolde:* should.
3262 *passe over:* disregard it; *game:* sport, fun.
3263 *rede:* read; *auctours:* authors; *trete:* treat.
3264 *heere:* hear.

3266 *kan:* know.
3267 *sond:* sand; *myrily:* pleasantly.
3268 *lith:* lies; *by:* nearby.
3269 *agayn:* in; *free:* noble.

3270 *soong:* sang; *see:* sea.
3271 *Phisiologus:* the collection of Latin beast fables, morally interpreted; *sikerly:* certainly.

3273 *bifel:* it befell; *yë:* eye.
3274 *wortes:* herbs; *boterflye:* butterfly.

He was war of this fox that lay ful lowe. *3275*
No thyng ne liste hym thanne for to crowe,
But cride anon, "Cok! cok!" and up he sterte,
As man that was affrayed in his herte;
For naturelly a beest desireth flee
Fro his contrarie if he may it see, *3280*
Though he nevere erst hadde seen it with his yë.
This Chauntecleer, whan he gan hym espye,
He wolde han fled, but that the fox anon
Seyde, "Gentil sire, allas, wher wol ye gon?
Be ye affrayd of me that am youre freend? *3285*
Now certes, I were worse than a feend
If I to yow wolde harm or vileynye!
I am nat come youre conseil for t'espye,
But trewely, the cause of my comynge
Was oonly for to herkne how that ye synge. *3290*
For trewely, ye have as myrie a stevene
As any aungel hath that is in hevene.
Therwith ye han in musyk moore feelynge
Than hadde Boece, or any that kan synge.
My lord your fader—God his soule blesse!— *3295*
And eek youre moder, of hire gentilesse,
Han in myn hous ybeen, to my greet ese.
And certes, sire, ful fayn wolde I yow plese.
But for men speke of syngyng, I wol seye,
So mote I brouke wel myne eyen tweye, *3300*
Save yow, I herde nevere man so synge
As dide youre fader in the morwenynge.
Certes, it was of herte, al that he song.
And for to make his voys the moore strong,

3275 *war:* aware.
3276 *no thyng . . . hym:* not at all did he wish.
3277 *sterte:* jumped.
3278 *man:* one; *affrayed:* afraid.
3279 *flee:* to flee.

3280 *contrarie:* philosophy held that every object has its contrary toward which it has a natural antipathy.
3281 *erst:* before; *yë:* eye.
3282 *gan:* did; *hym:* i.e., the fox; *espye:* espy.
3283 *but:* except.

3286 *certes:* certainly; *feend:* fiend, devil.
3287 *wolde:* intended.
3288 *conseil:* secrets.

3290 *herkne:* listen to.
3291 *myrie:* pleasant; *stevene:* voice.

3293 *therwith:* and in addition.
3294 Boethius was the author of a treatise on music.

3296 *of . . . gentilesse:* out of her nobility.
3297 *han ybeen:* have been; *ese:* satisfaction.
3298 *fayn:* gladly; *yow plese:* please you.
3299 *for:* since; *men* is used here in an impersonal construction, cf. Fr. *on dit:* "since singing is being discussed."
3300 *so mote I:* as I hope to; *brouke:* enjoy (the use of).
3301 *save:* except for.
3302 *morwenynge:* morning.
3303 *of herte:* from the heart.

He wolde so peyne hym that with bothe his yën *3305*
He moste wynke, so loude he wolde cryen,
And stonden on his tiptoon therwithal,
And strecche forth his nekke long and smal.
And eek he was of swich discrecion
That ther nas no man in no region *3310*
That hym in song or wisdom myghte passe.
I have wel rad in 'Daun Burnel the Asse,'
Among his vers how that ther was a cok,
For that a preestes sone yaf him a knok
Upon his leg whil he was yong and nyce, *3315*
He made hym for to lese his benefice.
But certeyn, ther nys no comparison
Bitwixe the wisdom and discrecion
Of youre fader and of his subtiltee.
Now syngeth, sire, for seinte charitee! *3320*
Lat se, konne ye youre fader countrefete?"
  This Chauntecleer his wynges gan to bete,
As man that koude his trayson nat espie,
So was he ravysshed with his flaterie.
  Allas, ye lordes, many a fals flatour *3325*
Is in youre courts, and many a losengeour,
That plesen yow wel moore, by my feith,
Than he that soothfastnesse unto yow seith!
Redeth Ecclesiaste of flaterye;
Beth war, ye lordes, of hir trecherye. *3330*
  This Chauntecleer stood hye upon his toos,
Strecchynge his nekke, and heeld his eyen cloos,
And gan to crowe loude for the nones.
And daun Russell the fox stirte up atones,

3305 *peyne hym:* exert himself; *yën:* eyes.
3306 *wynke:* blink, close the eyes.
3307 *tiptoon:* tiptoes.

3309 *discrecion:* discernment.

3310 *nas:* was not.
3311 *passe:* excel.
3312 *rad:* read; *Burnel . . .*: a twelfth-century satirical poem by Nigellus Wireker.
3314 *for:* (who) because; *preestes sone:* priest's son; *yaf:* gave; *knok:* blow.
3315 *he:* i.e., the priest's son; *nyce:* foolish.
3316 *he:* the cock; *lese:* lose; the day the young man was to be ordained the cock crowed late; the youth overslept and so lost his appointment to a church.
3317 *nys:* is not.
3319 *his subtiltee:* i.e., the ingeniousness of the cock in the story.
3320 *seinte:* holy.
3321 *lat se:* let it be seen; *konne:* can; *countrefete:* imitate.
3322 *gan:* began; *bete:* beat.
3323 *man:* one; *his:* the fox's; *espie:* spy.

3325 *flatour:* flatterer.
3326 *losengeour:* deceiver.
3327 *plesen:* pleases.
3328 *soothfastnesse:* truth.
3329 *redeth:* read; *of:* concerning; Ecclesiasticus 27:26 (see III:651) or Proverbs 29:5.
3330 *beth war:* be wary; *hir:* their.

3332 *cloos:* closed.
3333 *gan:* began; *nones:* occasion.
3334 *stirte:* jumped; *atones:* suddenly.

And by the gargat hente Chauntecleer, *3335*
And on his bak toward the wode him beer,
For yet ne was ther no man that hym sewed.
O destinee, that mayst nat been eschewed!
Allas that Chauntecleer fleigh fro the bemes!
Allas, his wif ne roghte nat of dremes! *3340*
And on a Friday fil al this meschaunce!
O Venus, that art goddesse of plesaunce,
Syn that thy servant was this Chauntecleer,
And in thy servyce dide al his power—
Moore for delit than world to multiplye— *3345*
Why woldestow suffre hym on thy day to dye?
O Gaufred, deere maister soverayn,
That, whan thy worthy kyng Richard was slayn
With shot, compleynedest his deeth so soore,
Why ne hadde I now thy sentence and thy loore, *3350*
The Friday for to chide as diden ye?
For on a Friday, soothly, slayn was he.
Thanne wolde I shewe yow how that I koulde pleyne
For Chauntecleres drede and for his peyne.
Certes, swich cry ne lamentacion *3355*
Was nevere of ladyes maad whan Ylion
Was wonne, and Pirrus with his streite swerd,
Whan he hadde hent kyng Priam by the berd
And slayn hym, as seith us Eneydos,
As maden alle the hennes in the cloos, *3360*
Whan they had seen of Chauntecleer the sighte.
But sovereynly dame Pertelote shrighte
Ful louder than dide Hasdrubales wyf,
Whan that hir housbonde hadde lost his lyf,

3335 *gargat:* throat; *hente:* seized.
3336 *his:* the fox's; *wode:* wood; *beer:* bore.
3337 *sewed:* pursued.
3338 *mayst:* may; *eschewed:* avoided.
3339 *fleigh:* flew; *bemes:* rafters.

3340 *roghte:* took heed of.
3341 Friday is Venus's day; *fil:* fell; *meschaunce:* misfortune.
3342 *plesaunce:* pleasure.
3343 *syn:* since; *servant:* i.e., Love's servant.
3344 *dide . . . power:* did his utmost.

3345 *delit:* delight; *world . . .:* i.e., to multiply his kind.
3346 *woldestow:* would you; *suffre:* allow.
3347 Geoffrey de Vinsauf, in his treatise on poetry, wrote an extravagant lament on the death of Richard I in which he chides Friday, the day of the king's death; *maister soverayn:* peerless master.
3349 *shot:* an arrow; *compleynedest:* lamented; *soore:* sorely.
3350 *sentence:* wisdom; *loore:* learning.

3352 *soothly:* truly.
3353 *shewe:* show; *pleyne:* lament.
3354 *drede:* fear.

3355 *certes:* certainly; *swich:* such.
3356 *of:* by; *maad:* made; *Ylion:* Troy.
3357 *Pirrus:* Pyrrhus, the Greek who slew Priam, king of Troy; *streite:* drawn.
3358 *hent:* seized.
3359 *seith:* tells; *Eneydos:* the *Aeneid.*
3360 *as maden:* as (the hens) made; *cloos:* yard.

3362 *sovereynly:* above all; *shrighte:* shrieked.
3363 Hasdrubal was the commanding Carthaginian general when the Romans burned the city in 146 B.C.

And that the Romayns hadden brend Cartage; *3365*
She was so ful of torment and of rage
That wilfully into the fyr she sterte,
And brende hirselven with a stedefast herte.
O woful hennes, right so cryden ye
As, whan that Nero brende the citee *3370*
Of Rome, cryden senatoures wyves
For that hir housbondes losten alle hir lyves—
Withouten gilt this Nero hath hem slayn.
Now wol I turne to my tale agayn.
This sely widwe and eek hir doghtres two *3375*
Herden thise hennes crye and maken wo,
And out at dores stirten they anon,
And syen the fox toward the grove gon,
And bar upon his bak the cok away,
And cryden, "Out! harrow! and weylaway! *3380*
Ha! ha! the fox!" and after hym they ran,
And eek with staves many another man.
Ran Colle oure dogge, and Talbot and Gerland,
And Malkyn, with a distaf in hir hand,
Ran cow and calf, and eek the verray hogges, *3385*
So fered for the berkyng of the dogges
And shoutyng of the men and wommen eek,
They ronne so hem thoughte hir herte breek.
They yelleden as feendes doon in helle;
The dokes cryden as men wolde hem quelle; *3390*
The gees for feere flowen over the trees;
Out of the hyve cam the swarm of bees;
So hydous was the noyse, a, *benedicite!*
Certes, he Jakke Straw and his meynee

3365 *brend:* burned.
3366 *torment:* anguish; *rage:* frenzy.
3367 *wilfully:* deliberately; *sterte:* leaped.

3369 *right:* just; *cryden:* cried.

3370 Legend tells that Nero burned Rome and put many of the senators to death.

3373 *withouten gilt:* (though they were) without guilt.

3375 *sely:* poor.
3376 *herden:* heard.
3377 *out at dores:* out of doors; *stirten:* ran.
3378 *syen:* saw.
3379 *bar:* bore.

3380 *out, harrow:* cries of alarm; *weylaway:* alas.

3382 *staves:* sticks.
3383 *Colle, Talbot, Gerland* are the names of dogs.
3384 *Malkyn:* a diminutive of Moll; *distaf:* the staff for holding the material being spun on a spinning wheel.

3386 *fered for:* frightened of; *berkyng:* barking.

3388 *ronne:* ran; *hem thoughte:* it seemed; *breek:* would break.
3389 *yelleden:* yelled.

3390 *dokes:* ducks; *as:* as if; *quelle:* kill.
3391 *gees:* geese; *feere:* fear; *flowen:* flew.

3393 *hydous:* hideous; *benedicite,* three syllables, bén-sĭ-té.
3394 Jack Straw was one of the leaders of the Peasants' Revolt in 1381, during which there was a massacre of Flemings in London; *meynee:* company.

Ne made nevere shoutes half so shrille *3395*
Whan that they wolden any Flemyng kille,
As thilke day was maad upon the fox.
Of bras they broghten bemes, and of box,
Of horn, of boon, in whiche they blewe and powped,
And therwithal they skriked and they howped— *3400*
It semed as that hevene sholde falle.
  Now goode men, I prey yow herkneth alle:
Lo, how Fortune turneth sodeynly
The hope and pryde eek of hir enemy.
This cok, that lay upon the foxes bak, *3405*
In al his drede unto the fox he spak,
And seyde, "Sire, if that I were as ye,
Yet sholde I seyn, as wys God helpe me,
'Turneth agayn, ye proude cherles alle!
A verray pestilence upon yow falle! *3410*
Now am I come unto this wodes syde;
Maugree youre heed, the cok shal here abyde.
I wol hym ete, in feith, and that anon.' "
  The fox answerde, "In feith, it shal be don."
And as he spak that word, al sodeynly *3415*
This cok brak from his mouth delyverly,
And hye upon a tree he fleigh anon.
  And whan the fox saugh that the cok was gon,
"Allas," quod he, "O Chauntecleer, allas!
I have to yow," quod he, "ydoon trespas, *3420*
In as muche as I maked yow aferd
Whan I yow hente and broghte out of the yerd.
But sire, I dide it in no wikke entente;
Com doun, and I shal telle yow what I mente.

3397 *thilke:* that.
3398 *bemes:* trumpets (of brass, wood, horn, and bone); *box:* boxwood.
3399 *powped:* tooted.
3400 *howped:* whooped.

3403 *turneth:* overturns.
3404 *hir:* her.

3407 *were as ye:* were you.
3408 *as wys:* as sure as; *helpe:* may help.
3409 *turneth agayn:* turn back; *cherles:* churls.

3411 *wodes syde:* wood's edge.
3412 *maugree:* in spite of, i.e., in spite of anything you can do.

3416 *brak:* broke; *delyverly:* nimbly.
3417 *fleigh:* flew.

3420 *ydoon trespas:* done wrong.
3421 *in as muche as:* in that; *aferd:* afraid.
3422 *hente:* seized.
3423 *wikke entente:* evil intention.
3424 *mente:* meant.

I shal seye sooth to yow, God help me so!" 3425
"Nay thanne," quod he, "I shrewe us bothe two;
And first I shrewe myself, bothe blood and bones,
If thow bigile me ofter than ones.
Thou shalt namoore, thurgh thy flaterye,
Do me to synge and wynke with myn yë; 3430
For he that wynketh whan he sholde see,
Al wilfully, God lat him nevere thee!"
"Nay," quod the fox, "but God yeve hym meschaunce,
That is so undiscreet of governaunce
That jangleth whan he sholde holde his pees!" 3435
Lo, swich it is for to be recchelees
And necligent, and truste on flaterye.
But ye that holden this tale a folye,
As of a fox, or of a cok and hen,
Taketh the moralitee, goode men. 3440
For Seint Paul seith that al that writen is
To oure doctryne it is ywrite, ywis:
Taketh the fruyt, and lat the chaf be stille.
Now goode God, if that it be thy wille,
As seith my lord, so make us alle goode men, 3445
And bringe us to his heighe blisse. Amen.

Heere is ended the Nonnes Preestes Tale.

EPILOGUE

"Sire Nonnes Preest," oure Hooste seide anoon,
"Yblessed be thy breche and every stoon!
This was a murie tale of Chauntecleer.

3425 *sooth:* truth.
3426 *shrewe:* curse.

3428 *bigile:* fool; *ofter:* oftener.

3430 *do:* gct.
3431 *wynketh:* closes his eyes; *sholde:* ought to.
3432 *al wilfully:* deliberately; *lat:* let; *thee:* prosper.
3433 *yeve:* give; *meschaunce:* misfortune.
3434 *undiscreet:* indiscreet; *governaunce:* self-control.

3435 *jangleth:* chatters; *pees:* peace.
3436 *swich:* so.

3438 *holden:* regard as; *folye:* silly thing.

3440 *taketh the moralitee:* consider the moral.
3441 *al that writen is:* everything that is written.
3442 *to:* for; *doctryne:* instruction; see Romans 15:4.
3443 *fruyt:* grain; *lat . . . be stille:* let the chaff alone.

3445 *my lord:* this allusion is not certainly understood.

3448 *breche:* breeches; *stoon:* testicle.

But by my trouthe, if thou were seculer 3450
Thou woldest been a tredefoul aright;
For if thou have corage as thou hast myght
Thee were nede of hennes, as I wene,
Ya, mo than seven tymes seventene.
See whiche braunes hath this gentil preest, 3455
So greet a nekke, and swich a large breest!
He looketh as a sperhauk with his yën;
Hym nedeth nat his colour for to dyen
With brasile ne with greyn of Portyngale.
Now sire, faire falle yow for youre tale." 3460
And after that he with ful merie chere,
Seide unto another as ye shuln heere.

Fragments VIII, IX, and X complete the work. The first contains the tale of the Second Nun, a legend of St. Cecelia, and the tale of the Canon's Yeoman, who joins the pilgrimage en route. The latter has been an assistant to an alchemist and narrates a swindling trick presumably not uncharacteristic of that profession. Fragment IX consists entirely of the *Manciple's Tale,* which is a digressive and moralized version of an old folk tale. It is preceded by an amusing passage between the Manciple and the almost helplessly drunk Cook. Fragment X, the *Parson's Tale,* is rather a sermon than a tale, being a systematic treatise on the Seven Deadly Sins. The Tales are concluded by the interesting "retracciouns" in which the author requests forgiveness for his inditings of "worldly vanitees," gives thanks to God that he has been allowed to present his works of "moralitee and devocioun," and closes with a prayer for the "grace of verray penitence."

3450 *seculer:* a layman.
3451 *woldest:* would have; *tredefoul:* a cock used for breeding purposes.
3452 *corage:* spirit, desire; *myght:* physical strength.
3453 *thee . . .:* you would have need of; *wene:* suppose.
3454 *ya:* yea; *mo:* more.
3455 *whiche:* what; *braunes:* muscles.
3456 *breest:* chest.
3457 *as:* like; *sperhauk:* sparrow hawk; *yën:* eyes.
3458 *dyen:* dye, i.e., to put color in his cheeks with dye.
3459 *brasile, greyn:* red dyes; *Portyngale:* Portugal.

3460 *faire falle yow:* good luck befall you.

ANCHOR BOOKS

LITERARY ESSAYS AND CRITICISM

THE ALICE B. TOKLAS COOK BOOK—Alice B. Toklas, A196
THE AMERICAN NOVEL AND ITS TRADITION—Richard Chase, A116
AN APPROACH TO SHAKESPEARE, in two volumes—D. A. Traversi, A74a, b
ART AND REALITY—Joyce Cary, A260
THE BIBLE FOR STUDENTS OF LITERATURE AND ART—G. B. Harrison, ed., A394
THE BIRTH OF TRAGEDY AND THE GENEALOGY OF MORALS—Friedrich Nietzsche; Francis Golffing, trans., A81
BLAKE: PROPHET AGAINST EMPIRE—David V. Erdman, AO12
THE BOOK OF THE COURTIER—Baldesar Castiglione; Charles S. Singleton, trans.; Edgar de N. Mayhew, ed. of illustrative material, A186
CLASSIC, ROMANTIC AND MODERN—Jacques Barzun, revised and expanded second edition of Romanticism and the Modern Ego, A255
A COLLECTION OF ESSAYS—George Orwell, A29
COMEDY, "Laughter"—Henri Bergson, and "Essay on Comedy"; George Meredith, intro. and supplementary essay by Wylie Sypher, A87
A COMPANION TO SHAKESPEARE STUDIES—H. Granville-Barker and G. B. Harrison, eds., A191
THE COMPLETE POEMS AND SELECTED LETTERS AND PROSE OF HART CRANE—Brom Weber, ed., A537
DR. BOWDLER'S LEGACY: A History of Expurgated Books in England and America—Noel Perrin, A786
FORM AND VALUE IN MODERN POETRY—R. P. Blackmur, A96
FOUR STAGES OF RENAISSANCE STYLE: Transformations in Art and Literature 1400–1700—Wylie Sypher, A44
FROM RITUAL TO ROMANCE—Jessie Weston, A125
FROM SHAKESPEARE TO EXISTENTIALISM—Walter Kaufmann, A213
GOOD-BYE TO ALL THAT—Robert Graves, second edition revised, A123
A GUIDE TO ENGLISH LITERATURE—F. W. Bateson, second edition revised, A418a
THE LIBERAL IMAGINATION: Essays on Literature and Society—Lionel Trilling, A13
MIDDLE ENGLISH ANTHOLOGY—Ann S. Haskell, AO10
ON NATIVE GROUNDS: An Interpretation of Modern American Prose Literature—Alfred Kazin, abridged, A69
THE POETRY AND PROSE OF WILLIAM BLAKE—David V. Erdman, ed., commentary by Harold Bloom, AO17
POETRY IN OUR TIME—Babette Deutsch, A344
THE PROSE OF JOHN MILTON—J. Max Patrick, ed., ACO10

SCIENCE AND LITERATURE: New Lenses for Criticism–Edward M. Jennings, ed., A756

THE SEVENTEENTH-CENTURY BACKGROUND–Basil Willey, A19

SHAKESPEARE–Mark Van Doren, A11

SHAKESPEARE OUR CONTEMPORARY–Jan Kott; Boleslaw Taborski, trans., A449

A STRESS ANALYSIS OF A STRAPLESS EVENING GOWN and Other Essays for a Scientific Age–Robert A. Baker, ed., A648

TECHNIQUES OF FICTION WRITING–Leon Surmelian, intro. by Mark Schorer, A549

THE THEATRE OF THE ABSURD–Martin Esslin, revised edition, A279

TRAGEDY AND PHILOSOPHY–Walter Kaufmann, A689

WHITE MAN, LISTEN!–Richard Wright, A414

ANCHOR BOOKS

FICTION

ARROW OF GOD–Chinua Achebe, intro. by K. W. J. Post, A698
THE COUNTRY OF THE POINTED FIRS AND OTHER STORIES–Sarah Orne Jewett, A26
A DIFFERENT DRUMMER–William Melvin Kelley, A678
DOWN SECOND AVENUE–Ezekiel Mphahlele, A792
DREAM OF THE RED CHAMBER–Tsao Hsueh-Chin; Chi-Chen Wang, trans., A159
ENVY AND OTHER WORKS–Yuri Olesha; Andrew R. MacAndrew, trans., A571
GOD'S BITS OF WOOD–Ousmane Sembene, A729
HALF-WAY TO THE MOON: New Writing From Russia–Patricia Blake and Max Hayward, eds., A483
A HERO OF OUR TIME–Mihail Lermontov; Vladimir Nabokov and Dmitri Nabokov, trans., A133
INFERNO, ALONE AND OTHER WRITINGS–August Strindberg; in new translations, Evert Sprinchorn, ed., A492c
A MAN OF THE PEOPLE–Chinua Achebe, A594
MOTHER EARTH AND OTHER STORIES–Boris Pilnyak; Vera T. Reck and Michael Green, trans. and eds., A625
19 NECROMANCERS FROM NOW: An Anthology of Original American Writing for the 70s–Ishmael Reed, A743
POCHO–José Antonio Villarreal, intro. by Dr. Ramon Ruiz, A744
POOR PEOPLE and A LITTLE HERO–Fyodor Dostoevsky; David Magarshack, trans., A619
REDBURN–Herman Melville, A118
RETURN TO LAUGHTER–Elenore Smith Bowen, Foreword by David Riesman, N36
THE SCARLET LETTER and YOUNG GOODMAN BROWN–Nathaniel Hawthorne, Alfred Kazin, ed., A732
THE SECRET AGENT–Joseph Conrad, A8
THE SHADOW-LINE AND TWO OTHER TALES–Joseph Conrad, intro. by Morton Dauwen Zabel, A178
SISSIE–John A. Williams, A710
THE TALE OF GENJI, I–Lady Murasaki; Arthur Waley, trans., A55
TEN GERMAN NOVELLAS–Harry Steinhauer, ed. and trans., A707
THREE SHORT NOVELS OF DOSTOEVSKY–Constance Garnett, trans.; Avraim Yarmolinsky, ed. and revised, A193
UNDER WESTERN EYES–Joseph Conrad, intro. by Morton Dauwen Zabel, A323
VICTORY–Joseph Conrad, A106
THE WANDERER (LE GRAND MEAULNES)–Henri Alain-Fournier; Françoise Delisle, trans., A14
WHAT MAISIE KNEW–Henry James, A43

ANCHOR BOOKS

POETRY

THE AENEID OF VIRGIL—C. Day Lewis, trans., A20
AMERICAN POETRY AND POETICS: Poems and Critical Documents from the Puritans to Robert Frost—Daniel G. Hoffman, ed., A304
THE ANCHOR ANTHOLOGY OF SEVENTEENTH-CENTURY VERSE, Volume 1—Louis L. Martz, ed., ACO13a
THE ANCHOR ANTHOLOGY OF SEVENTEENTH-CENTURY VERSE, Volume 2—Richard S. Sylvester, ACO13b
AN ANTHOLOGY OF FRENCH POETRY from Nerval to Valery, in English Translation with French Originals—Angel Flores, ed., A134
AN ANTHOLOGY OF SPANISH POETRY from Garcilasco to Garcia Lorca, in English Translation with Spanish Originals—Angel Flores, ed., A268
ANTIWORLDS AND "THE FIFTH ACE"—Andrei Voznesensky; Patricia Blake, and Max Hayward, eds., a bilingual edition, A595
BRATSK STATION AND OTHER NEW POEMS—Yevgeny Yevtushenko; Tina Tupikina-Glaessner, Geoffrey Dutton, and Igor Nezhakoff-Koriakin, trans., intro. by Rosh Ireland, A558
THE CANTERBURY TALES OF GEOFFREY CHAUCER—Daniel Cook, ed., A265
COLLECTED POEMS—Robert Graves, A517
THE COMPLETE POETRY OF JOHN MILTON—John T. Shawcross, ed., revised edition, ACO15
THE COMPLETE POEMS AND SELECTED LETTERS AND PROSE OF HART CRANE—Brom Weber, ed., A537
THE COMPLETE POETRY OF JOHN DONNE—John T. Shawcross, ed., ACO11
THE COMPLETE POETRY OF RICHARD CRASHAW—George Walton Williams, ed., ACO14
A CONTROVERSY OF POETS: An Anthology of Contemporary American Poetry—Paris Leary and Robert Kelly, eds., A439
ENGLISH RENAISSANCE POETRY: A Collection of Shorter Poems from Skelton to Jonson—John Williams, ed., A359
ENGLISH ROMANTIC POETRY, Volume I: Blake, Wordsworth, Coleridge and Others—Harold Bloom, ed., A347a
ENGLISH ROMANTIC POETRY, Volume II: Byron, Shelley, Keats and Others—Harold Bloom, ed., A347b
THE FAR FIELD—Theodore Roethke, AO20
FORM AND VALUE IN MODERN POETRY—R. P. Blackmur, A96
GOETHE'S FAUST—Walter Kaufmann, trans., bilingual edition, A328
IN PRAISE OF KRISHNA: Songs from the Bengali—Denise Levertov and Edward C. Dimock, Jr., trans.; Anju Chaudhuri, illus., A545
INSIDE OUTER SPACE: New Poems of the Space Age—Robert Vas Dias, ed., A738

AN INTRODUCTION TO HAIKU: An Anthology of Poems and Poets from Basho to Shiki–Harold G. Henderson, trans., A150
MIDDLE ENGLISH ANTHOLOGY–Ann S. Haskell, AO10
MY NAME IS AFRIKA–Keorapetse Kgositsile, AO19
THE ODYSSEY–Homer; Robert Fitzgerald, trans.; Hans Erni, illus., A333
THE POETRY AND PROSE OF WILLIAM BLAKE–David V. Erdman, ed., Commentary by Harold Bloom, AO17
POETRY OF OUR TIME–Babette Deutsch, A344
QUICKLY AGING HERE: Some Poets of the 1970s–Geof Hewitt, ed., A631
SELECTED POEMS AND LETTERS OF EMILY DICKINSON–Robert Linscott, ed., A192
SEVENTEENTH-CENTURY AMERICAN POETRY–Harrison T. Meserole, ed., ACO12
TECHNICIANS OF THE SACRED: A Range of Poetries from Africa, America, Asia and Oceania–Jerome Rothenberg, ed., AO6
WHERE IS VIETNAM? American Poets Respond–Walter Lowenfels, ed., A572
ZEN: Poems, Prayers, Sermons, Anecdotes, Interviews–Lucien Stryk and Takashi Ikemoto, eds., A485

ANCHOR BOOKS

DRAMA

AN ANTHOLOGY OF GERMAN EXPRESSIONIST DRAMA: A Prelude to the Absurd–Walter H. Sokel, ed., A365

AN APPROACH TO SHAKESPEARE, in two volumes–D. A. Traversi, A74a, b

THE BIRTH OF TRAGEDY AND THE GENEALOGY OF MORALS–Friedrich Nietzsche; Francis Golffing, trans., A81

BRECHT: THE MAN AND HIS WORK–Martin Esslin, revised edition, A245

BRAND–Henrik Ibsen; Michael Meyer, trans., intro. by W. H. Auden, A215a

THE CLASSIC THEATRE: Volume I: Six Italian Plays–Eric Bentley, ed., A155a

THE CLASSIC THEATRE: Volume II: Five German Plays–Eric Bentley, ed., A155b

THE CLASSIC THEATRE: Volume III: Six Spanish Plays–Eric Bentley, ed., A155c

THE CLASSIC THEATRE: Volume IV: Six French Plays–Eric Bentley, ed., A155d

COMEDY–Henri Bergson; George Meredith, A87

A COMPANION TO SHAKESPEARE STUDIES–H. Granville-Barker and G. B. Harrison, ed., A191

FIVE COMEDIES OF ARISTOPHANES–Benjamin Bickley Rogers, trans.; Andrew Chiappe, ed., A57

FIVE PLAYS OF STRINDBERG–Elizabeth Sprigge, trans., A219

GHOSTS AND THREE OTHER PLAYS–Henrik Ibsen; Michael Meyer, trans., A215e

GOETHE'S FAUST–Walter Kaufmann, trans., bilingual edition, A328

HAMLET AND OEDIPUS–Ernest Jones, A31

HEDDA GABLER AND THREE OTHER PLAYS–Henrik Ibsen; Michael Meyer, trans., A215c

INFERNO, ALONE AND OTHER WRITINGS–August Strindberg, new translations, Evert Sprinchorn, ed., A492c

MIDDLE ENGLISH ANTHOLOGY–Ann S. Haskell, AO10

THE MODERN THEATRE, Volume 1, Eric Bentley, ed., A48a

THE MODERN THEATRE, Volume 2, Eric Bentley, ed., A48b

THE MODERN THEATRE, Volume 3, Eric Bentley, ed., A48c

THE MODERN THEATRE, Volume 5, Eric Bentley, ed., A48e

THE PEOPLED WOUND, The Work of Harold Pinter–Martin Esslin, A739

PEER GYNT–Henrik Ibsen; Michael Meyer, trans., A215d

REFLECTIONS: Essays on the Modern Theatre–Martin Esslin, A771

SHAKESPEARE OUR CONTEMPORARY–Jan Kott; Boleslaw Taborski, trans., A499

SIX PLAYS OF STRINDBERG–Elizabeth Sprigge, trans., A54

4Ab

THEATRE EXPERIMENT: An Anthology of American Plays–Michael Benedikt, ed., A636
THE THEATRE OF THE ABSURD–Martin Esslin, revised edition, A279
TRAGEDY AND PHILOSOPHY–Walter Kaufmann, A689